Introduction to Matrices and Linear Transformations

A Series of Books in Mathematics

R. A. Rosenbaum, EDITOR

Introduction to Matrices and Linear Transformations (Second Edition)
  Daniel T. Finkbeiner, II

Introduction to Probability and Statistics (Third Edition)
  Henry L. Alder and Edward B. Roessler

The USSR Olympiad Problem Book: Selected Problems and
  Theorems of Elementary Mathematics
  D. O. Shklarsky, N. N. Chentzov, and I. M. Yaglom

Mathematics: The Man-made Universe
  Sherman K. Stein

Set Theory and Logic
  Robert R. Stoll

Problems in Differential Equations
  J. L. Brenner

Foundations of Linear Algebra
  A. I. Mal'cev

Computational Methods of Linear Algebra
  D. K. Faddeev and V. N. Faddeeva

Geometry and Analysis of Projective Spaces
  C. E. Springer

University Mathematics, I and II
  Jack R. Britton, R. Ben Kriegh, and Leon W. Rutland

GOLDEN GATE EDITIONS

A Concrete Approach to Abstract Algebra
  W. W. Sawyer

A Modern View of Geometry
  Leonard M. Blumenthal

Sets, Logic, and Axiomatic Theories
  Robert R. Stoll

The Solution of Equations in Integers
  A. O. Gelfond

An Elementary Introduction to the Theory of Probability
  B. V. Gnedenko and A. Ya. Khinchin

The Real Number System in an Algebraic Setting
  J. B. Roberts

Elements of Astromechanics
  Peter van de Kamp

Introduction to Matrices and Linear Transformations

BY

DANIEL T. FINKBEINER, II

Kenyon College

SECOND EDITION

 W. H. FREEMAN AND COMPANY

San Francisco and London

Library of Congress Catalogue Card Number: 65-19559

(C2)

PREFACE TO THE
SECOND EDITION

DURING the five years since this book was first published, many people have kindly taken time to send me their comments. Unsparing in exposing specific defects but generous in endorsing the text in general, their observations stimulated me to undertake this revision and influenced the nature of the changes which appear.

The approach to linear algebra and the organization of its content remain basically unchanged from the first edition. Proofs and text interpretations are revised in numerous places for greater clarity. The concept of the dual space is introduced at an early stage to provide a geometric interpretation of the transpose of a matrix. Much later it is used to study normal transformations and to express the primal and dual problems of linear programming. Chapter 7 combines the content of Chapters 7 and 8 of the first edition. It includes an improved derivation of the canonical form for a nilpotent matrix, using cyclic subspaces; this yields the Jordan canonical form for any square matrix. In Chapter 8 (formerly Chapter 9) the discussion of metric concepts is carried out for both real and complex vector spaces, and material on Hermitian functions and on normal transformations is developed. In Chapter 9 the discussion of combinatorial equivalence (formerly Appendix B) has been expanded to indicate its relevance to linear programming. Finally, a new Appendix B has been added to clarify distinctions which arise in the literature because of different conventions of notation for matrices.

I realize that change does not necessarily imply improvement; that elimination of errors does not prevent the introduction of new ones. I shall be most grateful for further suggestions from people who use this book. Especially, I wish to thank my friends at the University of Western Australia, whose incomparable hospitality in 1964 pleasantly leavened the work of this revision.

September, 1965   D. T. FINKBEINER

PREFACE TO THE
FIRST EDITION

MATRIX THEORY, or more generally linear algebra, is a relatively recent mathematical development. Its roots extend back 100 years to the work of Hamilton, Cayley, and Sylvester, but it has attracted widespread interest only in the past two or three decades. Today matrices are effective tools in quantum theory as well as classical mechanics; in aeronautical, mechanical, and electrical engineering; in statistics and linear programming and therefore in all the social sciences which these theories serve.

Even a cursory glance at current mathematical literature reveals that matrix theory is in a stage of active growth. It is rather surprising therefore that the mathematical background required for an understanding of matrix theory is sufficiently modest that a substantial first course can be mastered by undergraduates. The major prerequisite is not a specific list of courses in mathematics, but rather the ability to reason abstractly, to proceed logically from hypothesis to conclusion. Anyone who possesses this quality, even latently, is capable of understanding the material presented here, whether he be an economist, psychologist, engineer, chemist, physicist, or mathematician. The necessary mathematical background is normally acquired in one or two years of college mathematics.

Courses in matrix theory are currently presented in several ways. A computational course can be offered in which the calculations themselves are emphasized more than their meaning. Alternately, the study of matrices can be motivated from the familiar problem of solving systems of linear equations, the important connection between matrices and linear transformations being deferred until the end of the course. A third procedure, and the one chosen here, systematically employs the elegant techniques of abstract algebra to develop simultaneously the algebra of matrices and the geometry of linear transformations.

Although an axiomatic approach places a greater burden at the outset of the course on both the instructor and the student, the ultimate gain in understanding linear algebra, and indeed modern mathematics as a whole, amply justifies this extra effort. Undeniably, the understanding of abstract concepts is aided by frequent illustrations from familiar contexts, and a serious attempt has been made here to retain firm contact with concrete ideas while steadily developing a higher degree of generality.

The obvious purpose of this book is to present a lucid and unified introduction to linear algebra at a level which can be understood by undergraduates who possess reasonable mathematical aptitude, and thus to lay a solid foundation from which each student can apply these notions and techniques to the field of his interest. A more subtle but equally serious objective is to prepare the student for advanced scientific work by developing his powers of abstract reasoning. Linear algebra is admirably suited to this purpose.

The present text is a revised form of mimeographed lecture notes written in 1951 for the second semester of a survey course in abstract algebra at Kenyon College. Because linear algebra is a cohesive body of knowledge which blends a variety of algebraic and geometric concepts, I believe that it provides a more natural introduction to abstract algebra than does the usual survey course. The first chapter, supplemented by Appendix A, presents the algebraic notions needed for this study; thus the text can be used by students who have no previous experience with modern algebraic techniques.

The remaining material has been selected and arranged to proceed directly to the problem of equivalence relations and canonical forms. The duality of geometry and algebra is emphasized, but computational aspects are not ignored. Metric notions are deferred until Chapter 9, principally because they are not essential for the major part of this work. Depending upon the ability of the class, there is adequate material for a course of 60 class hours. Chapter 10, and to a lesser extent Chapter 9, may be omitted without interfering seriously with the major aims of this presentation.

Since some results of general interest are stated as exercises, each student is urged to make a practice of reading all exercises and learning the facts stated therein, even though he might choose not to prove all of them.

Revision of the original notes was performed during my tenture as a Science Faculty Fellow of the National Science Foundation. I am greatly indebted to the Foundation for its support, to Princeton University for the use of its facilities during this period, and to Kenyon College for assistance with the original version. Personal gratitude is expressed to J. G. Wendel for mathematical discussions extending over a decade, to A. W. Tucker for making available his recent work on combinatorial equivalence, to W. D. Lindstrom for reading critically selected parts of the manuscript, and to the editors and advisers of the publisher for many helpful suggestions. Appreciation is expressed also to Mrs. Richard Anderson and Mrs. Charles Helsley for their help in preparing the original and revised manuscripts.

February, 1960   D. T. FINKBEINER

CONTENTS

CHAPTER 1

Abstract Systems

§1.1. *Introduction*

When a student begins the study of matrices he soon discovers properties which seem to have no counterpart in his previous mathematical experience. This is as unavoidable as it is exciting. The concepts he considers and the methods he employs are markedly different from those he has encountered in mathematics through school and into college.

Elementary school mathematics is concerned primarily with the arithmetic of number systems, beginning with the positive integers and developing gradually to include all of the integers and the rational numbers. The later use of letters to represent numbers is a real stride toward abstraction, and the corresponding study is called algebra instead of arithmetic. The algebraic problem of solving quadratic equations reveals the need for still more comprehensive number systems, which leads to the study of real and complex numbers.

An exception to the emphasis on numbers occurs in plane geometry, where the elements studied are called points and lines rather than numbers and equations, and where the relations between geometric figures are no longer numerical equality or inequality but congruence, similarity, parallelism, or perpendicularity. Geometry normally is the student's first excursion from the world of numbers to a realm of deductive thought which is essentially nonnumerical.

Trigonometry and analytic geometry provide a bridge between numerical and geometric concepts by using numbers and equations to describe geometric figures. The objects studied are geometric, but the methods used in investigating their properties are numerical. This gradual transition from the study of numbers to the study of nonnumerical elements is continued in calculus, in which functions and operations on functions are described numerically but have significant geometric interpretations.

Likewise, matrices are described numerically and have important geometric interpretations. Matrices form a type of number system, and in this study we shall be concerned with developing the algebraic properties of this system. However, since matrices are intrinsically related to geometry, while their relation to arithmetic is comparatively superficial, a geometric interpretation of matrix theory is both natural and efficient. After this introductory chapter we turn immediately to a description of the geometric setting for our later work, *finite-dimensional vector spaces*. In Chapter 3 we study *linear transformations* of such spaces, and not until Chapter 4 do we study *matrices* themselves.

It is evident from the Table of Contents that various mathematical systems are discussed in this book, many of which may now be unfamiliar to you. Therefore, we shall begin by describing mathematical systems generally. In order to suggest that our present interest lies primarily in the internal structure of the system, rather than in its relation to the physical world, we speak of an *abstract system*. You are asked not to interpret the word "abstract" as meaning that familiar systems will not arise as particular examples of abstract systems. As we shall see, an abstract system is often defined as a synthesis of some concrete system.

This introductory chapter, which discusses abstract systems from the point of view of modern algebra, has three objectives: to introduce the basic notation used in this book, to extend and modernize the student's mathematical vocabulary, and to capture some of the spirit of abstract mathematics.

To most mathematicians the esthetic appeal of an abstract system is sufficient justification for its study. From a more practical standpoint, the investigation of abstract systems has greatly clarified and unified the fundamental concepts of mathematics, and has provided a description of such important notions as relations, functions, and operations in terms of the simple and intuitive notion of *set*. Such a description is given in Appendix A. If you have a flair for abstraction or a desire for more precision than is afforded in this introductory chapter, you may wish to study Appendix A immediately. Or you may prefer to proceed more gradually, deferring a general study of basic concepts until you have acquired some experience with these ideas in the specific systems considered in this book. In either event, you should not expect to attain immediate and comfortable familiarity with all of the ideas presented here. You should study the text material carefully and work through the examples and exercises in detail, steadily increasing your facility for abstract thought and enhancing your insight into the nature of mathematics.

Exercises

1. Assume that a club of two or more students is organized into committees in such a way that each of the following statements (postulates) is true.

(a) Every committee is a collection of one or more students.

(b) For each pair of students there is exactly one committee on which both serve.

(c) No single committee is composed of all the students in the club.

(d) Given any committee and any student not on that committee, there exists exactly one committee on which that student serves which has no students of the first committee in its membership.

Prove each of the statements (theorems) in the following sequence, justifying each step of your proof by appealing to one of the five postulates or to an earlier theorem of the sequence. (Although this system may appear more concrete than abstract, its general nature is indicated by Exercise 2 of this section and Exercise 2 of § 1.2.)

(i) Every student serves on at least two committees.

(ii) Every committee has at least two members.

(iii) There are at least four students in the club.

(iv) There are at least six committees in the club.

2. (i) Translate the description of the system of the previous exercise into geometric language by calling the club a "geometry," a student a "point," and a committee a "line," and by making other changes as needed to carry out the geometric flavor without changing the inherent meaning of the statements.

(ii) Translate the four theorems into geometric language, and similarly translate your proof of the first theorem.

(iii) Find the geometric system with the smallest number of points which satisfies the four postulates. (Such a system is called a finite geometry; other theorems about the system can be discovered and proved.)

(iv) Which of the four postulates are consistent with the axioms of Euclidean plane geometry?

§1.2. *Sets*

Before we attempt to describe abstract systems, we should first recognize that it is quite hopeless for two individuals to try to carry on an intelligent conversation unless they share some basic knowledge. We now state two general assumptions about the basic knowledge that is used as a foundation for our later discussion:

There is a common understanding of the basic language which we shall use to define other terms.

There is a common understanding of the system of logical reasoning with which we proceed from hypothesis to conclusion.

These assumptions are so general that they now appear to be quite elusive; presently we shall be more specific. In effect, the first assumption recognizes the futility of trying to define all terms which will be needed, and thereby establishes the need for *undefined terms*. The second assumption is a declaration that no formal treatment of the rules of deduction will appear in this book.

More specifically, as part of our basic language we assume an intuitive understanding of the notion of a *set*. The word *set* is used to denote a *collection, class, family,* or *aggregate* of objects, which are called *elements* or *members* of the set. It is evident that this explanation does not define a set or the concept of membership in a set. These concepts are part of the undefined language which is assumed for this book.

It is customary to denote a set by a capital letter and the elements of a set by small letters. To denote that an element b *is a member of* a set S, we write

$$b \in S,$$

which can also be read as "b belongs to S." To denote that b does *not* belong to S we write

$$b \notin S.$$

There are two common ways of specifying a set:

by listing all its elements within braces,

by stating a characteristic property which determines whether or not any given object is an element of that set.

The notation which we adopt for the second method comprises two parts, separated by a vertical line, within braces. The first part tells us what type of elements are being considered, and the second part specifies the characteristic property. For example, let I denote the set of all integers, and let S denote the set of all integers whose square is less than seven. The two methods of writing S are

$$S = \{-2, -1, 0, 1, 2\},$$

where we attach no importance to the order in which the elements are listed, and

$$S = \{x \in I \mid x^2 < 7\},$$

which is read, "S is the set of all integers x such that x^2 is less than 7."

We use the symbol Φ to denote the *void* or *empty* set, which contains no elements at all. While the void set may seem at first to be an artificial notion, its acceptance as a bona fide set is convenient.

Sets S and T are said to be *equal* if and only if they contain exactly the same elements. In terms of the membership relation, this is expressed as:

$$T = S \text{ means "} x \in T \text{ if and only if } x \in S\text{."}$$

The next concept is that of a *subset*. If S and T are sets, T is said to be a subset of S, written $T \subseteq S$, if and only if every element of T is an element of S; that is,

$$T \subseteq S \text{ means "if } x \in T, \text{ then } x \in S\text{."}$$

The subset notation $T \subseteq S$ can also be written $S \supseteq T$. This notation is analogous to the notation for inequality of numbers: $a \leq b$ means the same as $b \geq a$. It is readily verified that equality of sets can be expressed in terms of the subset notation as:

$$T = S \text{ means "} T \subseteq S \text{ and } S \subseteq T\text{."}$$

It is clear from the definition of subset that any set is a subset of itself. Also, since the void set has no elements, the statement "If $x \in \Phi$, then $x \in S$" is logically valid for any set S. Thus we have

$$\Phi \subseteq S \text{ and } S \subseteq S \text{ for every set } S.$$

T is said to be a *proper subset* of S if and only if every element of T is an element of S, but not every element of S is an element of T. This is written:

$$T \subset S \text{ if and only if } T \subseteq S \text{ and } T \neq S.$$

In practice it is sometimes useful to adopt geometric language for sets, calling an element a point even though the element may have no obvious geometric character. When we adopt such descriptive language we must bear in mind that this is done only for convenience, and we must carefully refrain from assuming any properties which may be suggested by our language but which are not otherwise legitimately established.

A geometric interpretation of sets suggests the use of sketches, called *Venn diagrams*, to represent sets and relations between sets. Thus the subset relation $T \subseteq S$ can be shown graphically as in Figure 1.1. Such diagrams provide

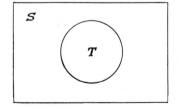

Figure 1.1

insight concerning sets, and often they suggest methods by which statements about sets can be proved or disproved. However, diagrams are not valid substitutes for formal proofs.

We now turn our attention to several ways in which sets can be combined to produce other sets. Let S be any set, and let K denote the collection of all subsets of S. (The elements of K are the subsets of S.) We shall define three operations on sets, called *union, intersection*, and *complementation:*

Union:	$A \cup B = \{x \in S \mid x \in A \text{ or } x \in B\}$,
Intersection:	$A \cap B = \{x \in S \mid x \in A \text{ and } x \in B\}$,
Complementation:	$A' = \{x \in S \mid x \notin A\}$.

Thus if A and B are any elements of K, the set "A union B" consists of all elements of S which belong to A, or to B, or to both. The set "A intersec tion B" consists of all elements of S which belong to both A and B. The "complement of A in S" consists of all elements of S which do not belong to A. If $A \cap B = \Phi$ (the void set), we say that A and B are *disjoint.* Venn diagrams which illustrate these operations are shown in Figure 1.2. More generally,

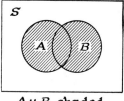
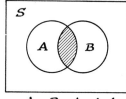
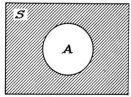

| **A ∪ B shaded** | **A ∩ B shaded** | **A′ shaded** |

Figure 1.2

the union and intersection of any family F of subsets of S are defined in an analogous way:

$$\bigcup_{A \in F} A = \{x \in S \mid x \in A \text{ for some } A \in F\},$$

$$\bigcap_{A \in F} A = \{x \in S \mid x \in A \text{ for all } A \in F\}.$$

Having made these definitions, we now have before us a concrete example of an abstract system, the general nature of which will be discussed in § 1.5. To pave the way for that description, it will be useful to recognize that we have been developing an algebraic system in which the objects of our attention are the various subsets of a fixed set S. We have defined two relations for subsets, the equality relation and the subset relation. Furthermore, we have introduced two methods, union and intersection, by which any two subsets of S may be combined to produce another subset of S. A third operation, complementation, provides a means by which each subset of S determines some other subset of S. If we chose to do so, we could now undertake a thorough investigation of the properties of this system, proving theorems about the algebra of sets. A few such theorems are listed below as exercises, while a more complete and systematic discussion is given in Appendix A, § A.6.

Exercises

1. (i) List all the subsets of $S = \{a, b, c, d\}$.

(ii) If S is a finite set having m elements, how many subsets does S have? Prove your answer.

2. Referring to Exercise 1, § 1.1, translate the description of the system into the abstract language and notation of sets. Also translate the four theorems (but you need not prove them again).

3. Let A and B be arbitrary subsets of a given set S. Use the definitions of set theory to prove the following theorems.

(i) $A \subseteq B$ if and only if $A \cup B = B$.

(ii) $A \cup (B \cap C) = (A \cup B) \cap (A \cup C)$.

(iii) $(A \cup B)' = A' \cap B'$.

4. The *difference* of two subsets of S is defined by

$$A - B = \{x \in A \mid x \notin B\}.$$

(i) Find and prove an equation which expresses $A - B$ in terms of the basic set operations ($\cup$, $\cap$, and $'$). Draw an illustrative Venn diagram.

(ii) Prove: $(A - B)' = A' \cup B$.

(iii) Is set difference a commutative operation? That is, are $A - B$ and $B - A$ equal? Prove your answer.

5. The *symmetric difference* $A \ominus B$ of two subsets of S is the set of all elements which belong either to A or to B, but not to both A and B.

(i) Find and prove an expression for $A \ominus B$ in terms of the basic set operations ($\cup$, $\cap$, and $'$). Draw an illustrative Venn diagram.

(ii) Prove that $(A \ominus B)' = (A' \cup B) \cap (A \cup B')$.

(iii) Is symmetric difference a commutative operation? That is, are $A \ominus B$ and $B \ominus A$ equal? Prove your answer.

(iv) Discover a simple description of the set $(A \ominus B) \ominus C$.

(v) Is symmetric difference an associative operation? That is, are $(A \ominus B) \ominus C$ and $A \ominus (B \ominus C)$ equal? Prove your answer.

6. Show that set union can be expressed in terms of intersection and complementation.

7. Considering only finite sets, let $n(S)$ denote the number of elements in S.

(i) Prove $n(A \cup B) = n(A) + n(B) - n(A \cap B)$.

(ii) Discover and prove a similar result for $n(A \cup B \cup C)$.

§1.3. *Relations*

Given any set S, it is often necessary to know how the elements of S are related, one to another. Two objects might be of the same color, but one might be heavier than the other. Line L might intersect line M but be parallel to line N. In general, then, we wish to consider all ordered pairs (a, b) of elements of S, and to have some means of distinguishing certain of those pairs from other pairs. The pairs which are thus distinguished constitute a *binary relation* on S, and we say that a is related to b if and only if the pair (a, b) is a distinguished pair.

To proceed more formally, we first define the *cartesian product* of a set S with itself to be the set $S \times S$ of all ordered pairs of elements of S:

$$S \times S = \{(a, b) \mid a \in S \text{ and } b \in S\}.$$

Two pairs are *equal* if and only if their first components are the same and their second components are the same. Then a *binary relation* $\mathbf{R}$ on S is simply a subset of $S \times S$. If $(a, b) \in \mathbf{R}$ we say that a *is related to* b by the relation $\mathbf{R}$, and we write $a \mathbf{R} b$. If $(a, b) \notin \mathbf{R}$, we write $a \not\mathbf{R} b$.

Examples

(a) If R is the set of all real numbers, representing the points on a real coordinate axis, then $R \times R$ is the set of all ordered pairs of real numbers, representing the points on a real coordinate plane. The relation of equality is described by the set $\{(a, a) \mid a \in R\}$, consisting of all points on the line $y = x$. The relation $a < b$ is represented by all points which lie above the line $y = x$.

(b) If I is the set of integers, $I \times I$ is represented by the set of all points of the plane for which both coordinates are integers, called "lattice points." The relation "$a - b$ is evenly divisible by 3," written $a \equiv b \pmod 3$, is represented by all lattice points which lie on any line of slope 1 through the points $(3n, 0)$, $n \in I$.

In linear algebra, as elsewhere throughout mathematics, we are particularly interested in binary relations which have the abstract properties of equality. These are

Reflexivity:	$a \mathbf{R} a$ for every $a \in S$,
Symmetry:	if $a \mathbf{R} b$ then $b \mathbf{R} a$,
Transitivity:	if $a \mathbf{R} b$ and $b \mathbf{R} c$, then $a \mathbf{R} c$.

Any relation $\mathbf{R}$ on S which has these three properties is called an *equivalence relation.*

One of the major investigations that we shall undertake in this book concerns a description of various equivalence relations which arise in a natural manner in the study of matrices. Therefore, before reading Chapter 6 you will need to become thoroughly familiar with the concept of binary relations and especially equivalence relations. These notions are developed more generally and completely in Appendix A.

Exercises

1. Given the set $S = \{1, 2, 6, 8\}$.

(i) Represent $S \times S$ geometrically.

(ii) Represent geometrically the subset of $S \times S$ which is determined by the relation "a divides b evenly" for $a, b \in S$.

(iii) Represent geometrically the subset of $S \times S$ which is determined by the relation "$a > b$" for $a, b \in S$.

2. Show that if S has more than three elements, then $S \times S$ has more than 60,000 subsets.

3. Since the void set Φ and $A \times A$ are subsets of $A \times A$, each represents a relation on A. Describe each of these two relations.

4. Let I be the set of all positive integers. For any fixed $n \in I$ we define on I the relation *congruence modulo n* by writing

$$a \equiv b(\mathrm{mod}\ n)$$

if and only if $a - b$ is divisible by n.

(i) Prove that this is an equivalence relation on I.

(ii) Prove that if $a \equiv b(\mathrm{mod}\ n)$ and if $c \equiv d(\mathrm{mod}\ n)$, then

$$a + c \equiv b + d(\mathrm{mod}\ n) \quad \text{and} \quad ac \equiv bd(\mathrm{mod}\ n).$$

(iii) Show by an example that if $c \not\equiv 0(\mathrm{mod}\ n)$ and if $ac \equiv bc(\mathrm{mod}\ n)$, it does not necessarily follow that $a \equiv b(\mathrm{mod}\ n)$.

§1.4. *Functions and Mappings*

It is assumed that you are familiar with numerical functions from your previous mathematical experience; our purpose here is to describe functions in a more general setting. Recall that each numerical function f has a *domain* of definition (a set D of numbers), and that to each $x \in D$ the function f assigns a unique number $f(x)$, which is called the *value* of f at x. As x varies over D, the numbers $f(x)$ form a set R which is called the *range* of f.

A generalization from numerical functions to arbitrary functions is made very easily—we simply drop the requirement that D and R be sets of numbers, and consider them to be abstract sets.

A *function F from a set A into a set B* consists of

1. a nonvoid subset $D \subseteq A$, called the *domain* of F,
2. a correspondence such that to each $a \in D$ there is associated one and only one $b \in B$.

The element $b \in B$ which is associated with $a \in D$ by the function F is often denoted $F(a)$. The *range* of F is the subset $R \subseteq B$, defined by

$$R = \{b \in B \mid b = F(a) \text{ for some } a \in D\}.$$

If $R = B$, we say that F is a function from A *onto* B.

Here again a translation to geometric language is useful. The domain D and range R are sets of points, and the function F associates with each point of D exactly one point of R.

A reasonable geometric synonym of function is *mapping*, a terminology suggested by Figure 1.3. Likewise, the point $F(x)$ is called the *image of x*

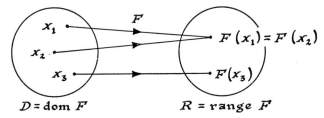

Figure 1.3

under the mapping F. For functions of abstract sets this geometric terminology is more descriptive than that used for numerical functions. There is also a useful notational change which we shall adopt—instead of denoting the image of x under F by the functional notation $F(x)$, we shall omit the parentheses and show $\mathbf{F}$ in boldface type to the right of x. In this new notation a function will be indicated thus:

$$\mathbf{F}: x \longrightarrow x\mathbf{F}, \quad \text{for all } x \in \text{dom } \mathbf{F}.$$

Thus for each $x \in \text{dom } \mathbf{F}$ the symbol $x\mathbf{F}$ denotes the image of x under the mapping $\mathbf{F}$.

It is important to observe that although a mapping $\mathbf{F}$ assigns a unique image $x\mathbf{F}$ to each $x \in \text{dom } \mathbf{F}$, it is quite possible that a point of range $\mathbf{F}$ is the image of *more than one* point of dom $\mathbf{F}$; that is, from the equation $x_1\mathbf{F} = x_2\mathbf{F}$ we cannot deduce that $x_1 = x_2$. Therefore, mappings in general are *many-to-one*, in the sense that many distinct points of the domain may be mapped into the same point of the range. Just as with numerical functions, if it happens that each point of range $\mathbf{F}$ is the image of *exactly* one point of dom $\mathbf{F}$, then an *inverse mapping* $\mathbf{F}^*$ can be defined from range $\mathbf{F}$ onto dom $\mathbf{F}$, such that if $y = x\mathbf{F} \in$ range $\mathbf{F}$, then

$$y\mathbf{F}^* = (x\mathbf{F})\mathbf{F}^* = x \quad \text{for every } x \in \text{dom } \mathbf{F}.$$

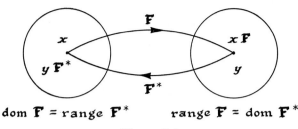

dom **F** = range **F***   range **F** = dom **F***

Figure 1.4

In summary, we say that a mapping **F** is *one-to-one* (or *reversible*) if and only if $x_1\mathbf{F} = x_2\mathbf{F}$ implies $x_1 = x_2$. If **F** is one-to-one, then an inverse function **F*** can be defined from range **F** to dom **F** such that for each $x \in$ dom **F**, $(x\mathbf{F})\mathbf{F}^* = x$.

The equation $(x\mathbf{F})\mathbf{F}^* = x$ states that if x is mapped first by **F** and if the image $x\mathbf{F}$ is then mapped by **F***, the resultant image is x itself. This is a special instance of the more general concept of *successive mappings*. Suppose that A, B, and C are sets, that **F** is a mapping from A into B, and that **G** is a mapping from B into C. Whenever the range of **F** is a subset of the domain of **G**, we can define a direct mapping **FG** from A into C as

$$\mathbf{FG}:x \longrightarrow x\mathbf{FG} = (x\mathbf{F})\mathbf{G} \quad \text{for all } x \in \text{dom } \mathbf{F}.$$

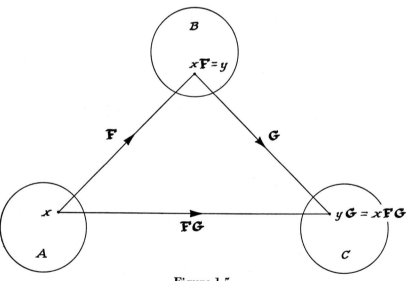

Figure 1.5

The concept of composite function is very important in linear algebra because matrix multiplication can be interpreted in terms of successive mappings of vector spaces into vector spaces. The right-hand notation which we have adopted for functions places the symbol for a mapping to the *right* of the symbol for the object which is mapped, a convention which is particularly convenient for composite functions. Thus, the image of x under the composite mapping "**F** followed by **G**" is denoted by x**FG**, the individual symbols written from left to right in their natural order of occurrence. By contrast, in the familiar left-hand notation which is used for functions in introductory analysis the corresponding notation is $G(F(x))$, and the term "function of a function" is used. As we shall see later when we represent linear mappings by matrices, there are important differences in the form of that representation, depending upon whether mappings are written in right-hand or left-hand notation. Both systems are widely used.

Exercises

1. Let S, T, U, and V be sets, and let **F**, **G**, and **H** be mappings whose domains are S, T, and U, and whose ranges are subsets of T, U, and V, respectively.

(i) Describe the domain and range of **FG** and **GH**.

(ii) Show that **F(GH)** = **(FG)H**.

(iii) Suppose that **F** and **G** are both reversible (one-to-one). Show that **(FG)*** = **G*F***, and that **(F*)*** = **F**.

(iv) Suppose $U = S$. Describe the domain and range of **FG** and **GF**. Are these two functions equal? Explain.

(v) Suppose $U = T = S$. Are **FG** and **GF** equal functions? Explain.

2. Let **F** and **G** both be mappings from the real numbers to the real numbers. Since multiplication of real numbers is defined, a *product* **F** $\odot$ **G** of mappings can be defined by

$$x(\mathbf{F} \odot \mathbf{G}) = (x\mathbf{F})(x\mathbf{G}).$$

(The symbol $\odot$ is used to prevent confusion with the successive application of mappings, **FG**, as in Exercise 1.) Prove **F** $\odot$ **G** = **G** $\odot$ **F**.

3. The zero mapping **O** is defined by $x\mathbf{O} = 0$ for all real x. Let

$$x\mathbf{F} = |x| + x,$$
$$x\mathbf{G} = |x| - x.$$

Prove **F** $\neq$ **O**, **G** $\neq$ **O**, but **F** $\odot$ **G** = **O**, where $\odot$ is defined as in Exercise 2.

§1.5. *Abstract Systems*

We are now ready to describe the nature of an abstract system. First a system must have a nonvoid set of *elements*, the building blocks of the system. These elements are regarded as having no properties other than those which are prescribed by the system, even though we might use geometric terms or other descriptive names for them.

Example

To illustrate this discussion we shall use the specific example of the collection K of all subsets of a given set S. The system which we describe in this example has K as its set of elements. Thus an element of the system is a *subset* of S, not an element of S.

Next we need a set of *relations* between elements. One of the relations must be a definition of equality, which provides a criterion for distinguishing one element from another. Generalized forms of equality, called *equivalence relations*, play a vital role in matrix theory. (See § 6.1 and Appendix A.)

Example

Equality of two elements of K means that they are the same subset of S. Furthermore, a second relation, denoted $\subseteq$, is defined between various elements of K.

A system will also include a set of *operations*, ways of combining elements to produce other elements of the system. Since we are working entirely within a given system, we require that the result of an operation on any elements of the system be an element of that system. Such an operation is called a *closed operation*, and we consider only operations with this property. An operation which combines any *two* elements of a system to produce a single element of the system is called a *binary* operation. Similarly, a *unary* operation maps each *single* element of the system into a corresponding element of the system.

Example

For the elements of K we list three operations: union, intersection, and complementation. Union and intersection combine two elements of K to produce an element of K, and therefore can be regarded as mappings of $K \times K$ into K. Complementation operates on any element of K to produce another element of K, and thus can be considered as a mapping of K into K.

To endow the elements, relations, and operations of a system with desired properties, a set of *postulates* is prescribed. These are statements or axioms which are assumed to be valid for the system. Indeed, the postulates are initially the only description of the system.

From the postulates certain deductions can be made by means of the rules of logic which are part of the basic knowledge underlying the system. These deductions are *theorems* of the system and, once proved, they possess the same validity in the system as do the original postulates.

Another important feature of a system is its set of *definitions*, which are agreements concerning terminology for concepts constructed from the skeleton of the system. By means of definitions, new relations and operations can be introduced, or elements with special properties can be given distinctive names. As theorems are proved and the known facts of the system grow in number and complexity, a proper use of definitions helps to classify the information of the system and to simplify its internal language.

A brief discussion of the postulates, theorems, and definitions of the system of all subsets of a given set is contained in § A.6.

In summary, an abstract system S consists of

> a set E of elements,
> a set R of relations,
> a set O of operations,
> a set of postulates,
> a set of theorems,
> a set of definitions.

Of course, the heart of the system is the set of postulates, and all else is derived from the postulates. For notational purposes, however, it is convenient to emphasize the elements, relations, and operations by writing

$$S = \{E; R; O\}$$

to denote the system. Here E denotes a set of elements, R a set of relations, and O a set of operations.

When we speak of an element x of a system S, we refer to a member of E. However, it is customary in mathematical literature to ignore the distinction between the system itself and the set of elements of the system; thus we shall often write $x \in S$ when, strictly speaking, we mean $x \in E$.

Most of the systems which we shall study are defined by postulates which describe the elements and the operations. A few of the postulates occur in so many different systems that it is convenient to assign special terminology to them. To do so, we suppose that S is an abstract system whose set of elements is denoted by E. For the sake of clarity you might wish to interpret the following discussion in terms of a familiar example, such as the system of integers with addition and multiplication as operations, or the system of subsets of a set with union and intersection as operations.

First we consider three properties of binary operations.

Associativity: The operation $*$ is *associative* if and only if for all a, b, $c \in E$,

$$a * (b * c) = (a * b) * c.$$

Commutativity: The operation $*$ is *commutative* if and only if for all $a, b \in E$,

$$a * b = b * a.$$

Distributivity: The operation $\odot$ is *distributive* over the operation $*$ if and only if for all $a, b, c \in E$,

$$a \odot (b * c) = (a \odot b) * (a \odot c),$$
$$(b * c) \odot a = (b \odot a) * (c \odot a).$$

We say that $\odot$ is *left*-distributive over $*$ if the first of these two conditions is satisfied, and that $\odot$ is *right*-distributive over $*$ if the second condition is satisfied.

Observe that for integers, both addition and multiplication are associative and commutative, and multiplication is distributive over addition. For subsets, both union and intersection are associative and commutative, and each operation is distributive over the other.

Postulates about elements most often assert the *existence* of elements with unusual properties. We give three examples of such elements.

Identity element: An element $i \in E$ is called an *identity* relative to the operation $*$ if and only if, for every $x \in E$,

$$i * x = x = x * i.$$

Inverse element: Given an identity relative to $*$ and an arbitrary element $x \in E$, an element x' is called an *inverse* of x relative to $*$ if and only if

$$x * x' = i = x' * x.$$

Idempotent element: An element $x \in E$ is said to be *idempotent* relative to $*$ if and only if

$$x * x = x.$$

In the system of integers, 0 is an identity of addition, and 1 is an identity of multiplication. Both are idempotent relative to multiplication, but 0 is the only integer which is idempotent relative to addition. Each integer x has an additive inverse, $-x$, but 1 and -1 are the only integers that have a multiplicative inverse which is an integer.

In the system of subsets of S, the void set Φ is an identity of set union and S is an identity of set intersection. Every set is idempotent relative to both union and intersection. The void set Φ is self-inverse relative to union, and S is self-inverse relative to intersection, and these are the only sets which have either type of inverse.

Exercises

1. Prove the following about an abstract system $S = \{E; *, \odot\}$, assuming no properties of the system other than those stated for each case.

(i) Each operation can have at most one identity element.

(ii) If $*$ is associative and has an identity $i \in E$, then each $x \in E$ can have at most one inverse element relative to $*$.

(iii) If an identity element of an operation exists, it is idempotent relative to that operation.

(iv) If $\odot$ is distributive over $*$, if i is an identity of $\odot$, and if e is an identity of $*$, then e is idempotent relative to both $\odot$ and $*$. Is i idempotent relative to $*$?

Interpret these results for the special case of addition and multiplication of real numbers.

2. In each case below determine whether or not the given function describes a closed operation on the given set.

(i) Multiplication of even integers.
(ii) Multiplication of odd integers.
(iii) Addition of odd integers.
(iv) Addition of even integers.
(v) Multiplication of real functions which are differentiable.
(vi) Differentiation of real functions which are differentiable.
(vii) Differentiation of polynomials.

3. Let P be the set of points of the plane. For $p, q \in P$ define $p * q$ to be the midpoint of the segment from p to q.

(i) Is $*$ a closed operation on P?
(ii) Is $*$ commutative?
(iii) Is $*$ associative?

Substantiate your answers.

4. Let a mapping $\mathbf{T}_1$ of the points of the real coordinate axis into itself be defined by

$$x\mathbf{T}_1 = a_1 + b_1 x,$$

where a_1 and b_1 are fixed real numbers with $b_1 \neq 0$. Another mapping $\mathbf{T}_2$ of this form would be defined by

$$x\mathbf{T}_2 = a_2 + b_2 x, \ b_2 \neq 0.$$

We define the "product" $\mathbf{T}_1 * \mathbf{T}_2$ of such mappings by

$$x(\mathbf{T}_1 * \mathbf{T}_2) = (x\mathbf{T}_1)\mathbf{T}_2.$$

Prove that

(i) $*$ is associative,
(ii) an identity of $*$ exists,
(iii) each $\mathbf{T}$ has an inverse,
(iv) $*$ is not commutative.

Interpret each such mapping geometrically as a change of coordinates on the real line, after considering the two special cases

$$a \text{ arbitrary, } b = 1;$$

$$a = 0, b \text{ arbitrary.}$$

§1.6. *Fields*

To illustrate the discussion of § 1.5 let us turn our attention to several familiar systems of numbers—rational numbers, real numbers, and complex numbers—which occupy a central position in many phases of mathematics. In all of these number systems the four fundamental operations of arithmetic can be performed, and many algebraic properties are shared in common. Our aim is to extract these common features and thereby to construct an abstract system which is a useful generalization of each of the three concrete examples.

We begin by recognizing that the three examples comprise different number systems; that is, the set of elements is different in each case. Thus for the abstract representation, we consider an unspecified nonvoid set F of elements; we may call any such element a "number" if we wish, but we take the position that the only properties these objects possess are those which we specify in the stated postulates and their logical consequences. Next we turn our attention to the arithmetic operation of addition, which in the abstract system we denote by the symbol $\oplus$. In each example, the sum of two numbers of a given type is again a number of that type; hence $\oplus$ denotes a closed operation on F. Of the many general properties of addition we select the following as postulates.

A1. $\oplus$ is associative.
A2. $\oplus$ is commutative.
A3. There exists in F an identity element o, relative to $\oplus$.
A4. For each element $a \in F$ there exists in F an inverse element a_-, relative to $\oplus$.

In each of the three concrete examples, subtraction can be defined in terms of addition, so we make no specific assumptions about subtraction in the abstract system; our definition of subtraction would take the form

$$a \ominus b = a \oplus b_-$$

in imitation of the known examples.

Multiplication in the general system will be denoted $\odot$; it is a closed operation on F and possesses properties similar to those we have postulated for $\oplus$, with one notable exception—the number zero does not have a multiplicative inverse. Hence we adopt the following postulates.

M1. $\odot$ is associative.

M2. $\odot$ is commutative.

M3. There exists in F an identity element i, relative to $\odot$, and $i \neq o$.

M4. For each $a \in F$ such that $a \neq o$, there exists an inverse a' relative to $\odot$.

Finally, we need to recognize that a connection exists between addition and multiplication in number systems which can be expressed by a distributive postulate.

D. $\odot$ is distributive over $\oplus$.

Thus, an abstract generalization of the rational, real, and complex numbers is a system $\mathfrak{F} = \{F; \oplus, \odot\}$ which satisfies the nine postulates A1–A4, M1–M4, and D. Any such system is called a *field*.

The similarity between the properties of addition and multiplication in a field shows that any field contains two simpler subsystems, one additive and one multiplicative. Thus we are led naturally to consider a system which has a single associative and commutative operation and has an identity element and an inverse for each element. Any such system is called a *commutative group*, and a brief discussion of groups may be found in § A.7. This terminology allows us to restate the definition of a field in simpler form.

A *field* $\mathfrak{F}$ is a system $\mathfrak{F} = \{F; \oplus, \odot\}$ having two closed operations and satisfying the following postulates.

F1. The system $\{F; \oplus\}$ is a commutative group whose identity will be denoted by o.

F2. The system $\{F_o; \odot\}$ is a commutative group whose identity will be denoted by i, where $F_o = \{x \in F \mid x \neq o\}$.

F3. The operation $\odot$ is distributive over $\oplus$.

In order to distinguish the two inverses of an element $a \neq o$ relative to the two operations, we denote by a_- the inverse of a relative to $\oplus$, and by a' the inverse of a relative to $\odot$. The distributive law forms a connection between the two operations; for example, the theorem $a \odot o = o$ is valid for any field. Similarly, we can prove for arbitrary fields such well known properties of numbers as

$$a_- \odot b = (a \odot b)_- = a \odot b_-,$$

$$(a \odot b') \oplus (c \odot d') = [(a \odot d) \oplus (b \odot c)] \odot (b \odot d)',$$

and many others. You should read these theorems carefully, making sure that you understand the meaning of each term in the abstract sense rather than only for a numerical interpretation.

The concept of a field is a genuine extension of the three examples of number systems from which our investigation began; that is, there are many examples of fields other than the rational, real, and complex numbers. From the field postulates it is evident that any field must contain at least two elements, o and i, which are distinct, since $i \in F_o$ but $o \notin F_o$. Hence the smallest possible field contains two elements; it is easily verified that the field postulates are satisfied for the two-element system whose operations are defined by the tables below. In the $\oplus$-table, the element $x \oplus y$ appears in the row which is labeled x at the left and in the column which is labeled y at the top; the $\odot$-table is read similarly.

$\oplus$	o	i
o	o	i
i	i	o

$\odot$	o	i
o	o	o
i	o	i

This is an example of a finite field.

In the study of vector spaces and matrices we constantly make use of elements of a field. Although most of the results are valid regardless of the choice of the field, we occasionally need to require that the field have special algebraic properties. For example, we sometimes stipulate that the field satisfy the condition $i \oplus i \neq o$, which excludes the two-element field described above.

Exercises

1. Prove that the following theorems are valid in any field.

   (i) $a \odot o = o$.
   (ii) $a_- \odot b = (a \odot b)_-$.
   (iii) $(b')_- = (b_-)'$ if $b \neq o$.

2. Which of the field axioms are not satisfied for the system of integers with addition and multiplication defined in the usual way?

3. Prove that the set of all numbers of the form $a + b\sqrt{3}$, where a and b are rational numbers, together with numerical addition and multiplication, form a field.

4. Prove that the set of all rational functions forms a field relative to the usual addition and multiplication of functions. (A rational function is the ratio of two polynomials with real coefficients, the denominator being different from the zero polynomial.)

5. Let $C = R \times R$, where R is the set of real numbers. We define equality, addition, and multiplication in C as

$(a, b) = (c, d)$ if and only if $a = c$ and $b = d$ in R,

$(a, b) + (c, d) = (a + c, b + d)$,

$(a, b) \bullet (c, d) = (ac - bd, ad + bc)$.

Prove that the system $\{C; =; +, \bullet\}$ is a field.

6. Show that commutativity of addition is a consequence of the remaining eight postulates for a field.

CHAPTER 2

Vector Spaces

§2.1. *Introduction*

The purpose of this chapter is to develop a geometric system, called a *vector space*, upon which most of our study of matrices will be based. Before proceeding to a general definition, however, we shall consider three familiar examples of vector spaces which in all essential respects provide an accurate model of the general system.

First consider the cartesian plane, in which each point is represented uniquely by an ordered pair of real numbers (relative to a chosen rectangular coordinate system). To represent a physical quantity which has both magnitude and direction, such as force, we sometimes think of a vector as an arrow starting at the origin and proceeding to some point, say (a_1, a_2). These coordinates are called the *components* of the vector. The direction of the arrow is chosen as the direction of the force, and the length of the arrow

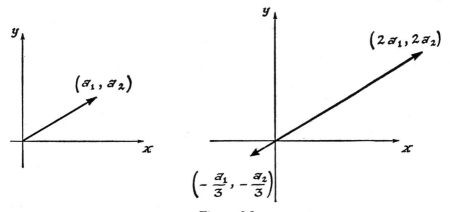

Figure 2.1

as the magnitude of the force. If this force is multiplied by a factor k, the resulting vector is described as (ka_1, ka_2); each of its components is multiplied by k.

If a second force is represented by the vector (b_1, b_2), the resultant physical effect of (a_1, a_2) and (b_1, b_2) acting simultaneously on a point (the origin) is described by the parallelogram principle: the resultant vector is the diagonal (from the origin) of the parallelogram having the two given vectors as adjacent sides. An easy application of analytic geometry shows that the resultant vector is described as $(a_1 + b_1, a_2 + b_2)$.

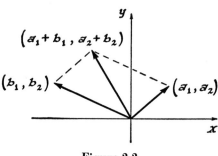

Figure 2.2

Now we observe that neither the magnitude nor the direction of the vector appears in this description of a vector, although each can be calculated from the components of the description. Likewise, the effect of multiplying a vector by a constant and the effect of combining two vectors into their resultant, both can be described very simply directly from the components. As we shall see in the material to follow, a surprising amount of geometry can be developed for vector spaces without any reference to the basically geometric concepts of length and angle; such metric considerations are deferred until Chapter 8.

But, we may ask, if length, distance, and angle do not form the basis of this geometry, what concepts are used? The answer has already been given in the first example: multiplication of a vector by a constant, and resultant addition of two vectors.

The second example is even more realistically allied to physical considerations, since we are inclined to believe that we live in three-dimensional space. A vector from the origin to a point in space is represented by the three coordinates (relative to a rectangular coordinate system) of the terminal point, (a_1, a_2, a_3). As in the plane, multiplying (a_1, a_2, a_3) by a constant k yields a vector whose coordinates are (ka_1, ka_2, ka_3); the resultant of (a_1, a_2, a_3) and (b_1, b_2, b_3) is $(a_1 + b_1, a_2 + b_2, a_3 + b_3)$, again by the parallelogram principle. This consistency of form of the representation of vectors enables us to consider vector spaces of higher dimensions, where geometric intuition is likely to fail and where physical experiments are not readily conceived. In particular, we note that in each of these examples the vectors form a commutative group relative to the "resultant" operation, which is called vector addition. Concerning the multiplication of a vector by constants, we observe that

1. $[k_1 + k_2](a_1, a_2) = k_1(a_1, a_2) + k_2(a_1, a_2)$,
2. $k[(a_1, a_2) + (b_1, b_2)] = k(a_1, a_2) + k(b_1, b_2)$,
3. $[k_1 k_2](a_1, a_2) = k_1[k_2(a_1, a_2)]$,
4. $1(a_1, a_2) = (a_1, a_2)$,

and similarly for vectors in three-dimensional space. This particular selection of observations may seem arbitrary, especially number 4, which appears almost too obvious to record. However, it is important to notice that a strong connection exists between the addition of vectors and the multiplication of vectors by constants. In that sense, numbers 1 and 2 resemble distributivity, number 3 resembles associativity, and number 4 is not unlike an identity.

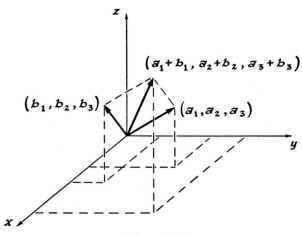

Figure 2.3

Our third example is of a different nature, for the objects which we call vectors are not pairs or triples of numbers; rather, a "vector" in this example is a real-valued function f which is continuous on the interval $0 \leq x \leq 1$. We recall that the product of a real number and a continuous function is a continuous function, and that the sum of two continuous functions is continuous. As usual we define kf and $f + g$ by the rules

$$(kf)(x) = kf(x),$$
$$(f + g)(x) = f(x) + g(x).$$

It is easily verified that multiplication of a function by a constant satisfies the four properties cited above. Furthermore, we observe that addition of functions is associative and commutative, the zero function is continuous and is the identity element relative to addition, and $-f$ is the additive inverse of f. Hence continuous functions form a commutative group relative to addition.

Exercises

1. Let (a_1, a_2) and (b_1, b_2) be two points of the plane which form a triangle with $(0, 0)$. For each of the conditions specified below, describe geometrically the set of points $\{k_1(a_1, a_2) + k_2(b_1, b_2)\}$.

    (i) $k_1 = 1, k_2 = 1$.
    (ii) $k_1 = 1, k_2 = -1$.
    (iii) $0 \leq k_1 \leq 1, k_2 = 0$.
    (iv) $0 \leq k_1 \leq 1, k_2 = 1$.
    (v) All $k_1, k_2 = 0$.
    (vi) $0 \leq k_1 \leq 1, 0 \leq k_2 \leq 1$.
    (vii) $0 \leq k_1 \leq 1, 0 \leq k_2 \leq 1, k_1 + k_2 = 1$.
    (viii) $0 \leq k_1, 0 \leq k_2 \leq 1$.
    (ix) All $k_1, 0 \leq k_2$.
    (x) All k_1, all k_2.

2. Which of the sets in Exercise 1 form an additive group?

3. (i) Consider the collection of all polynomials with real coefficients and of degree not exceeding 2:

$$a(x) = a_1 x^2 + a_2 x + a_3.$$

The sum of two such polynomials and the product of a polynomial by a real number are defined in the usual way, thus forming an abstract system with two operations. In what way does this system resemble the system of points in three-dimensional space as described in this section?

(ii) How might we define "the angle between two polynomials of degree not exceeding 2"?

§2.2. *Vector Spaces over a Field*

Having examined several examples of vector spaces, we now undertake to construct an abstract system which embodies these examples. From the first two examples of § 2.1 we might be tempted to say that a vector is an n-tuple of members, but the third example reminds us that it will be better not to specify too precisely the representation of a vector. We shall say simply that we have a set V of abstract elements called *vectors* and denoted by small Greek letters. In comparison with the abstract systems described in the first chapter, a vector space appears to be more complicated, because there is a second set of elements involved. In the examples considered, these elements are real numbers. For a general description, however, we shall only assume that the second set is a field F whose elements are called *scalars* and are denoted by small Latin letters. There are two field operations, denoted $+$ and $\cdot$, and two operations involving vectors. "Addition" of two vectors α and β produces a vector denoted $\alpha \oplus \beta$, and vectors form a commutative group relative to vector addition. Finally, "multiplication" of a scalar a and a vector α produces a vector $a \odot \alpha$, and scalar multiplication satisfies the four properties observed in § 2.1.

Definition 2.1. A system $\mathcal{V} = \{V, F; +, \cdot, \oplus, \odot\}$ is called a *vector space over the field* $\mathfrak{F}$ if and only if

(a) $\{F; +, \cdot\}$ is a field $\mathfrak{F}$ whose identity elements are denoted by 0 and 1,
(b) $\{V; \oplus\}$ is a commutative group whose identity element is denoted θ,
(c) for all $a, b \in F$ and all $\alpha, \beta \in V$, $a \odot \alpha \in V$, and

    (i) $(a + b) \odot \alpha = (a \odot \alpha) \oplus (b \odot \alpha)$,
    (ii) $a \odot (\alpha \oplus \beta) = (a \odot \alpha) \oplus (a \odot \beta)$,
    (iii) $(ab) \odot \alpha = a \odot (b \odot \alpha)$,
    (iv) $1 \odot \alpha = \alpha$.

Fortunately, the notation used above can be simplified. From the type of letters involved it is always clear whether we are adding two scalars or two vectors, or multiplying two scalars or a scalar and a vector; therefore, we can use $+$ to indicate both types of addition and juxtaposition to indicate both types of multiplication. Thus $(c + a)(\beta + d\alpha)$ denotes

$$(c + a) \odot [\beta \oplus (d \odot \alpha)].$$

Some of the theory of vector spaces is valid even if the scalars form only a *division ring* (a system which satisfies all field postulates except the commutative law of multiplication). For an introduction to vector spaces, however, such generality can be dispensed with. In fact, the field $\mathfrak{F}$ plays a subordinate role in our consideration most of the time. Except in the later chapters, where the nature of $\mathfrak{F}$ is clearly specified, you may think of $\mathfrak{F}$ as the field of real numbers without any curtailment of general understanding. Our first theorem concerns multiplication of special scalars and special vectors.

Theorem 2.1. Let θ denote the zero vector, and let $-\alpha$ denote the group inverse of α. Then for all $\alpha \in V$, $a \in F$,

(a) $0\alpha = \theta$,
(b) $(-1)\alpha = -\alpha$,
(c) $a\theta = \theta$.

PROOF: (a) $\alpha = 1\alpha = (1 + 0)\alpha = 1\alpha + 0\alpha = \alpha + 0\alpha$ by (iv) and (i) of Definition 2.1. Adding $-\alpha$ to both sides, we have $\theta = 0\alpha$.

(b) $\alpha + (-1)\alpha = 1\alpha + (-1)\alpha = (1 - 1)\alpha = \theta$. Hence $(-1)\alpha$ is an inverse of α, and (b) follows from the uniqueness of the group inverse.

(c) $a\theta = a[\alpha + (-\alpha)] = a\alpha + a(-\alpha) = a\alpha + (-a\alpha) = \theta$.

A geometric interpretation of this theorem is instructive, even though the results are not at all surprising. You are encouraged to make such interpretations of algebraic statements, and dually, to recognize algebraic implications of geometric results.

Examples of Vector Spaces Over the Field of Real Numbers

(a) For a fixed positive integer n, the set of all n-tuples of real numbers forms a vector space if addition of vectors and multiplication of a scalar and a vector are defined by

$$(x_1, \ldots, x_n) + (y_1, \ldots, y_n) = (x_1 + y_1, \ldots, x_n + y_n)$$

and

$$a(x_1, \ldots, x_n) = (ax_1, \ldots, ax_n).$$

For $n = 2, 3$ these are the two examples of § 2.1.

(b) A completely trivial example is that in which the zero n-tuple $(0, 0, \ldots, 0)$ is the only vector and the scalar field is the field of real numbers.

(c) Another trivial example is provided by considering the real numbers themselves as vectors and also as scalars. This space is represented geometrically by a line. More generally, if the elements of any field are considered both as vectors and scalars, and if the vector operations are defined to be the corresponding field operations, the resulting system is a vector space.

(d) For fixed n let V be the set of all polynomials in x with real coefficients and of degree not exceeding n together with the zero polynomial. Vector sum and scalar multiples are defined as the usual polynomial sum and product by real numbers.

(e) Let V be the set of all real valued functions which are differentiable on the interval $0 \leq x \leq 1$, with operations defined by

$$(f + g)(x) = f(x) + g(x),$$
$$(af)(x) = af(x).$$

Exercises

1. Verify that each of the preceding five examples satisfies the postulates of a vector space.

2. How are the vector spaces of Examples (a) and (d) related? (See Exercise 3, § 2.1.)

3. Let V be the set of all polynomials (of all degrees) with real coefficients, with the sum of polynomials and the product of a polynomial by a real number defined in the usual way. Prove that this system is a vector space.

4. Let V be the set of all sequences of real numbers, with the sum of sequences and the product of a sequence by a real number defined in the usual way. Prove that this system is a vector space. How is this example related to the vector space of Exercise 3?

5. Let V be the set of all real valued functions which attain a relative maximum or relative minimum value at $x = 0$, with the sum of two functions and the product of a function by a real number defined in the usual way. Is this system a vector space?

6. Consider the set of all triples of real numbers (a_1, a_2, a_3) subject to the conditions stated below. In each case determine whether the system forms a vector space relative to addition of triples and multiplication of a triple by a real number.

   (i) $a_1 = 0$; a_2 and a_3 arbitrary.
   (ii) $a_1 = -a_3$; a_2 arbitrary.
   (iii) a_1, a_2 arbitrary, $a_3 = 1 + a_1 - a_2$.
   (iv) a_1, a_2 arbitrary, $a_3 = 3a_1 - 4a_2$.
   (v) $a_1 a_2 \geq 0$, a_3 arbitrary.

7. Consider the set S of all solutions of a homogeneous differential equation of order n:
$$y^{(n)} + a_1(x)y^{(n-1)} + \cdots + a_{n-2}(x)y'' + a_{n-1}(x)y' + a_n(x)y = 0.$$
Prove that S forms a vector space relative to addition and scalar multiples of functions.

8. Given a set of m linear, homogeneous equations in n unknowns, with real coefficients:
$$a_{11}x_1 + a_{12}x_2 + \cdots + a_{1n}x_n = 0,$$
$$a_{21}x_1 + a_{22}x_2 + \cdots + a_{2n}x_n = 0,$$
$$\vdots$$
$$a_{m1}x_1 + a_{m2}x_2 + \cdots + a_{mn}x_n = 0.$$
Prove that the set S of all solutions of this system forms a vector space over the real numbers.

§2.3. *Subspaces*

In the study of any abstract system we are usually interested not only in the full system but also in various subsystems. When considering three-dimensional space our interest is in lines and planes, particularly in those lines and planes which pass through the origin and thereby constitute vector spaces in themselves. A general description of subspaces is given as follows.

> **Definition 2.2.** Given a vector space $\mathcal{U}$ over $\mathcal{F}$. A subset S of vectors is said to form a *subspace* $\mathcal{S}$ of $\mathcal{U}$ if and only if the subsystem $\mathcal{S} = \{S, F; +, \cdot, \oplus, \odot\}$ is a vector space.

Again we are made conscious of the fact that our language and notation can be simplified by ignoring the distinction between a system $\mathcal{S}$ and the set S of elements of the system. Henceforth we shall use $\mathcal{U}$ to denote both a vector space and the set of vectors of a vector space. With this simplification, a subspace $\mathcal{S}$ is a subset of $\mathcal{U}$ which, within itself, forms a vector space; it is understood that the field and the operations for $\mathcal{S}$ are the same as for $\mathcal{U}$.

The postulate that the vectors of a vector space form a group relative to vector addition implies that the zero vector θ is in every subspace. Trivially, the vector space which consists of θ alone is a subspace of every $\mathcal{U}$; likewise, $\mathcal{U}$ is a subspace of $\mathcal{U}$. In three-dimensional space, the nontrivial subspaces are simply all those lines and planes which pass through the origin.

We now seek a simple way of determining whether a given subset $S \subseteq \mathcal{U}$ is a subspace, because it is needlessly tedious to verify that each of the postulates of a vector space is satisfied for S; the next theorem provides an easily applied criterion.

> **Theorem 2.2.** A nonvoid subset S of $\mathcal{U}$ is a subspace if and only if S is closed under the two operations of vector sum and multiplication of vectors by scalars, as defined for $\mathcal{U}$; that is, for every $\alpha, \beta \in S$ and every $c \in \mathcal{F}$, $\alpha + \beta \in S$ and $c\alpha \in S$.
>
> P R O O F : The condition is clearly necessary. Conversely, assume that S is closed under the operations. Then $(-1)\alpha = -\alpha \in S$ for every $\alpha \in S$, and $\alpha + (-\alpha) = \theta \in S$. Vector addition in S is the same as in $\mathcal{U}$, so it is associative and commutative, and S forms a commutative group. The other postulates are satisfied in S because those properties are inherited from $\mathcal{U}$.

Examples of Subspaces

(a) In Example (a) of § 2.2, let S be the set of all n-tuples with $x_1 = 0$.

(b) In Example (a) of § 2.2, let S be the set of all n-tuples with $x_1 = kx_2$ for a fixed scalar k.

(c) In Example (e) of § 2.2, let S be the set of all constant functions on the interval $0 \le x \le 1$.

A general means of generating subspaces is provided by the following definition.

Definition 2.3. Given a vector space υ, let A be a nonvoid set of vectors. The set $[A]$ of all *linear combinations* of vectors of A is the collection of all finite sums of the form

$$a_1\alpha_1 + a_2\alpha_2 + \cdots + a_m\alpha_m,$$

where $a_i \in \mathfrak{F}$, $\alpha_i \in A$, and $m = 1, 2, 3, \ldots$.

Linear combinations of vectors are so vital in the study of vector spaces that the term *linear space* is used as a synonym for vector space, and the study of certain mappings of such spaces is called *linear algebra*. In the following theorem, which may be proved as an exercise, we have an example of the importance of linear combinations of vectors.

Theorem 2.3. The set of all linear combinations of any nonvoid set of vectors of υ is a subspace of υ.

Definition 2.4. The set of all linear combinations of a nonvoid set A of vectors is called the *subspace spanned by* A and is denoted $[A]$.

The concept of subspaces of υ is roughly analogous to that of subsets of a set, but important distinctions exist. An arbitrary subset of vectors is not a subspace, nor is the void set a subspace. We recall that subsets can be combined by the set operations of union and intersection to produce other subsets. A similar combination is possible for subspaces, but again the analogy is not perfect since the set union of two subspaces is not necessarily a subspace.

Definition 2.5. Let $\mathcal{S}$ and $\mathfrak{I}$ be subspaces of υ. The *sum* of $\mathcal{S}$ and $\mathfrak{I}$, denoted $\mathcal{S} + \mathfrak{I}$, is the set of all vectors $\sigma + \tau$, where $\sigma \in \mathcal{S}$ and $\tau \in \mathfrak{I}$.

Definition 2.6. The *intersection* of $\mathcal{S}$ and $\mathfrak{I}$, denoted $\mathcal{S} \cap \mathfrak{I}$, is the set of all vectors common to $\mathcal{S}$ and $\mathfrak{I}$.

Theorem 2.4. If $\mathcal{S}$ and $\mathfrak{I}$ are subspaces of υ, then $\mathcal{S} + \mathfrak{I}$ and $\mathcal{S} \cap \mathfrak{I}$ are subspaces of υ.

P R O O F : $\mathcal{S} + \mathfrak{I}$ is a subspace by Theorem 2.3, since any linear combination of vectors from $\mathcal{S}$ and $\mathfrak{I}$ can be written as the sum of a vector from $\mathcal{S}$ and a vector from $\mathfrak{I}$ because $\mathcal{S}$ and $\mathfrak{I}$ are subspaces. Indeed, $\mathcal{S} + \mathfrak{I}$ is simply the subspace generated by the set union of $\mathcal{S}$ and $\mathfrak{I}$. Now let $\alpha, \beta \in \mathcal{S} \cap \mathfrak{I}$, and let $c \in \mathfrak{F}$. Then $\alpha + \beta \in \mathcal{S}$, $\alpha + \beta \in \mathfrak{I}$, $c\alpha \in \mathcal{S}$, and $c\alpha \in \mathfrak{I}$, since $\mathcal{S}$ and $\mathfrak{I}$ are subspaces. Thus $\alpha + \beta \in \mathcal{S} \cap \mathfrak{I}$ and $c\alpha \in \mathcal{S} \cap \mathfrak{I}$. The operations in $\mathcal{S} \cap \mathfrak{I}$ are therefore closed, and $\mathcal{S} \cap \mathfrak{I}$ is a subspace by Theorem 2.2.

This theorem justifies the terminology given in Definitions 2.5 and 2.6. The set intersection of two subspaces turns out to be a subspace. However, the set union of two subspaces is not a subspace; the smallest subspace which contains this union is simply the set $[\text{S} \cup \text{J}]$ of all linear combinations of vectors chosen from $\text{S} \cup \text{J}$. Since any such vector is of the form $\sigma + \tau$, where $\sigma \in \text{S}$ and $\tau \in \text{J}$, we write $\text{S} + \text{J}$ to remind us of this fact. We recognize that further ambiguity is introduced in this use of the sign $+$, but once we are aware of the fact, the ambiguity is of no consequence.

Example

Consider the vector space V_3 of all triples of real numbers, as described in § 2.1, and let

$$\alpha = (1, 1, 0),$$
$$\beta = (0, 0, 1),$$
$$\gamma = (1, 0, 0),$$
$$\delta = (0, 2, 1),$$
$$\text{S} = [\alpha, \beta],$$
$$\text{J} = [\gamma, \delta].$$

The space $[\alpha]$ spanned by α is the line $y = x$ in the $z = 0$ plane—that is, the set of all real multiples of α. Similarly for the other vectors. Then S is the vertical plane $y = x$, since a point of S is any vector of the form $a\alpha + b\beta =$

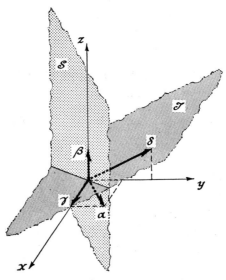

Figure 2.4

(a, a, b) for any real numbers a, b. Similarly, J is the set of all vectors of the form $c\gamma + d\delta = (c, 2d, d)$, a sloping plane $y = 2z$ containing the x-axis.

These two planes intersect in $S \cap \mathfrak{I}$, the line $x = y = 2z$ along the vector $2\gamma + \delta = (2, 2, 1) = 2\alpha + \beta$. It is easily verified that $S + \mathfrak{I} = \mathcal{V}_3$, since an arbitrary vector (x, y, z) of $\mathcal{V}_3$ can be expressed as $\sigma + \tau$, where $\sigma = y\alpha + z\beta \in S$ and $\tau = (x - y)\gamma \in \mathfrak{I}$.

We observe two related facts about this representation of (x, y, z). First, the representation is not unique, for we can write

$$\sigma' = \sigma - k(2\alpha + \beta) = (y - 2k)\alpha + (z - k)\beta,$$
$$\tau' = \tau + k(2\gamma + \delta) = (x - y + 2k)\gamma + k\delta,$$

for any real k, where $2\alpha + \beta \in S \cap \mathfrak{I}$. Then $(x, y, z) = \sigma' + \tau'$.

Second, the vector δ is not needed, for if we let $\mathfrak{R} = [\gamma]$, then $\tau \in \mathfrak{R}$ and $S + \mathfrak{R} = \mathcal{V}_3$, and $\mathfrak{R}$ is a line which intersects the plane S only at the origin. Thus $S \cap \mathfrak{R} = [\theta]$. As we shall see, any vector of $\mathcal{V}_3$ can be expressed *uniquely* as the sum of a vector in S and a vector in $\mathfrak{R}$.

Definition 2.7. Let $\mathfrak{M}$ and $\mathfrak{N}$ be subspaces of a vector space $\mathcal{V}$. $\mathcal{V}$ is said to be the *direct sum* of $\mathfrak{M}$ and $\mathfrak{N}$, written

$$\mathcal{V} = \mathfrak{M} \oplus \mathfrak{N},$$

if and only if $\mathfrak{M} + \mathfrak{N} = \mathcal{V}$ and $\mathfrak{M} \cap \mathfrak{N} = [\theta]$.

Theorem 2.5. $\mathcal{V} = \mathfrak{M} \oplus \mathfrak{N}$ if and only if every vector $\xi \in \mathcal{V}$ has a unique representation

$$\xi = \mu + \nu,$$

for some $\mu \in \mathfrak{M}$ and some $\nu \in \mathfrak{N}$.

P R O O F : Assume that $\mathcal{V} = \mathfrak{M} \oplus \mathfrak{N}$. Then since $\mathcal{V} = \mathfrak{M} + \mathfrak{N}$, each $\xi \in \mathcal{V}$ can be expressed as $\xi = \mu + \nu$ for suitable $\mu \in \mathfrak{M}$ and $\nu \in \mathfrak{N}$, and we need only prove uniqueness. Suppose also that $\xi = \mu_1 + \nu_1$. Then

$$\mu_1 + \nu_1 = \mu + \nu,$$

$$\mu_1 - \mu = \nu - \nu_1.$$

But $\mu_1 - \mu \in \mathfrak{M}$ and $\nu - \nu_1 \in \mathfrak{N}$, and by hypothesis $\mathfrak{M}$ and $\mathfrak{N}$ have only the zero vector in common. Hence $\mu_1 = \mu$ and $\nu_1 = \nu$, so the representation is unique. To prove the converse, assume that each $\xi \in \mathcal{V}$ is expressed uniquely as the sum of some $\mu \in \mathfrak{M}$ and $\nu \in \mathfrak{N}$. Clearly, $\mathfrak{M} + \mathfrak{N} = \mathcal{V}$. Let $\alpha \in \mathfrak{M} \cap \mathfrak{N}$. Then

$$\alpha = \alpha + \theta, \text{ where } \alpha \in \mathfrak{M} \text{ and } \theta \in \mathfrak{N}$$

$$= \theta + \alpha, \text{ where } \theta \in \mathfrak{M} \text{ and } \alpha \in \mathfrak{N}.$$

Since any such representation of α is unique, we have $\alpha = \theta$. Hence $\mathfrak{M} \cap \mathfrak{N} = [\theta]$, and therefore $\mathcal{V} = \mathfrak{M} \oplus \mathfrak{N}$.

Exercises

1. If $\mathcal{U}$ is the space of all real-valued functions which are continuous on $-1 \le x \le 1$, which of the following subsets are subspaces of $\mathcal{U}$?

(i) All differentiable functions.

(ii) All polynomials of degree two.

(iii) All polynomials of degree less than five.

(iv) All polynomials of degree greater than three.

(v) All odd functions $[f(-x) = -f(x)]$.

(vi) All even functions $[f(-x) = f(x)]$.

(vii) All functions for which $f(0) = 0$.

(viii) All nonnegative functions.

(ix) All constant functions.

(x) All functions for which $f^2(x) \le 0$.

2. Consider the collection of all subspaces $\mathcal{S}$ of a vector space $\mathcal{U}$, together with the operation $+$, sum of subspaces.

(i) Show that $+$ is associative and commutative.

(ii) Show that an identity subspace exists relative to $+$.

(iii) Is this system a commutative group?

3. Prove Theorem 2.3.

4. In the cartesian space of three dimensions, suppose that $\alpha = (2, 1, 0)$, $\beta = (1, 0, -1)$, $\gamma = (-1, 1, 1)$, $\delta = (0, -1, 1)$. Let $\mathcal{S} = [\alpha, \beta]$, $\mathcal{I} = [\gamma, \delta]$. Describe $\mathcal{S} \cap \mathcal{I}$ and $\mathcal{S} + \mathcal{I}$.

5. Show that $(\mathcal{R} + \mathcal{S}) \cap \mathcal{I} \supseteq (\mathcal{R} \cap \mathcal{I}) + (\mathcal{S} \cap \mathcal{I})$. Show by an example in the plane that equality need not hold.

6. Prove that if $\mathcal{R} \subseteq \mathcal{I}$, $(\mathcal{R} + \mathcal{S}) \cap \mathcal{I} = \mathcal{R} + (\mathcal{S} \cap \mathcal{I})$.

7. Referring to Exercise 4, find a vector $\xi \in \mathcal{I}$ such that $\mathcal{U} = \mathcal{S} \oplus [\xi]$. Is the choice of ξ uniquely determined? Explain your answer geometrically.

8. Let $\mathcal{S}$ be a subspace of a vector space $\mathcal{U}$ over $\mathcal{F}$. For each vector $\xi \in \mathcal{U}$, the $\mathcal{S}$-*coset of* ξ is defined to be the set

$$(\xi + \mathcal{S}) = \{\xi + \sigma \mid \sigma \in \mathcal{S}\}.$$

(Geometrically in $\mathcal{U}_3$ if $\mathcal{S}$ is a plane through the origin, $(\xi + \mathcal{S})$ is a plane which is parallel to $\mathcal{S}$ and passes through the tip of the vector ξ.)

(i) Show that $(\xi + \mathcal{S})$ is a subspace if and only if $\xi \in \mathcal{S}$.

(ii) Show that $(\xi + \mathcal{S}) = (\eta + \mathcal{S})$ if and only if $\xi - \eta \in \mathcal{S}$.

A new vector space over $\mathcal{F}$ can be formed from the collection C of all $\mathcal{S}$-cosets by defining the sum of two cosets and the scalar multiple of a coset:

$$(\xi_1 + \mathcal{S}) \oplus (\xi_2 + \mathcal{S}) = (\xi_1 + \xi_2 + \mathcal{S}),$$
$$a \odot (\xi_1 + \mathcal{S}) = (a\xi_1 + \mathcal{S}).$$

(iii) Show that these operations are unambiguously defined; that is, if $\eta_1 \in (\xi_1 + S)$ and $\eta_2 \in (\xi_2 + S)$, then

$$(\xi_1 + S) + (\xi_2 + S) = (\eta_1 + \eta_2 + S),$$
$$a \odot (\xi_1 + S) = (a\eta_1 + S).$$

(iv) Show that the system $\{C, F; +, \cdot, \oplus, \odot\}$ is a vector space. This space is called the *quotient space of* $\mathcal{V}$ *modulo* S and is denoted $\mathcal{V}/S$.

§2.4. *Linear Independence*

We now come to one of the most useful concepts in the theory of vector spaces, that of linear independence.

Definition 2.8. Let $\mathcal{V}$ be a vector space over a field $\mathcal{F}$ and let $S = \{\alpha_1, \ldots, \alpha_k\}$ be a finite subset of $\mathcal{V}$. S is said to be *linearly independent* if and only if every equation of the form

$$a_1\alpha_1 + a_2\alpha_2 + \cdots + a_k\alpha_k = \theta, \qquad a_i \in \mathcal{F},$$

implies that $a_1 = a_2 = \cdots = a_k = 0$.

An infinite set T is said to be linearly independent if and only if every finite subset of T is linearly independent. The void set is linearly independent. Any set of vectors which is not linearly independent is said to be *linearly dependent*.

The definition states that the zero vector can be obtained as a linear combination of independent vectors *only* in the trivial way, in which every scalar of the linear combination is zero. But if the zero vector is a nontrivial linear combination of vectors γ_i, we have

$$c_1\gamma_1 + c_2\gamma_2 + \cdots + c_m\gamma_m = \theta$$

where not all scalars c_i are zero. Let c_j be the first nonzero scalar. We obtain

$$\gamma_j = -\frac{1}{c_j} (c_{j+1}\gamma_{j+1} + \cdots + c_m\gamma_m).$$

In this case the vector γ_j *depends* linearly on the other vectors in the sense that γ_j is a linear combination of the others. Clearly any set of vectors is either linearly independent or linearly dependent, any set which contains the zero vector is dependent, and any set which consists of a single nonzero vector is independent.

To regard the void set as independent may appear at first glance to be a strange convention. However, that definition is logically consistent with the defining condition for independence of nonvoid finite sets. A corresponding agreement can be adopted to extend Definitions 2.3 and 2.4: the set of all linear combinations of the void set is defined to be the set consisting of the zero vector alone. Thus $[\Phi] = [\theta]$ by definition. By adopting these conventions for the void set, we can obtain a consistent theory of vector spaces in which many theorems concerning nonvoid sets of vectors remain valid even for the void set. The following is an example.

Theorem 2.6. Any subset of an independent set is independent, and any set containing a dependent subset is dependent.

P R O O F : Exercise.

On many occasions we shall need to construct linearly independent sets of vectors. We can begin by choosing any nonzero vector, but how should the next choice be made? The following theorem provides an answer.

Theorem 2.7. Let $S \subseteq \mathcal{V}$ be linearly independent and let $\mathfrak{I} = [S]$. Then for any vector ξ, $S \cup \{\xi\}$ is linearly independent if and only if $\xi \notin \mathfrak{I}$.

P R O O F : Let S, $\mathfrak{I}$, and ξ be as described. First suppose that $\xi \in \mathfrak{I}$; then for suitable scalars a_i and vectors $\alpha_i \in S$,

$$\xi = a_1\alpha_1 + a_2\alpha_2 + \cdots + a_k\alpha_k.$$

If $a_i = 0$ for each i, then $\xi = \theta$ and $S \cup \{\xi\}$ is linearly dependent. If some $a_i \neq 0$, again $S \cup \{\xi\}$ is linearly dependent. Conversely, suppose that $\xi \notin \mathfrak{I}$, and consider any equation of the form

$$b_1\alpha_1 + b_2\alpha_2 + \cdots + b_m\alpha_m + b_{m+1}\xi = \theta,$$

where each $\alpha_i \in S$. If $b_{m+1} \neq 0$, then ξ is a linear combination of vectors of S, and so $\xi \in \mathfrak{I}$, contrary to our assumption. Hence $b_{m+1} = 0$, and since S is linearly independent, $b_i = 0$ for all $i \leq m$. Then $S \cup \{\xi\}$ is linearly independent.

Thus a linearly independent set S of vectors may be extended to a larger linearly independent set by adjoining any vector which does not lie in the space spanned by S; of course it is possible that no such vector exists, since S might span $\mathcal{V}$. The next two theorems concern the selection of a linearly independent subset of a dependent set of vectors.

Theorem 2.8. Let $S = \{\alpha_1, \ldots, \alpha_k\}$ be a finite set of nonzero vectors. Then S is dependent if and only if

$$\alpha_m \in [\alpha_1, \ldots, \alpha_{m-1}]$$

for some $m \leq k$.

P R O O F : If for some m, $\alpha_m \in [\alpha_1, \ldots, \alpha_{m-1}]$, then $\{\alpha_1, \ldots, \alpha_m\}$ is dependent and so is S (Theorem 2.6). Conversely, suppose S is dependent and let m be the least integer such that $\{\alpha_1, \ldots, \alpha_m\}$ is dependent. Then for suitable scalars $c_1, \ldots, c_m$, not all zero,

$$\sum_{i=1}^{m} c_i \alpha_i = \theta.$$

If $c_m = 0$, then $\{\alpha_1, \ldots, \alpha_{m-1}\}$ is dependent, contradicting the definition of m. Hence

$$\alpha_m = -c_m^{-1}(c_1 \alpha_1 + \cdots + c_{m-1}\alpha_{m-1}) \in [\alpha_1, \ldots, \alpha_{m-1}].$$

Theorem 2.9. If $\mathfrak{I} \neq [\theta]$ is spanned by the set $S = \{\alpha_1, \ldots, \alpha_k\}$, there exists a linearly independent subset of S which also spans $\mathfrak{I}$.

FIRST PROOF: If S is independent, there is nothing to prove. Otherwise, by Theorem 2.7 there is a least integer i such that $\alpha_i \in [\alpha_1, \ldots, \alpha_{i-1}]$. Let $S_1 = S - \alpha_i$. Clearly $\mathfrak{I} = [S_1]$, and the argument can be repeated on S_1. Either S_1 is independent, in which case the proof is complete, or for some j, $S_2 = S_1 - \alpha_j$ spans $\mathfrak{I}$. The theorem follows by repeating the argument a finite number of times.

SECOND PROOF: Let $\alpha_{r_1} \neq \theta$ and let $\mathfrak{I}_1 = [\alpha_{r_1}]$. Then $\mathfrak{I}_1 \subseteq \mathfrak{I}$, and equality holds if $\alpha_i \in \mathfrak{I}_1$ for $i = 1, \ldots, k$, in which case the proof is complete. Otherwise, by Theorem 2.6, $\{\alpha_{r_1}, \alpha_{r_2}\}$ is linearly independent for some α_{r_2}. Let $\mathfrak{I}_2 = [\alpha_{r_1}, \alpha_{r_2}]$. Clearly $\mathfrak{I}_2 \subseteq \mathfrak{I}$, and the argument can be repeated to construct a linearly independent subset of S which spans $\mathfrak{I}$.

In each of these proofs we constructed an independent subset S' of S such that $[S'] = [S]$. Thus for every $\xi \in \mathfrak{I}$, $\{S', \xi\}$ is dependent, and if S'' is any set of vectors of $\mathfrak{I}$ which contains S' as a subset, either $S'' = S'$ or S'' is dependent. An independent set which has the property that it cannot be extended in $\mathfrak{I}$ to a larger independent set is called a *maximal independent subset* of $\mathfrak{I}$. This concept is used in the next section.

Corollary. Any finite set of nonzero vectors contains a maximal independent subset.

This corollary may be strengthened by dropping the word "finite," but we have no need here for the stronger result, and shall pursue the idea no further.

Exercises

1. (i) Referring to the vectors of Exercise 3, § 2.3, select an independent subset of $\{\alpha, \beta, \gamma, \delta\}$, containing three vectors.

(ii) Prove that the vectors of your answer to (i) form a maximal independent subset of $\mathcal{V}$.

(iii) Still referring to Exercise 3, § 2.3, choose any nonzero vector $\xi_1 \in S \cap \mathfrak{I}$. Find vectors ξ_2 and ξ_3 such that $S = [\xi_1, \xi_2]$ and $\mathfrak{I} = [\xi_1, \xi_3]$. Prove that $[\xi_1, \xi_2, \xi_3] = S + \mathfrak{I}$.

2. Select a maximal linearly independent subset of each of the following sets of vectors.

(i) $(1, 0, 1, 0)$, $(0, 1, 0, 1)$, $(1, 1, 1, 1)$, $(-1, 0, 2, 0)$.

(ii) $(0, 1, 2, 3)$, $(3, 0, 1, 2)$, $(2, 3, 0, 1)$, $(1, 2, 3, 0)$.

(iii) $(1, -1, 1, -1)$, $(-1, 1, -1, -1)$, $(1, -1, 1, -2)$, $(0, 0, 0, 1)$.

3. For each example of the preceding exercise in which the largest independent subset contains fewer than four vectors, adjoin vectors (a_1, a_2, a_3, a_4) to obtain a linearly independent set of four vectors.

4. Prove Theorem 2.5.

5. In the space of real n-tuples prove that the vectors

$$\alpha_1 = (1, 1, 1, \ldots, 1, 1),$$
$$\alpha_2 = (0, 1, 1, \ldots, 1, 1),$$
$$\alpha_3 = (0, 0, 1, \ldots, 1, 1),$$
$$\cdot$$
$$\cdot$$
$$\cdot$$
$$\alpha_n = (0, 0, 0, \ldots, 0, 1),$$

are linearly independent.

§2.5. *Basis*

At the beginning of the chapter, when we first discussed the physical concept of a vector in three-dimensional space, our description was made in terms of that ordered triple of numbers which specified the coordinates of the end point of the "arrow," relative to a rectangular coordinate system. We shall now examine this idea more carefully. First we observe that

$$(a_1, a_2, a_3) = a_1(1, 0, 0) + a_2(0, 1, 0) + a_3(0, 0, 1)$$
$$= a_1\epsilon_1 + a_2\epsilon_2 + a_3\epsilon_3,$$

where ϵ_i, $i = 1, 2, 3$, represents the triple whose ith component is 1 and whose other components are zero. Clearly, $\{\epsilon_1, \epsilon_2, \epsilon_3\}$ spans the space and is linearly independent. Therefore, this set is a maximal linearly independent subset of the space. These three vectors are unit vectors along three coordinate axes, and every point in the space acquires a unique system of coordinates relative to these vectors, the coordinates being the three scalars used to represent a given vector as a linear combination of the ϵ_i.

From the proofs of Theorem 2.9 it is clear that there is nothing unique about the way we might choose a maximal independent subset of a space. Many such subsets exist for three-dimensional space, and indeed for any space $\mathcal{V} \neq [\theta]$. For example, a second maximal linearly independent set in three-dimensional space is

$$\beta_1 = (0, 1, 1),$$
$$\beta_2 = (1, 0, 1),$$
$$\beta_3 = (1, 1, 0),$$

and if we let $s = \frac{1}{2}(a_1 + a_2 + a_3)$ we have the linear representation

$$(a_1, a_2, a_3) = (s - a_1)\beta_1 + (s - a_2)\beta_2 + (s - a_3)\beta_3.$$

The scalars of this representation are uniquely determined, but they are different from the scalars which represent the same point relative to the ϵ_i vectors. We now turn to a general consideration of these observations.

Definition 2.9. A maximal linearly independent subset of a vector space $\mathcal{V}$ is called a *basis* of $\mathcal{V}$. If $\mathcal{V}$ contains a finite basis, $\mathcal{V}$ is said to be *finite-dimensional;* otherwise $\mathcal{V}$ is *infinite-dimensional*.

In this book we shall devote our attention to finite-dimensional spaces except for occasional comments and examples to illustrate similarities or differences between the two types of spaces.

Since a basis for $\mathcal{V}$ spans $\mathcal{V}$, every vector $\xi \in \mathcal{V}$ is a linear combination of basis vectors,

$$\xi = c_1\alpha_1 + \cdots + c_k\alpha_k.$$

The scalars in this representation are unique; for suppose

$$\xi = b_1\alpha_1 + \cdots + b_k\alpha_k.$$

Then $\theta = \xi - \xi = (c_1 - b_1)\alpha_1 + \cdots + (c_k - b_k)\alpha_k$, and since the α_i are linearly independent, $c_i - b_i = 0$ for every $i = 1, \ldots, k$. We have proved the following theorem.

Theorem 2.10. If $\mathcal{V} \neq [\theta]$, every vector of $\mathcal{V}$ has a unique representation as a linear combination of the vectors of a fixed basis of $\mathcal{V}$.

This theorem reveals a significant interpretation of bases. Given a basis $\{\alpha_1, \ldots, \alpha_n\}$, each vector ξ can be represented in one and only one way as a linear combination of basis vectors:

$$\xi = c_1\alpha_1 + \cdots + c_n\alpha_n.$$

Thus ξ determines uniquely an n-tuple of scalars, $(c_1, \ldots, c_n)$, which can be regarded as the coordinates of ξ relative to the α-basis. Hence each basis of $\mathcal{V}$ determines a system of coordinates for $\mathcal{V}$. This suggests that any n-dimensional vector space is not unlike the space of all n-tuples of scalars, a fact which we later prove. We shall make repeated use of this interpretation of a basis as a coordinate system for $\mathcal{V}$.

Examples of Bases

(a) Consider the space of ordered pairs of real numbers, represented geometrically by the cartesian plane. The unit vectors (vectors of unit length along the chosen x- and y-axes) are $\epsilon_1 = (1, 0)$ and $\epsilon_2 = (0, 1)$, respectively. These two vectors form a basis since they are independent, and $(x, y) = x\epsilon_1 + y\epsilon_2$, so that ϵ_1 and ϵ_2 span the space. But also, $\alpha_1 = (a, 0)$ and $\alpha_2 = (0, b)$ form a basis for any a and b different from zero. Furthermore, $\beta_1 = (1, 1)$ and $\beta_2 = (-2, 1)$ form a basis. As shown in Figure 2.5, any pair of vectors which do not lie on the same line forms a basis for the plane.

(b) More generally for the space of all real n-tuples, let ϵ_i be the n-tuple whose ith component is 1, the other components being zero, $i = 1, 2, \ldots, n$. The ϵ_i are linearly independent, and $(a_1, \ldots, a_n) = a_1\epsilon_1 + \cdots + a_n\epsilon_n$, so the ϵ_i form a basis. Throughout this book we shall reserve the symbols ϵ_i to represent the vectors of this particular basis, and reserve the symbol $\mathcal{E}_n$ to represent the space of real n-tuples with this choice of basis.

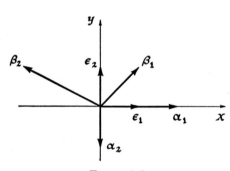

Figure 2.5

(c) Consider the space of all real polynomials of degree not exceeding a fixed natural number n. Then $x^0 = 1, x^1, \ldots, x^n$ form a basis.

(d) An example of an infinite-dimensional space is the space of all real polynomials. Each polynomial is of finite degree but we include *all* finite degrees. The polynomials x^k, $k = 0, 1, 2, \ldots$, form a basis.

We have seen that any vector space has many bases; however, every basis has the important property stated in the following theorem.

Theorem 2.11. Every basis for a finite-dimensional vector space $\mathcal{V}$ has the same number of elements.

P R O O F : Let $A = \{\alpha_1, \ldots, \alpha_k\}$ and $B = \{\beta_1, \ldots, \beta_m\}$ be bases for $\mathcal{V}$. Each set is a maximal independent set, so $B_1 = \{\alpha_1, \beta_1, \beta_2, \ldots, \beta_m\}$ is dependent. By Theorem 2.8 some β_i is a linear combination of the vectors which precede it, and there exists a subset B_1' of B_1 which contains α_1 as the first vector and which is a basis for $\mathcal{U}$. Then $B_2 = \{\alpha_2, B_1'\}$ is dependent, and some vector is a linear combination of the ones which precede it. This vector cannot be α_1 or α_2 since A is linearly independent. Hence there exists a subset B_2' of B_2 which contains α_2 and α_1 as the first and second vectors and which is a basis for $\mathcal{U}$. Let $B_3 = \{\alpha_3, B_2'\}$ and repeat the argument. If all the β_i are removed in this way before k steps, we obtain the basis $B_j = \{\alpha_j, \alpha_{j-1}, \ldots, \alpha_1\}$ for $j < k$, which contradicts the independence of A, since $\alpha_k \in [B_j]$. Hence k steps are required to remove all of the β_i, one or more at a time, so $k \leq m$. Reversing the roles of A and B in the replacement process, we obtain $m \leq k$, so the proof is complete.

Exercises

1. Verify that the several sets described in Examples (a) to (d) of this section are bases.

2. Let $\{\alpha_1, \ldots, \alpha_n\}$ be a basis for $\mathcal{U}$, and let c_i be arbitrary nonzero scalars, $i = 1, 2, \ldots, n$. Prove that $\{c_1\alpha_1, c_2\alpha_2, \ldots, c_n\alpha_n\}$ is a basis for $\mathcal{U}$. Interpret geometrically for $n = 3$.

3. Show that any three points which do not lie in a plane through the origin determine a basis for three-dimensional space.

4. Beginning with $\alpha_1 = (-1, 1, 2)$, construct two bases for the space of all real triples in such a way that if $\{\alpha_1, \alpha_2, \alpha_3\}$ and $\{\alpha_1, \alpha_2', \alpha_3'\}$ are the two bases, then $\{\alpha_2, \alpha_3, \alpha_3'\}$ is also a basis.

5. Given the basis $\alpha_1 = (1, 1, 1, 1)$, $\alpha_2 = (0, 1, 1, 1)$, $\alpha_3 = (0, 0, 1, 1)$, $\alpha_4 = (0, 0, 0, 1)$, express each vector ϵ_i, $i = 1, 2, 3, 4$, as a linear combination of the α's. Likewise express each α_i as a linear combination of the ϵ's.

6. Let $\{\alpha_1, \ldots, \alpha_n\}$ and $\{\beta_1, \ldots, \beta_n\}$ be two bases for the space of all real n-tuples. Define the mapping $\mathbf{T}$ of the space into itself by the statement,

$$\text{if } \xi = \sum_{i=1}^{n} c_i\alpha_i, \quad \text{then } \xi\mathbf{T} = \sum_{i=1}^{n} c_i\beta_i.$$

Verify that

    (i) $\mathbf{T}$ maps α_i onto β_i, $i = 1, \ldots, n$,

    (ii) $\mathbf{T}$ is a one-to-one mapping,

    (iii) $(\xi + \eta)\mathbf{T} = \xi\mathbf{T} + \eta\mathbf{T}$,

    (iv) $(k\xi)\mathbf{T} = k(\xi\mathbf{T})$.

7. Let $\mathcal{U}$ be a finite-dimensional vector space.

    (i) Prove that if $\{\alpha_1, \ldots, \alpha_n\}$ is a basis for $\mathcal{U}$, if $\mathcal{S} = [\alpha_1, \ldots, \alpha_k]$, and if $\mathcal{J} = [\alpha_{k+1}, \ldots, \alpha_n]$, then $\mathcal{U} = \mathcal{S} \oplus \mathcal{J}$.

(ii) Prove, conversely, that if S and 𝔍 are any subspaces of $\mathcal{V}$ such that $\mathcal{V} = S \oplus 𝔍$, if $\{\alpha_1, \ldots, \alpha_k\}$ is a basis for S, and if $\{\beta_1, \ldots, \beta_m\}$ is a basis for 𝔍, then $\{\alpha_1, \ldots, \alpha_k, \beta_1, \ldots, \beta_m\}$ is a basis for $\mathcal{V}$.

§2.6. *Dimension*

Now that the number of elements in any basis for $\mathcal{V}$ has been shown to be unique, we use this number as a definition of the dimension of a vector space.

Definition 2.10. The *dimension* of a finite-dimensional vector space is the number of vectors in any basis. The dimension of $\mathcal{V}$ is denoted $d(\mathcal{V})$.

By definition, a set of vectors is a basis of $\mathcal{V}$ if and only if two conditions are satisfied:

1. the set must be linearly independent, *and*
2. the set must span $\mathcal{V}$.

However, for an n-dimensional space and a set of n vectors, these two conditions turn out to be equivalent. This result (Theorem 2.13) simplifies the task of verifying that a given set is a basis. We first prove another useful theorem.

Theorem 2.12. Any linearly independent set of vectors in an n-dimensional space $\mathcal{V}$ can be extended to a basis.

P R O O F : Let $\{\alpha_1, \ldots, \alpha_k\}$ be linearly independent, and let $\{\beta_1, \ldots, \beta_n\}$ be a basis. Let $𝔍_k = [\alpha_1, \ldots, \alpha_k]$. If $\beta_i \in 𝔍_k$ for $i = 1, \ldots, n$, then $𝔍_k = \mathcal{V}$. Otherwise, for some j, $\beta_j \notin 𝔍_k$, so by Theorem 2.7 $\{\alpha_1, \ldots, \alpha_k, \beta_j\}$ is independent. Thus the original set has been extended to a larger independent set, and the theorem follows by repeating the argument until the enlarged set spans $\mathcal{V}$.

Theorem 2.13. Let $A = \{\alpha_1, \ldots, \alpha_n\}$ be an arbitrary set of n vectors of an n-dimensional space $\mathcal{V}$.
(a) A is a basis for $\mathcal{V}$ if and only if A is linearly independent.
(b) A is a basis for $\mathcal{V}$ if and only if $[A] = \mathcal{V}$.

P R O O F : If A is linearly independent, A may be extended to a basis by Theorem 2.12. But a basis contains only n vectors, so A is a basis. To prove the second statement, suppose $\mathcal{V} = [A]$. By Theorem 2.9 a linearly independent subset of A also spans $\mathcal{V}$ and hence is a basis. But any basis contains n vectors, so A itself must be that subset. The "only if" statements of (a) and (b) are valid by the definition of a basis.

If S and $\mathcal{J}$ are subspaces of $\mathcal{V}$, what can be said about the dimensions of the spaces $S + \mathcal{J}$ and $S \cap \mathcal{J}$ (§ 2.3)? A partial answer is available.

Theorem 2.14. $d(S + \mathcal{J}) + d(S \cap \mathcal{J}) = d(S) + d(\mathcal{J})$.

P R O O F : Of the four subspaces involved in this theorem, $S \cap \mathcal{J}$ is a subspace of each of the others, and both S and $\mathcal{J}$ are subspaces of $S + \mathcal{J}$. Our proof begins with the choice of a basis $\{\alpha_1, \ldots, \alpha_k\}$ for $S \cap \mathcal{J}$, where $k = d(S \cap \mathcal{J})$. Then $d(S) = k + i$ and $d(\mathcal{J}) = k + j$ for some non-negative i and j. The basis for $S \cap \mathcal{J}$ can be extended to a basis $\{\alpha_1, \ldots, \alpha_k, \beta_{k+1}, \ldots, \beta_{k+i}\}$ for S. A different extension similarly produces a basis $\{\alpha_1, \ldots, \alpha_k, \gamma_{k+1}, \ldots, \gamma_{k+j}\}$ for $\mathcal{J}$. Combining these two bases gives a set $\{\alpha_1, \ldots, \alpha_k, \beta_{k+1}, \ldots, \beta_{k+i}, \gamma_{k+1}, \ldots, \gamma_{k+j}\}$ of $k + i + j$ vectors. The theorem follows immediately when it is proved that this set is a basis for $S + \mathcal{J}$, which is left as an exercise. (Remember that since the dimension of $S + \mathcal{J}$ is not yet known to be $k + i + j$, it must be shown that this set is linearly independent *and* spans $S + \mathcal{J}$.)

It should be noticed that Theorem 2.14 is similar in form to Exercise 7 of § 1.2, concerning the number of elements in the union and intersection of finite sets. In geometric terms, Theorem 2.14 proves, for example, that in three-dimensional space any two distinct planes through the origin intersect in a line through the origin.

Exercises

1. Prove Theorem 2.14 in detail.
2. Determine the dimension of each of the five spaces given as examples in § 2.2.
3. Show that if subspaces $\mathcal{R}$ and S have the same dimension and if $\mathcal{R} \subseteq S$, then $\mathcal{R} = S$.
4. Let S be a k-dimensional subspace of the n-dimensional space $\mathcal{V}$, $k \geq 1$.
   (i) Show that an $(n - k)$-dimensional subspace $\mathcal{J}$ exists such that $S \cap \mathcal{J} = [\theta]$.
   (ii) Deduce that $S \oplus \mathcal{J} = \mathcal{V}$.
   (iii) Show that $\mathcal{J}$ is *not* uniquely determined by S and $\mathcal{V}$.
5. (i) Referring to Exercise 5, § 2.3, if necessary, prove that for subspaces $\mathcal{R}$, S, $\mathcal{J}$ of $\mathcal{V}$ $d(\mathcal{R} + S + \mathcal{J}) \leq d(\mathcal{R}) + d(S) + d(\mathcal{J}) - d(\mathcal{R} \cap S) - d(\mathcal{R} \cap \mathcal{J}) - d(S \cap \mathcal{J}) + d(\mathcal{R} \cap S \cap \mathcal{J})$.
   (ii) Compare (i) with the corresponding formula for the number of elements in finite subsets (Exercise 7(ii), § 1.2).
   (iii) Show that the result of (i) cannot be strengthened to equality in all cases (Exercise 5, § 2.3).

§2.7. *Isomorphism of Vector Spaces*

We now turn our attention to a problem which has been constantly in the background of our development of vector spaces. We began by making an informal description of the spaces $\mathcal{E}_2$ and $\mathcal{E}_3$, which were familiar from our knowledge of analytic geometry, and then generalized the form of our observations in order to define an abstract vector space. Abstract vector spaces are of two types—finite-dimensional or infinite-dimensional—and we agreed that we shall study only finite-dimensional spaces in this book. But in considering bases we began to suspect that any n-dimensional space over a field is essentially the same as the space $\mathcal{F}_n$ of n-tuples of field elements.

In order to formulate our suspicions more precisely, we must first agree upon a meaning of the phrase "essentially the same." This is a problem of importance for all abstract systems, but we confine our attention here to vector spaces; a more general discussion is given in Appendix A.

Consider two vector spaces,

$$\mathcal{V} = \{V, F; +, \cdot, \oplus, \odot\}$$

and

$$\mathcal{W} = \{W, F; +, \cdot, +, \bullet\},$$

over the same field $\mathcal{F}$. The vectors of the two systems might have different mathematical names, as suggested by the various examples of vector spaces given in § 2.2, and the vector operations of the two systems might be defined in different ways. However, suppose we can rename the vectors of the first system, assigning to each vector of the first system the name of a vector of the second system, with different names being given to distinct vectors. Suppose further that the new names are assigned in such a way that the vector operations of the renamed first system coincide exactly with the corresponding operations of the second system. Then we would agree that the two systems are identical twins which are distinguishable by name only, and not by behavior. This is what we mean by "essentially the same"; the mathematical term for this concept is *isomorphism*. We first define the more general notion of *homomorphism*.

Definition 2.11. Let

$$\mathcal{V} = \{V, F; +, \cdot, \oplus, \odot\}$$

and

$$\mathcal{W} = \{W, F; +, \cdot, +, \bullet\}$$

be vector spaces over a field $\mathcal{F}$. A mapping **H** of V into W is called a *homomorphism*, provided that for all $\alpha, \beta \in \mathcal{V}$ and all $a \in \mathcal{F}$,

$$(\alpha \oplus \beta)\mathbf{H} = \alpha\mathbf{H} + \beta\mathbf{H},$$

and

$$(a \odot \alpha)\mathbf{H} = a \bullet \alpha\mathbf{H}.$$

If every vector of $\mathcal{W}$ is in the range of $\mathbf{H}$, $\mathbf{H}$ is said to be a *homomorphism* of $\mathcal{V}$ *onto* $\mathcal{W}$.

Definition 2.12. A *one-to-one* homomorphism $\mathbf{J}$ of $\mathcal{V}$ onto $\mathcal{W}$ is called an *isomorphism*. If such a mapping exists, $\mathcal{V}$ and $\mathcal{W}$ are said to be *isomorphic*.

Thus, to establish that two vector spaces $\mathcal{V}$ and $\mathcal{W}$ over the same field $\mathcal{F}$ are isomorphic, we need to exhibit a one-to-one mapping of $\mathcal{V}$ onto $\mathcal{W}$ which preserves the two operations of vector sum and multiplication of a vector by a scalar. We are now ready to prove the following theorem.

Theorem 2.15. Any n-dimensional vector space $\mathcal{V}$ over $\mathcal{F}$ is isomorphic to the space $\mathcal{F}_n$ of all n-tuples of elements of $\mathcal{F}$.

P R O O F : Let $\{\alpha_1, \ldots, \alpha_n\}$ be a basis for $\mathcal{V}$. By Theorem 2.10 every $\xi \in \mathcal{V}$ has a unique representation as a linear combination of the α_i:

$$\xi = c_1\alpha_1 + \cdots + c_n\alpha_n.$$

To each $\xi \in \mathcal{V}$ we associate the corresponding n-tuple $(c_1, \ldots, c_n) \in \mathcal{F}_n$. This is a mapping of $\mathcal{V}$ onto $\mathcal{F}_n$, and distinct vectors of $\mathcal{V}$ map into distinct vectors of $\mathcal{F}_n$. Furthermore, let $\xi = \sum_{i=1}^n c_i\alpha_i$ and $\eta = \sum_{i=1}^n b_i\alpha_i$. Then

$$\xi + \eta = \sum_{i=1}^n (c_i + b_i)\alpha_i \longrightarrow (c_1 + b_1, \ldots, c_n + b_n)$$
$$= (c_1, \ldots, c_n) + (b_1, \ldots, b_n)$$

and

$$k\xi = \sum_{i=1}^n (kc_i)\alpha_i \longrightarrow (kc_1, \ldots, kc_n) = k(c_1, \ldots, c_n).$$

Hence vector sum and scalar multiplication are preserved by the mapping, and the systems are isomorphic.

This result tells us that any two vector spaces of the same finite dimension n are isomorphic, since each is isomorphic to $\mathcal{F}_n$. (See Exercise 4, below.) It allows us to think of any such abstract space in terms of the more familiar space of n-tuples.

The isomorphism theorem suggests that for finite-dimensional spaces our attempt to obtain generality by giving an abstract definition of vector spaces was not wholly successful. Any n-dimensional space over $\mathcal{F}$ is isomorphic to the space of n-tuples of elements of $\mathfrak{F}$. However, the n-tuple notation is often unnecessarily cumbersome, so we prefer to use the general notation for vectors, remembering that we can represent vectors as n-tuples of field elements, without loss of generality, whenever that particular representation proves to be convenient. We shall denote by $\mathcal{V}_n$ a vector space of dimension n with any basis.

Exercises

1. Establish an isomorphism between the space of all polynomials of degree not exceeding n and the space $\mathfrak{F}_{n+1}$. What are the images of the basis vectors under the isomorphism?

2. Let **J** be an isomorphism of the spaces $\mathcal{V}_n$ and $\mathcal{W}_n$. Let $\{\alpha_1, \ldots, \alpha_k\}$ be a linearly independent set of vectors in $\mathcal{V}_n$, $k \leq n$. Prove that $\{\alpha_1\mathbf{J}, \ldots, \alpha_k\mathbf{J}\}$ is linearly independent in $\mathcal{W}_n$. Deduce that the isomorphic image of a basis is a basis.

3. Let **H** be a homomorphism of $\mathcal{V}_n$ into $\mathcal{W}_n$. Prove that **H** is an isomorphism if and only if, for every $\xi \neq \theta$ in $\mathcal{V}_n$, $\xi\mathbf{H} \neq \theta$ in $\mathcal{W}_n$.

4. Suppose that vector spaces $\mathcal{V}$ and $\mathcal{W}$ are both isomorphic to the same space $\mathcal{U}$. Show how these two isomorphisms can be combined to yield an isomorphism of $\mathcal{V}$ onto $\mathcal{W}$.

5. Let $\mathcal{V}$ and $\mathcal{W}$ be vector spaces over the same field $\mathfrak{F}$, and let $\mathcal{K}$ denote the collection of all homomorphisms from $\mathcal{V}$ into $\mathcal{W}$. The sum of two homomorphisms is defined by

$$\xi(\mathbf{H}_1 + \mathbf{H}_2) = \xi\mathbf{H}_1 + \xi\mathbf{H}_2 \qquad \text{for all } \xi \in \mathcal{V}.$$

Also, the product of a scalar and a homomorphism is defined by

$$\xi(a\mathbf{H}) = a(\xi\mathbf{H}) \qquad \text{for all } a \in \mathfrak{F}, \, \xi \in \mathcal{V}.$$

Show that $\mathbf{H}_1 + \mathbf{H}_2$ and $a\mathbf{H}$ are also homomorphisms from $\mathcal{V}$ into $\mathcal{W}$ and that $\mathcal{K}$ forms a vector space over $\mathfrak{F}$ relative to these operations.

6. Referring to Exercise 5, if $\mathcal{W} = \mathcal{V}$, then it is possible to define the product of two homomorphisms in $\mathcal{K}$ in terms of the rule for successive mappings:

$$\xi(\mathbf{H}_1\mathbf{H}_2) = (\xi\mathbf{H}_1)\mathbf{H}_2 \qquad \text{for all } \xi \in \mathcal{V}.$$

Show that $\mathbf{H}_1\mathbf{H}_2$ is a homomorphism from $\mathcal{V}$ into $\mathcal{V}$.

7. If we specialize Exercise 5 by choosing $\mathcal{W}$ to be the field $\mathfrak{F}$, considered as a vector space over itself, then the members of $\mathcal{K}$ are scalar valued functions defined on $\mathcal{V}$ and satisfying the properties of a homomorphism. Any such function is called a *linear functional*, and the vector space $\mathcal{K}$ of all linear functionals from $\mathcal{V}$ to $\mathfrak{F}$ is called the *dual space* of $\mathcal{V}$. Determine whether or not each of the following mappings is a linear functional.

(i) In $\mathfrak{F}_n$, the mappings

$$(a_1, \ldots, a_n)\mathbf{H} = 2a_1,$$
$$(a_1, \ldots, a_n)\mathbf{H} = a_1 + 2.$$

(ii) In the space of all real-valued functions which are differentiable on the interval $-1 \le x \le 1$, the mappings

$$f\mathbf{H} = f'(0),$$
$$f\mathbf{H} = f(0)f'(0).$$

(iii) In the space of all real-valued functions which are continuous on the interval $0 \le x \le 1$, the mappings

$$f\mathbf{H} = \int_0^1 f(t)e^{-t}dt,$$
$$f\mathbf{H} = \int_0^1 f(te^{-t})dt,$$
$$f\mathbf{H} = \int_0^1 e^{-f(t)}dt.$$

8. Associated with any subspace $\mathcal{S}$ of $\mathcal{U}$ there is a family of homomorphisms from $\mathcal{U}$ to $\mathcal{S}$ called *projections*. Each such projection $\mathbf{P}_\mathcal{S}$ is determined by the choice of a subspace $\mathfrak{I}$ such that $\mathcal{U} = \mathcal{S} \oplus \mathfrak{I}$ (Exercise 4, § 2.6). Since each $\xi \in \mathcal{U}$ has a unique representation $\xi = \sigma + \tau$, where $\sigma \in \mathcal{S}$ and $\tau \in \mathfrak{I}$, the mapping $\mathbf{P}_\mathcal{S}$ is defined by

$$\xi\mathbf{P}_\mathcal{S} = \sigma$$

and is called the projection of $\mathcal{U}$ onto $\mathcal{S}$ along $\mathfrak{I}$. Similarly, the mapping $\mathbf{P}_\mathfrak{I}$,

$$\xi\mathbf{P}_\mathfrak{I} = \tau,$$

is called the projection of $\mathcal{U}$ onto $\mathfrak{I}$ along $\mathcal{S}$. Prove that

(i) $\mathbf{P}_\mathcal{S}$ and $\mathbf{P}_\mathfrak{I}$ are homomorphisms of $\mathcal{U}$ onto $\mathcal{S}$ and onto $\mathfrak{I}$, respectively.

(ii) $\mathbf{P}_\mathcal{S}$ and $\mathbf{P}_\mathfrak{I}$ are idempotent relative to the operation of successive mapping operations (Exercise 6).

(iii) $\mathbf{P}_\mathcal{S}\mathbf{P}_\mathfrak{I} = \mathbf{Z} = \mathbf{P}_\mathfrak{I}\mathbf{P}_\mathcal{S}$, where $\xi\mathbf{Z} = \theta$ for every $\xi \in \mathcal{U}$.

(iv) $\mathbf{P}_\mathcal{S} + \mathbf{P}_\mathfrak{I} = \mathbf{I}$, where $\xi\mathbf{I} = \xi$ for every $\xi \in \mathcal{U}$.

CHAPTER 3

Linear Transformations

§3.1. *Homomorphisms of Vector Spaces*

A study of vector spaces can be extended beyond the preliminary investigations of the preceding chapter, and we shall develop further theory as it is needed. For the present, however, we turn our attention from the spaces themselves to the subject of homomorphisms of vector spaces. In this chapter and the next we shall see that such homomorphisms are intimately related to matrices.

We assume that $\mathcal{V}$ and $\mathcal{W}$ are vector spaces over the same field $\mathcal{F}$. From Definition 2.11, a homomorphism of $\mathcal{V}$ into $\mathcal{W}$ is a mapping $\mathbf{H}$ which preserves the two operations involving vectors; that is, for all α, $\beta \in \mathcal{V}$, $a \in \mathcal{F}$, the following equations hold in $\mathcal{W}$:

1. $(\alpha + \beta)\mathbf{H} = \alpha\mathbf{H} + \beta\mathbf{H}$,
2. $(a\alpha)\mathbf{H} = a(\alpha\mathbf{H})$.

We now show that equations 1 and 2 can be replaced by the single condition

3. $(a\alpha + b\beta)\mathbf{H} = a(\alpha\mathbf{H}) + b(\beta\mathbf{H})$.

Clearly, equation 1 follows from equation 3 by selecting $a = 1 = b$, and equation 2 follows by choosing $b = 0$. Conversely,

$$(a\alpha + b\beta)\mathbf{H} = (a\alpha)\mathbf{H} + (b\beta)\mathbf{H}$$

by equation 1, which then reduces to $a(\alpha\mathbf{H}) + b(\beta\mathbf{H})$ by equation 2.

Condition 3 is the requirement of linearity, and since a homomorphism is a mapping, it is reasonable to use geometric language to describe mappings. Henceforth we shall call such a homomorphism a *linear transformation*. The terms *linear mapping* and *linear operator* are also used as synonyms.

Definition 3.1. A *linear transformation* **T** from a vector space $\mathcal{U}$ to a vector space $\mathcal{W}$, both over the scalar field $\mathcal{F}$, is a mapping of $\mathcal{U}$ into $\mathcal{W}$ such that for all $\alpha, \beta \in \mathcal{U}$ and for all $a, b \in \mathcal{F}$,

$$(a\alpha + b\beta)\mathbf{T} = a(\alpha\mathbf{T}) + b(\beta\mathbf{T}).$$

This definition is stated more elegantly in the form "a linear transformation from $\mathcal{U}$ to $\mathcal{W}$ is a homomorphism of $\mathcal{U}$ into $\mathcal{W}$." We remark that either form of the definition includes the possibility that $\mathcal{W}$ and $\mathcal{U}$ are the same space.

Before proceeding we call attention to our choice of notation for linear transformations, which will have important consequences for the notation which we later adopt for matrices. Since a linear transformation **T** is a function from $\mathcal{U}$ to $\mathcal{W}$ we could use standard functional notation in which $\mathbf{T}(\alpha)$ represents the "value" of the function **T** at the vector α. But, as we observed in § 1.4, if we wish to emphasize the geometric character of **T** as a mapping, and particularly if successive mapping (function of a function) is considered often, the notation $\alpha\mathbf{T}$ is a useful substitute for $\mathbf{T}(\alpha)$. In this respect the notation for linear transformations is not standardized, and you are advised when consulting other books to ascertain whether the author uses $\mathbf{T}(\alpha)$ (left-hand notation) or $\alpha\mathbf{T}$ (right-hand notation) for linear transformations and matrices. Right-hand notation is used in this book. However, to facilitate the translation of major results from one notational system to the other, a summary of results in both systems is given in Appendix B.

We shall regard linear transformations as the elements of an abstract system whose nature is to be investigated. First we need to decide upon the relations and operations of the system. Since linear transformations are functions, we accept the notion of equality of functions as a definition of equality of linear transformations.

Definition 3.2. Two linear transformations $\mathbf{T}_1$ and $\mathbf{T}_2$ from $\mathcal{U}$ to $\mathcal{W}$ are said to be *equal* if and only if $\alpha\mathbf{T}_1 = \alpha\mathbf{T}_2$ for all $\alpha \in \mathcal{U}$.

This means that equal transformations determine the same mapping of the vectors of $\mathcal{U}$ into vectors of $\mathcal{W}$, and that a linear transformation is determined by its effect on the vectors of $\mathcal{U}$. We use this method of description to define operations on linear transformations.

Definition 3.3. The *sum* $\mathbf{T}_1 \oplus \mathbf{T}_2$ and *scalar multiple* $c \odot \mathbf{T}_1$ of linear transformations from $\mathcal{U}$ to $\mathcal{W}$ are defined, respectively, by

(a) $\alpha(\mathbf{T}_1 \oplus \mathbf{T}_2) = \alpha\mathbf{T}_1 + \alpha\mathbf{T}_2$, all $\alpha \in \mathcal{U}$,
(b) $\alpha(c \odot \mathbf{T}_1) = c(\alpha\mathbf{T}_1)$, all $\alpha \in \mathcal{U}$, $c \in \mathcal{F}$.

Thus, given a field $\mathfrak{F}$ and two vector spaces $\mathcal{V}$ and $\mathcal{W}$ over $\mathfrak{F}$, the set L of all linear transformations forms a system $\mathcal{L}$ for which two operations are defined.

Sum: $\mathbf{T}_1 \oplus \mathbf{T}_2,$ all $\mathbf{T}_1, \mathbf{T}_2 \in L.$
Scalar multiple: $c \odot \mathbf{T}_1,$ all $c \in \mathfrak{F}, \mathbf{T}_1 \in L.$

Theorem 3.1. Let $\mathfrak{F}$ be a field, $\mathcal{V}$ and $\mathcal{W}$ vector spaces over $\mathfrak{F}$, and L the set of all linear transformations from $\mathcal{V}$ to $\mathcal{W}$. The system

$$\mathcal{L} = \{L, F; +, \cdot, \oplus, \odot\}$$

is a vector space over $\mathfrak{F}$.

P R O O F : Exercise. Except for minor changes of terminology, this is Exercise 5, § 2.7.

Most of our attention in the rest of this book will be devoted to the study of properties of the space $\mathcal{L}$ and its elements. Generally we shall consider linear mappings from one vector space $\mathcal{V}$ to another space $\mathcal{W}$. But frequently we shall specialize this general study by choosing $\mathcal{W}$ in one of two ways: either $\mathcal{W} = \mathcal{V}$ or $\mathcal{W} = \mathfrak{F}$, where we regard the field $\mathfrak{F}$ as a vector space over itself. These special cases are investigated in § 3.6 and § 3.4, respectively.

Definition 3.4. Let $\mathcal{V}$, $\mathcal{W}$, and $\mathcal{Y}$ be vector spaces over $\mathfrak{F}$, let $\mathbf{T}_1$ be a linear transformation from $\mathcal{V}$ to $\mathcal{W}$, and let $\mathbf{T}_2$ be a linear transformation from $\mathcal{W}$ to $\mathcal{Y}$. Then the *product* transformation $\mathbf{T}_1 \boxdot \mathbf{T}_2$ is the mapping from $\mathcal{V}$ to $\mathcal{Y}$ defined by

$$\alpha(\mathbf{T}_1 \boxdot \mathbf{T}_2) = (\alpha\mathbf{T}_1)\mathbf{T}_2 \qquad \text{for every } \alpha \in \mathcal{V}.$$

It is easily verified that $\mathbf{T}_1 \boxdot \mathbf{T}_2$ is linear. We note in particular that if we restrict our attention to the set L of linear transformations from $\mathcal{V}$ into $\mathcal{V}$ itself, then in addition to sum $\oplus$ and scalar multiple $\odot$, a third operation $\boxdot$ is defined for the system $\mathcal{L}$. Since $\boxdot$ is the successive mapping operation, it is associative. We shall return to this point in § 3.6.

Several special linear transformations merit our attention. The *zero* linear transformation $\mathbf{Z}$ is defined from $\mathcal{V}$ to $\mathcal{W}$ by

$$\alpha\mathbf{Z} = \theta \qquad \text{for every } \alpha \in \mathcal{V}.$$

Corresponding to each linear transformation $\mathbf{T}$ from $\mathcal{V}$ to $\mathcal{W}$, there is the *negative* linear transformation, denoted $-\mathbf{T}$ and defined by

$$\alpha(-\mathbf{T}) = -\alpha\mathbf{T} \qquad \text{for every } \alpha \in \mathcal{V}.$$

For each space $\mathcal{V}$ there is an *identity* linear transformation $\mathbf{I}$ from $\mathcal{V}$ onto $\mathcal{V}$, defined by

$$\alpha\mathbf{I} = \alpha \qquad \text{for every } \alpha \in \mathcal{V}.$$

Of course, if $\mathbf{T}$ is a linear transformation from $\mathcal{V}$ to $\mathcal{W}$, then both $\mathbf{I} \boxdot \mathbf{T}$ and

T □ **I** are defined, but in the former **I** represents the identity mapping on $\mathcal{U}$ and in the latter **I** represents the identity mapping on $\mathcal{W}$. You should verify that these names are justified; that is, that

$$\mathbf{T} \oplus \mathbf{Z} = \mathbf{T} \qquad \text{for every } \mathbf{T},$$
$$\mathbf{T} \oplus -\mathbf{T} = \mathbf{Z} \qquad \text{for every } \mathbf{T},$$
$$\mathbf{T} \square \mathbf{I} = \mathbf{I} \square \mathbf{T} = \mathbf{T} \qquad \text{for every } \mathbf{T}.$$

Once again we simplify our notation by using customary symbols for the operations on linear transformations.

Examples of Linear Transformations

(a) The space $\mathcal{E}_2$ of pairs of real numbers is represented geometrically by the plane. The transformation defined by $(x, y)\mathbf{T} = (kx, ky)$ for fixed scalar k is a linear transformation which maps each point P into the point Q which is collinear with P and the origin and k times as far from the origin as P is.

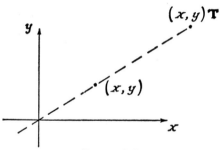

Figure 3.1

(b) Again in $\mathcal{E}_2$, the transformation defined by

$$(x, y)\mathbf{T} = (x \cos \Psi - y \sin \Psi, x \sin \Psi + y \cos \Psi)$$

is a linear transformation which rotates each point of the plane about the origin and through the angle Ψ.

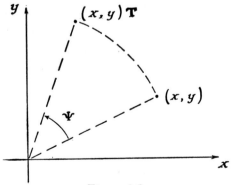

Figure 3.2

(c) In $\mathcal{E}_2$ let T_1, T_2, and T_3 be defined by

$$(x, y)T_1 = (x, 0),$$
$$(x, y)T_2 = (0, y),$$
$$(x, y)T_3 = (y, x).$$

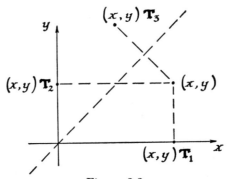

Figure 3.3

All of these transformations are linear. T_1 is a projection of each point of the plane onto the x-axis; T_2 is a projection onto the y-axis; T_3 is a reflection across the line $y = x$. Observe that $(x, y)T_1T_2 = (x, 0)T_2 = (0, 0)$, so $T_1T_2 = Z$ but $T_1 \neq Z$ and $T_2 \neq Z$. Hence *a product of nonzero transformations can be the zero transformation.* Also, $(x, y)T_2T_3 = (0, y)T_3 = (y, 0)$; however, $(x, y)T_3T_2 = (y, x)T_2 = (0, x)$. Hence $T_2T_3 \neq T_3T_2$, so the *multiplication of transformations is not commutative.* Finally, observe that $(x, y)T_1T_1 = (x, 0)T_1 = (x, 0) = (x, y)T_1$, so that $T_1^2 = T_1$. Thus *there exist idempotent transformations* other than I and Z.

(d) In the space of polynomials P of degree not exceeding n, let

$$P(x)D = \frac{d}{dx} P(x).$$

Familiar properties of the derivative show that D is linear. Observe also that $P(x)D^{n+1} = 0$ for every polynomial in the space, so $D^{n+1} = Z$. Thus *there exist nonzero transformations T such that a finite power of T is Z.* A transformation T is called *nilpotent of index k* if $T^k = Z$ but $T^{k-1} \neq Z$.

Exercises

1. Prove that the sum and scalar multiple of linear transformations are linear.

2. Show that the transformations Z, I, and $-T$ are entitled to the names zero, identity, and negative.

3. Verify that each transformation listed in Examples (a) to (d) is linear.

4. Prove that $\theta\mathbf{T} = \theta$ for any linear transformation $\mathbf{T}$.

5. If we regard the complex numbers as a vector space over the real field, is the conjugate mapping, $(a + ib)\mathbf{T} = a - ib$, a linear transformation?

6. Let $\mathbf{T}$ be a linear transformation of $\mathcal{V}$ into $\mathcal{W}$.

(i) Show that any subspace of $\mathcal{V}$ is mapped by $\mathbf{T}$ into a subspace of $\mathcal{W}$.

(ii) Conversely, show that if $\mathcal{Y}$ is a subspace of $\mathcal{W}$, the set of all vectors mapped into $\mathcal{Y}$ is a subspace of $\mathcal{V}$.

7. (i) Show that a linear transformation $\mathbf{T}$ from $\mathcal{V}_n$ to $\mathcal{W}$ is determined by the effect of $\mathbf{T}$ on any basis of $\mathcal{V}_n$.

(ii) Conversely, let $\{\alpha_1, \ldots, \alpha_n\}$ be a basis of $\mathcal{V}_n$ and let $\{\beta_1, \ldots, \beta_n\}$ be any set of n vectors in $\mathcal{W}$. Show how the correspondence $\alpha_i \longrightarrow \beta_i$ can be used to define a linear transformation from all of $\mathcal{V}_n$ into $\mathcal{W}$.

8. Which of the following transformations on $\mathcal{E}_3$ are linear? Describe the geometric effect of each.

(i) $(a_1, a_2, a_3)\mathbf{T} = (a_1 + 1, a_2 + 1, 0)$,
(ii) $(a_1, a_2, a_3)\mathbf{T} = (a_2, a_1, a_3)$,
(iii) $(a_1, a_2, a_3)\mathbf{T} = (a_1, a_2, 1)$,
(iv) $(a_1, a_2, a_3)\mathbf{T} = (a_1, -a_2, -a_3)$.

9. Let $\mathcal{V}, \mathcal{W}, \mathcal{X}, \mathcal{Y}$ be vector spaces over $\mathcal{F}$ and let $\mathbf{R}, \mathbf{S}, \mathbf{T}$ be linear mappings, respectively, of $\mathcal{V}$ into $\mathcal{W}$, $\mathcal{W}$ into $\mathcal{X}$, and $\mathcal{X}$ into $\mathcal{Y}$.

(i) Prove that $\mathbf{R} \boxdot \mathbf{S}$ is a linear mapping of $\mathcal{V}$ into $\mathcal{X}$.

(ii) Prove that $(\mathbf{R} \boxdot \mathbf{S}) \boxdot \mathbf{T} = \mathbf{R} \boxdot (\mathbf{S} \boxdot \mathbf{T})$.

10. In the space of all polynomials P of all degrees define mappings $\mathbf{M}$ and $\mathbf{D}$ by

$$P(x)\mathbf{D} = \frac{d}{dx}P(x),$$

$$P(x)\mathbf{M} = xP(x).$$

(i) Prove that both $\mathbf{D}$ and $\mathbf{M}$ are linear transformations.
(ii) Is $\mathbf{D}$ nilpotent on this space? Compare with $\mathbf{D}$ in Example (d).
(iii) Prove that $\mathbf{MD} - \mathbf{DM} = \mathbf{I}$.
(iv) Deduce that $(\mathbf{DM})^2 = \mathbf{D}^2\mathbf{M}^2 + \mathbf{DM}$.

§3.2. *Rank and Nullity of a Linear Transformation*

We recall that a linear transformation $\mathbf{T}$ is, by definition, a homomorphism from a space $\mathcal{V}$ into a space $\mathcal{W}$, where $\mathcal{V}$ and $\mathcal{W}$ may be the same space, but are not necessarily so. The domain of $\mathbf{T}$ is the space $\mathcal{V}$, and the range of $\mathbf{T}$ is a subset $\mathcal{R}_\mathbf{T}$ of $\mathcal{W}$, the set of all images $\alpha\mathbf{T}$ of the vectors of $\mathcal{V}$:

$$\mathcal{R}_\mathbf{T} = \{\beta \in \mathcal{W} \mid \beta = \alpha\mathbf{T} \text{ for some } \alpha \in \mathcal{V}\}.$$

It is easily proved that $\mathcal{R}_\mathbf{T}$ is actually a *subspace* of $\mathcal{W}$, for if $\beta,\, \gamma \in \mathcal{R}_\mathbf{T}$, then $\beta = \alpha_1\mathbf{T}$ and $\gamma = \alpha_2\mathbf{T}$. Hence $\beta + \gamma = \alpha_1\mathbf{T} + \alpha_2\mathbf{T} = (\alpha_1 + \alpha_2)\mathbf{T} \in \mathcal{R}_\mathbf{T}$. Similarly for $c \in \mathfrak{F}$, $c\beta = c(\alpha_1\mathbf{T}) = (c\alpha_1)\mathbf{T} \in \mathcal{R}_\mathbf{T}$. By Theorem 2.2, $\mathcal{R}_\mathbf{T}$ is a subspace of $\mathcal{W}$.

Another important set associated with any vector space homomorphism $\mathbf{T}$ is the *kernel* $\mathfrak{N}_\mathbf{T}$ of the homomorphism, which is defined to be the set of all vectors in $\mathcal{V}$ which are mapped into θ:

$$\mathfrak{N}_\mathbf{T} = \{\alpha \in \mathcal{V} \mid \alpha\mathbf{T} = \theta\}.$$

To see that $\mathfrak{N}_\mathbf{T}$ is a subspace of $\mathcal{V}$, let $\alpha,\, \beta \in \mathfrak{N}_\mathbf{T}$, $c \in \mathfrak{F}$. Then $(\alpha + \beta)\mathbf{T} = \alpha\mathbf{T} + \beta\mathbf{T} = \theta + \theta = \theta$, so $\alpha + \beta \in \mathfrak{N}_\mathbf{T}$; also $(c\alpha)\mathbf{T} = c(\alpha\mathbf{T}) = c\theta = \theta$, so $c\alpha \in \mathfrak{N}_\mathbf{T}$. Thus $\mathfrak{N}_\mathbf{T}$ is a subspace of $\mathcal{V}$.

These two subspaces, $\mathcal{R}_\mathbf{T}$ and $\mathfrak{N}_\mathbf{T}$, called, respectively, the *range space* of $\mathbf{T}$ and the *null space* of $\mathbf{T}$, are of major importance in the study of linear algebra, as are their dimensions.

Definition 3.5.
(a) The *range space* $\mathcal{R}_\mathbf{T}$ of a linear transformation $\mathbf{T}$ is the set of all images $\alpha\mathbf{T} \in \mathcal{W}$ as α ranges over $\mathcal{V}$.
(b) The *rank* $\rho(\mathbf{T})$ of a linear transformation $\mathbf{T}$ is the dimension of its range space.

Definition 3.6.
(a) The *null space* $\mathfrak{N}_\mathbf{T}$ of a linear transformation $\mathbf{T}$ is the set of all vectors $\alpha \in \mathcal{V}$ for which $\alpha\mathbf{T} = \theta \in \mathcal{W}$.
(b) The *nullity* $\nu(\mathbf{T})$ of a linear transformation $\mathbf{T}$ is the dimension of its null space.

Theorem 3.2. If $\mathbf{T}$ is a linear transformation from $\mathcal{V}$ to $\mathcal{W}$ and if $\mathbf{S}$ is a linear transformation from $\mathcal{W}$ to $\mathcal{Y}$, then
(a) $\mathcal{R}_\mathbf{TS} \subseteq \mathcal{R}_\mathbf{S}$ and $\rho(\mathbf{TS}) \leq \rho(\mathbf{S})$,
(b) $\mathfrak{N}_\mathbf{TS} \supseteq \mathfrak{N}_\mathbf{T}$ and $\nu(\mathbf{TS}) \geq \nu(\mathbf{T})$.

P R O O F : Exercise.

Thus we see that each linear transformation $\mathbf{T}$ from $\mathcal{V}$ to $\mathcal{W}$ automatically selects a subspace $\mathfrak{N}_\mathbf{T}$ of $\mathcal{V}$ and a subspace $\mathcal{R}_\mathbf{T}$ of $\mathcal{W}$. These two subspaces are related in an interesting manner, as indicated by the following theorem and its corollaries.

Theorem 3.3. Let $\{\alpha_1, \ldots, \alpha_{\nu(\mathbf{T})}\}$ be a basis for $\mathfrak{N}_\mathbf{T}$. Extend this basis to any basis $\{\alpha_1, \ldots, \alpha_{\nu(\mathbf{T})}, \alpha_{\nu(\mathbf{T})+1}, \ldots, \alpha_n\}$ for $\mathcal{V}_n$. Then $\{\alpha_{\nu(\mathbf{T})+1}\mathbf{T}, \ldots, \alpha_n\mathbf{T}\}$ is a basis for $\mathfrak{R}_\mathbf{T}$.

P R O O F : Let $\{\alpha_1, \ldots, \alpha_n\}$ be chosen as in the statement of the theorem. Any vector of $\mathfrak{R}_\mathbf{T}$ is of the form $\xi\mathbf{T}$ for some $\xi \in \mathcal{V}_n$. Let $\xi = \sum_{i=1}^{n} a_i\alpha_i$; then

$$\xi\mathbf{T} = \left(\sum_{i=1}^{n} a_i\alpha_i\right)\mathbf{T} = \sum_{i=1}^{n} a_i(\alpha_i\mathbf{T}) = \sum_{i=\nu(\mathbf{T})+1}^{n} a_i(\alpha_i\mathbf{T}),$$

since $\alpha_i\mathbf{T} = \theta$ for $i = 1, 2, \ldots, \nu(\mathbf{T})$. Hence $\{\alpha_{\nu(\mathbf{T})+1}\mathbf{T}, \ldots, \alpha_n\mathbf{T}\}$ spans $\mathfrak{R}_\mathbf{T}$. Since we do not know the dimension of $\mathfrak{R}_\mathbf{T}$ we must also prove linear independence. Suppose scalars b_i, not all zero, exist such that

$$\theta = \sum_{\nu(\mathbf{T})+1}^{n} b_i(\alpha_i\mathbf{T}) = \left(\sum_{\nu(\mathbf{T})+1}^{n} b_i\alpha_i\right)\mathbf{T}.$$

Then $\sum_{\nu(\mathbf{T})+1}^{n} b_i\alpha_i \in \mathfrak{N}_\mathbf{T}$; but $\{\alpha_1, \ldots, \alpha_{\nu(\mathbf{T})}\}$ spans $\mathfrak{N}_\mathbf{T}$, so for suitable scalars c_i,

$$\sum_{\nu(\mathbf{T})+1}^{n} b_i\alpha_i = \sum_{1}^{\nu(\mathbf{T})} c_i\alpha_i.$$

This contradicts the linear independence of $\{\alpha_1, \ldots, \alpha_n\}$, so the vectors $\{\alpha_{\nu(\mathbf{T})+1}\mathbf{T}, \ldots, \alpha_n\mathbf{T}\}$ are linearly independent and therefore form a basis for $\mathfrak{R}_\mathbf{T}$.

Theorem 3.4. If $\mathbf{T}$ is a linear transformation from $\mathcal{V}_n$ to $\mathcal{W}$, then $\rho(\mathbf{T}) + \nu(\mathbf{T}) = n$.

P R O O F : Exercise.

Now if we consider $\mathcal{W}$ and $\mathcal{V}_n$ to be the same space, then $\mathbf{T}, \mathbf{T}^2, \mathbf{T}^3, \ldots$ are all well-defined transformations of $\mathcal{V}_n$ into itself. The corresponding range and null spaces form chains, as indicated in the following result.

Theorem 3.5. If $\mathbf{T}$ is a linear transformation on $\mathcal{V}_n$, then

(a) $\mathcal{V}_n \supseteq \mathfrak{R}_\mathbf{T} \supseteq \mathfrak{R}_{\mathbf{T}^2} \supseteq \cdots \supseteq \mathfrak{R}_{\mathbf{T}^k} \supseteq \cdots,$
(b) $[\theta] \subseteq \mathfrak{N}_\mathbf{T} \subseteq \mathfrak{N}_{\mathbf{T}^2} \subseteq \cdots \subseteq \mathfrak{N}_{\mathbf{T}^k} \subseteq \cdots.$

Furthermore, if p is a positive integer such that $\mathfrak{R}_{\mathbf{T}^p} = \mathfrak{R}_{\mathbf{T}^{p+1}}$, then for every integer $k \geq 1$ we have $\mathfrak{R}_{\mathbf{T}^p} = \mathfrak{R}_{\mathbf{T}^{p+k}}$ and $\mathfrak{N}_{\mathbf{T}^p} = \mathfrak{N}_{\mathbf{T}^{p+k}}$.

P R O O F : The chains are established by repeated application of Theorem 3.2. Furthermore, in a finite-dimensional space equality must hold somewhere in each chain. The dimension relation of Theorem 3.4 shows that $\mathfrak{R}_{\mathbf{T}^p} = \mathfrak{R}_{\mathbf{T}^{p+k}}$ if and only if $\mathfrak{N}_{\mathbf{T}^p} = \mathfrak{N}_{\mathbf{T}^{p+k}}$. Now assume $\mathfrak{N}_{\mathbf{T}^p} = \mathfrak{N}_{\mathbf{T}^{p+1}}$, and let $\xi \in \mathfrak{N}_{\mathbf{T}^{p+k}}$. Then

$$\theta = \xi \mathbf{T}^{p+k} = (\xi \mathbf{T}^{k-1}) \mathbf{T}^{p+1}.$$

Hence $\xi \mathbf{T}^{k-1} \in \mathfrak{N}_{\mathbf{T}^{p+1}} = \mathfrak{N}_{\mathbf{T}^p}$. If $k > 1$, the argument may be repeated to give $\xi \mathbf{T}^{k-2} \in \mathfrak{N}_{\mathbf{T}^p}$, etc., so finally $\xi \in \mathfrak{N}_{\mathbf{T}^p}$. Thus $\mathfrak{N}_{\mathbf{T}^{p+k}} \subseteq \mathfrak{N}_{\mathbf{T}^p}$, and the chain relation gives $\mathfrak{N}_{\mathbf{T}^p} \subseteq \mathfrak{N}_{\mathbf{T}^{p+k}}$, so equality holds.

This result gives us a fairly clear picture of the range and null spaces of an iterated transformation. As $\mathbf{T}$ is iterated on $\mathcal{V}_n$, the corresponding null spaces form a *strictly increasing* sequence of subspaces up to a certain number $p \leq n$ of iterations, at which point the increase stops. Thereafter, further application of $\mathbf{T}$ maps into θ only those vectors which are mapped into θ by $\mathbf{T}^p$. Likewise, the range spaces form a *strictly decreasing* sequence up to p iterations, and further application of $\mathbf{T}$ maps $\mathfrak{R}_{\mathbf{T}^p}$ *onto* itself.

Exercises

1. Prove Theorem 3.2.
2. Prove Theorem 3.4.
3. Let $\mathbf{S}$ and $\mathbf{T}$ be linear transformations from $\mathcal{V}_n$ to $\mathcal{V}_n$; prove the following relations for rank and nullity.

   (i) $\rho(\mathbf{T} + \mathbf{S}) \leq \rho(\mathbf{T}) + \rho(\mathbf{S})$.
   (ii) $\nu(\mathbf{T} + \mathbf{S}) \geq \nu(\mathbf{T}) + \nu(\mathbf{S}) - n$.
   (iii) $\nu(\mathbf{T}) + \nu(\mathbf{S}) \geq \nu(\mathbf{TS}) \geq \max \{\nu(\mathbf{T}), \nu(\mathbf{S})\}$.
   (iv) $\rho(\mathbf{T}) + \rho(\mathbf{S}) - n \leq \rho(\mathbf{TS}) \leq \min \{\rho(\mathbf{T}), \rho(\mathbf{S})\}$.

4. Specify the range space and null space of each of the linear transformations given in the examples of § 3.1.
5. Illustrate the statements of Exercise 3 above by using the linear transformations $\mathbf{T}_2$ and $\mathbf{T}_3$ of Example (c), § 3.1.
6. Demonstrate by specific examples that the second inequality of Exercise 3(iii) and the first inequality of Exercise 3(iv) need not be valid when $\mathbf{T}$ is a linear transformation from $\mathcal{V}_n$ to $\mathcal{W}_m$ and $\mathbf{S}$ a linear transformation from $\mathcal{W}_m$ to $\mathcal{Y}_p$.
7. If $\mathbf{T}$ is a linear transformation of rank 1 from $\mathcal{V}$ to $\mathcal{V}$, prove that $\mathbf{T}^2 = c\mathbf{T}$ for some scalar c.
8. Let $\mathbf{T}$ be a nilpotent linear transformation on $\mathcal{V}$, so that for every $\eta \in \mathcal{V}$, $\eta \mathbf{T}^p = \theta$, but for some $\xi \in \mathcal{V}$, $\xi \mathbf{T}^{p-1} \neq \theta$.

   (i) Show that $\{\xi, \xi \mathbf{T}, \xi \mathbf{T}^2, \ldots, \xi \mathbf{T}^{p-1}\}$ is linearly independent.
   (ii) If $\mathcal{S}$ is the subspace spanned by the vectors of (i), show that $\sigma \mathbf{T} \in \mathcal{S}$ for every $\sigma \in \mathcal{S}$. (That is, $\mathbf{T}$ maps the space $\mathcal{S}$ into itself. Such a space is said to be *invariant under* $\mathbf{T}$, or $\mathbf{T}$-*invariant*.)

9. Let **T** be a linear transformation from $\mathcal{V}$ into $\mathcal{W}$. A mapping $\overline{\mathbf{T}}$ is defined from $\mathcal{V}/\mathfrak{N}_{\mathbf{T}}$ (Exercise 8, § 2.3) into $\mathcal{W}$ as follows:

$$(\xi + \mathfrak{N}_{\mathbf{T}})\overline{\mathbf{T}} = \xi\mathbf{T}.$$

Show that the mapping $\overline{\mathbf{T}}$ is unambiguously defined, linear, one-to-one, and onto $\mathfrak{R}_{\mathbf{T}}$. In short, $\overline{\mathbf{T}}$ is an isomorphism of $\mathcal{V}/\mathfrak{N}_{\mathbf{T}}$ onto $\mathfrak{R}_{\mathbf{T}}$.

§3.3. *Nonsingular Transformations*

The range and null spaces of a linear transformation **T** have an intrinsic connection with the concept of *nonsingularity* of **T**, which can be characterized in numerous ways. The essential idea is one-to-one-ness. A nonsingular linear transformation is distinguished from an arbitrary linear transformation in the same way that an isomorphism is distinguished from a homomorphism. This means, of course, that the null space of a nonsingular transformation is $[\theta]$, and therefore the mapping thus defined is reversible.

Definition 3.7. A linear transformation **T** from $\mathcal{V}$ into $\mathcal{W}$ is said to be *nonsingular* if and only if there exists a mapping **T*** from $\mathfrak{R}_{\mathbf{T}}$ onto $\mathcal{V}$ such that **TT*** = **I**, where **I** is the identity mapping on $\mathcal{V}$.

Although this definition does not explicitly require **T*** to be linear, it is necessarily so. To deduce this fact, let **T*** be a mapping from $\mathfrak{R}_{\mathbf{T}}$ onto $\mathcal{V}$ such that **TT*** = **I**. If $\alpha, \beta \in \mathfrak{R}_{\mathbf{T}}$, there exist $\xi, \eta \in \mathcal{V}$ such that $\xi\mathbf{T} = \alpha$, $\eta\mathbf{T} = \beta$. Then $\xi\mathbf{TT}^* = \alpha\mathbf{T}^* = \xi$ and $\beta\mathbf{T}^* = \eta$. For any $a, b \in \mathfrak{F}$,

$$(a\alpha + b\beta)\mathbf{T}^* = (a\xi\mathbf{T} + b\eta\mathbf{T})\mathbf{T}^* = (a\xi + b\eta)\mathbf{TT}^*$$
$$= (a\xi + b\eta)\mathbf{I} = a(\alpha\mathbf{T}^*) + b(\eta\mathbf{T}^*).$$

Thus the linearity of **T** and the property **TT*** = **I** imply that **T*** is linear. Furthermore, **T*** is uniquely determined by **T** if **T** is nonsingular.

Theorem 3.6. Let **T** be a linear transformation on $\mathcal{V}_n$ to $\mathcal{W}$; the following statements are equivalent.

(a) **T** is nonsingular.
(b) For all $\alpha, \beta \in \mathcal{V}_n$, if $\alpha\mathbf{T} = \beta\mathbf{T}$, then $\alpha = \beta$.
(c) $\mathfrak{N}_{\mathbf{T}} = [\theta]$.
(d) $\nu(\mathbf{T}) = 0$.
(e) $\rho(\mathbf{T}) = n$.
(f) **T** maps any basis for $\mathcal{V}_n$ onto a basis for $\mathfrak{R}_{\mathbf{T}}$.

P R O O F : Our proof consists of a cycle of implications.

(a) implies (b). Assume $\mathbf{T}$ is nonsingular and that $\alpha\mathbf{T} = \beta\mathbf{T}$. Then $(\alpha\mathbf{T})\mathbf{T}^* = (\beta\mathbf{T})\mathbf{T}^*$, $\alpha\mathbf{I} = \beta\mathbf{I}$, and $\alpha = \beta$.

(b) implies (c). If $\xi \in \mathfrak{N}_{\mathbf{T}}$, then $\xi\mathbf{T} = \theta = \theta\mathbf{T}$, so $\xi = \theta$. Hence $\mathfrak{N}_{\mathbf{T}} = [\theta]$.

(c) implies (d). Definition 3.6.

(d) implies (e). Theorem 3.4.

(e) implies (f). Theorem 3.3.

(f) implies (a). Let $\{\alpha_1, \ldots, \alpha_n\}$ be a basis for $\mathcal{V}_n$; then $\{\alpha_1\mathbf{T}, \ldots, \alpha_n\mathbf{T}\}$ is a basis for $\mathfrak{R}_{\mathbf{T}}$. Hence each $\eta \in \mathfrak{R}_{\mathbf{T}}$ has a unique expression of the form $\eta = \sum_{i=1}^{n} b_i(\alpha_i\mathbf{T})$. Let $\mathbf{T}^*$ be the mapping from $\mathfrak{R}_{\mathbf{T}}$ to $\mathcal{V}_n$ defined by $\eta\mathbf{T}^* = \sum_{i=1}^{n} b_i\alpha_i$. We must show that $\mathbf{TT}^* = \mathbf{I}$ on $\mathcal{V}_n$. For each $\xi \in \mathcal{V}_n$,

$$\xi = \sum_{i=1}^{n} a_i\alpha_i,$$

$$\xi\mathbf{T} = \left(\sum_{i=1}^{n} a_i\alpha_i\right)\mathbf{T} = \sum_{i=1}^{n} a_i(\alpha_i\mathbf{T}) \in \mathfrak{R}_{\mathbf{T}},$$

$$(\xi\mathbf{T})\mathbf{T}^* = \sum_{i=1}^{n} a_i\alpha_i = \xi \qquad \text{by definition of } \mathbf{T}^*.$$

Hence $\mathbf{TT}^* = \mathbf{I}$ on $\mathcal{V}_n$.

Since a linear transformation is a homomorphism of $\mathcal{V}$ onto $\mathfrak{R}_{\mathbf{T}}$, a nonsingular transformation is simply an isomorphism of $\mathcal{V}$ onto $\mathfrak{R}_{\mathbf{T}}$. This interpretation lends intuitive feeling to the statements of the preceding theorem, since in an isomorphism distinct vectors have distinct images, the kernel is trivial, and it seems entirely reasonable that dimension must be preserved. We remark that if $\mathbf{T}$ maps $\mathcal{V}$ into $\mathcal{V}$, then $\mathbf{T}$ *is nonsingular if and only if* $\mathfrak{R}_{\mathbf{T}} = \mathcal{V}$. If we insist on distinguishing $\mathcal{V}$ and $\mathcal{W}$, then it is still true that $\mathbf{T}$ is an isomorphism between $\mathcal{V}$ and $\mathfrak{R}_{\mathbf{T}}$ if and only if $\mathbf{T}$ is nonsingular.

Interestingly enough, these observations remain valid even when $\mathcal{V}$ and $\mathcal{W}$ are infinite-dimensional spaces. Of course in that case Theorem 3.6 must be amended by deleting statement (e) and the subscript on $\mathcal{V}_n$; otherwise, the theorem and most of the proof remain valid. In contrast to the definition of nonsingularity given here, a linear transformation $\mathbf{T}$ from $\mathcal{V}$ to $\mathcal{W}$ is sometimes defined to be nonsingular if and only if there exists a mapping $\mathbf{T}^*$ from $\mathcal{W}$ to $\mathcal{V}$ (instead of from $\mathfrak{R}_{\mathbf{T}}$ to $\mathcal{V}$) such that $\mathbf{TT}^*$ is the identity mapping on $\mathcal{V}$ and $\mathbf{T}^*\mathbf{T}$ is the identity mapping on $\mathcal{W}$ (instead of on $\mathfrak{R}_{\mathbf{T}}$). The two definitions coincide if $\mathcal{V}$ and $\mathcal{W}$ are finite-dimensional spaces of the same dimension, but not otherwise. (See Exercise 5.)

The significance of Theorem 3.6 (as well as other results we prove about linear transformations) will become more evident when the theory of matrices is developed in subsequent chapters. Indeed, for *every* theorem we prove about linear transformations there is a corresponding theorem about matrices. The next result is surprisingly simple to prove in terms of linear transformations, but a matrix proof of the corresponding result is relatively obscure.

Theorem 3.7. If $\mathbf{T}$ is a linear transformation from $\mathcal{V}$ to $\mathcal{W}$ and if $\mathbf{T}^*$ is a mapping from $\mathcal{R}_\mathbf{T}$ to $\mathcal{V}$ such that $\mathbf{TT}^* = \mathbf{I}$ on $\mathcal{V}$, then $\mathbf{T}^*\mathbf{T} = \mathbf{I}$ on $\mathcal{R}_\mathbf{T}$.

P R O O F : By hypothesis, $\mathbf{T}$ is nonsingular, so any $\beta \in \mathcal{R}_\mathbf{T}$ can be represented uniquely as $\beta = \alpha\mathbf{T}$ for some $\alpha \in \mathcal{V}$, by Theorem 3.6(b). Then $\beta(\mathbf{T}^*\mathbf{T}) = (\alpha\mathbf{T})(\mathbf{T}^*\mathbf{T}) = \alpha(\mathbf{TT}^*)\mathbf{T} = \alpha\mathbf{T} = \beta$. Hence $\mathbf{T}^*\mathbf{T} = \mathbf{I}$.

Thus in algebraic language $\mathbf{T}$ is nonsingular if and only if there exists a transformation $\mathbf{T}^*$ which is *both* a left inverse and a right inverse of $\mathbf{T}$. Hence we call $\mathbf{T}^*$ the *inverse* of $\mathbf{T}$ and write $\mathbf{T}^{-1}$ instead of $\mathbf{T}^*$. Observe that not every nonzero linear transformation has an inverse; for example, $\mathbf{T}_1$ of Example (c), § 3.1, has a one-dimensional range space and hence is singular but nonzero.

Theorem 3.8. Let $\mathcal{V}$, $\mathcal{W}_n$, $\mathcal{X}$, $\mathcal{Y}$ be vector spaces, and let $\mathbf{S}_1$, $\mathbf{T}$, and $\mathbf{S}_2$ be linear transformations defined, respectively, from $\mathcal{V}$ into $\mathcal{W}_n$, from $\mathcal{W}_n$ into $\mathcal{X}$, and from $\mathcal{R}_\mathbf{T}$ into $\mathcal{Y}$. If $\mathbf{T}$ is nonsingular, then $\rho(\mathbf{S}_1\mathbf{T}) = \rho(\mathbf{S}_1)$ and $\rho(\mathbf{TS}_2) = \rho(\mathbf{S}_2)$.

P R O O F : Since $\mathbf{T}$ is nonsingular, $\dim \mathcal{R}_{\mathbf{S}_1}\mathbf{T} = \dim \mathcal{R}_{\mathbf{S}_1}$; but $\mathcal{R}_{\mathbf{S}_1}\mathbf{T} = \mathcal{R}_{\mathbf{S}_1\mathbf{T}}$, so $\rho(\mathbf{S}_1) = \rho(\mathbf{S}_1\mathbf{T})$. Also $\mathcal{R}_{\mathbf{TS}_2} = \mathcal{R}_\mathbf{T}\mathbf{S}_2 = \mathcal{R}_{\mathbf{S}_2}$, so $\rho(\mathbf{TS}_2) = \rho(\mathbf{S}_2)$. As a particular case, if $\mathcal{V} = \mathcal{W}_n = \mathcal{X} = \mathcal{Y}$ and if $\mathbf{S}_1 = \mathbf{S}_2$, we have $\rho(\mathbf{TS}_1) = \rho(\mathbf{S}_1\mathbf{T}) = \rho(\mathbf{S}_1)$ whenever $\mathbf{T}$ is nonsingular.

It should be observed that $\mathcal{R}_{\mathbf{ST}}$ and $\mathcal{R}_\mathbf{S}$ need not be equal, since $\mathbf{T}$ might map a vector of $\mathcal{R}_\mathbf{S}$ into a vector which is not in $\mathcal{R}_\mathbf{S}$. All we know is that $\mathcal{R}_{\mathbf{ST}}$ and $\mathcal{R}_\mathbf{S}$ have the same dimension. As an example, let $\mathbf{T}$ be the rotation of the plane through an angle of $45°$, and let $\mathbf{S}$ be the projection of (x, y) onto $(x, 0)$. Then $\mathcal{R}_\mathbf{S}$ is the line $y = 0$ and $\mathcal{R}_{\mathbf{ST}}$ is the line $y = x$.

Theorem 3.9. Let $\mathbf{T}$ be a linear transformation from $\mathcal{V}$ into $\mathcal{W}$, and let $\mathbf{S}$ be a linear transformation from $\mathcal{R}_\mathbf{T}$ into $\mathcal{Y}$. Then $\mathbf{TS}$ is nonsingular if and only if $\mathbf{T}$ and $\mathbf{S}$ are nonsingular. If $\mathbf{TS}$ is nonsingular, then $(\mathbf{TS})^{-1} = \mathbf{S}^{-1}\mathbf{T}^{-1}$.

P R O O F : Exercise.

Theorem 3.10. If $\mathbf{T}$ is nonsingular, then $\mathbf{T}^{-1}$ is nonsingular, and
(a) $(\mathbf{T}^{-1})^{-1} = \mathbf{T}$,
(b) $(c\mathbf{T})^{-1} = c^{-1}\mathbf{T}^{-1}$, if $c \neq 0$.

P R O O F : Exercise.

Exercises

1. Prove Theorem 3.9.

2. Prove Theorem 3.10.

3. Any linear transformation of the plane is determined by its effect on the two vectors $\epsilon_1 = (1, 0)$ and $\epsilon_2 = (0, 1)$. Suppose $\epsilon_1 \mathbf{T} = (a, b)$ and $\epsilon_2 \mathbf{T} = (c, d)$. Express in terms of a, b, c, d a necessary and sufficient condition that $\mathbf{T}$ be nonsingular. Interpret geometrically.

4. Show that the set of all nonsingular linear transformations on $\mathcal{V}_n$ form a group. This group is called the *full linear group* $\mathcal{L}_n(\mathfrak{F})$.

5. Let $\mathcal{P}$ be the infinite-dimensional space of all real polynomials and let $\mathcal{P}_0$ be the subspace of all polynomials P for which $P(0) = 0$. Consider the linear transformations defined as follows:

$$P(x)\mathbf{J} \;=\; \int_0^x P(t)dt \qquad \text{for all } P(x) \in \mathcal{P},$$

$$P(x)\mathbf{D} \;=\; \frac{d}{dx} P(x) \qquad \text{for all } P(x) \in \mathcal{P},$$

$$P(x)\mathbf{D}_0 \;=\; \frac{d}{dx} P(x) \qquad \text{for all } P(x) \in \mathcal{P}_0.$$

(i) Determine the domain and range of each of the transformations $\mathbf{J}$, $\mathbf{D}$, $\mathbf{D}_0$, $\mathbf{JD}$, $\mathbf{DJ}$, $\mathbf{JD}_0$, $\mathbf{D}_0\mathbf{J}$.

(ii) Which of the four product transformations in (i) is the identity transformation on its domain?

(iii) Which of the seven transformations in (i) are nonsingular?

(iv) Explain wherein these results are consistent with Theorem 3.7 and Theorem 3.9.

6. Let $\mathcal{S}_k$ be a k-dimensional subspace of $\mathcal{V}_n$.

(i) Show that $\mathcal{S}_k$ is the null space of a suitably defined linear transformation $\mathbf{T}$ from $\mathcal{V}_n$ into $\mathcal{V}_n$. (Exercise 8, § 2.7.)

(ii) Deduce that the dimension of $\mathcal{V}_n/\mathcal{S}_k$ is $n - k$. (Exercise 9, § 3.2.)

(iii) Describe a basis for $\mathcal{V}_n/\mathcal{S}_k$ which is related in a natural way to a suitably chosen basis for $\mathcal{V}_n$.

§3.4. *Dual Space*

Up to this point we have been studying linear transformations from one vector space $\mathcal{V}$ over $\mathfrak{F}$ to any other vector space $\mathcal{W}$ over $\mathfrak{F}$, a study which is resumed in § 3.7. But now we digress slightly in order to investigate two special choices for $\mathcal{W}$; in this section and the next we let $\mathcal{W} = \mathfrak{F}$, and in

§ 3.6 we let $\mathcal{W} = \mathcal{V}$. In each case we obtain results which are peculiar to that situation, yet important for an understanding of general topics which will arise later in our study of linear algebra. A reader who prefers to move directly to § 3.7 may do so without any knowledge of the intervening topics, returning to these sections later.

We therefore turn our attention to scalar-valued linear functions defined on a vector space $\mathcal{V}$ over $\mathcal{F}$. Since $\mathcal{F}$ may be regarded as a vector space over itself, we consider the set of all linear transformations from $\mathcal{V}$ to $\mathcal{W}$, specialized to the case where $\mathcal{W} = \mathcal{F}$. (Exercise 7, § 2.7.) In this case a linear transformation $\mathbf{T}$ from $\mathcal{V}$ to $\mathcal{F}$ assigns to each vector $\xi \in \mathcal{V}$ a scalar $\xi\mathbf{T} \in \mathcal{F}$; of course linearity means that for all $\xi, \eta \in \mathcal{V}$ and all $a, b \in \mathcal{F}$, $(a\xi + b\eta)\mathbf{T} = a(\xi\mathbf{T}) + b(\eta\mathbf{T})$ in $\mathcal{F}$. From Theorem 3.1 it follows that the set of all linear functions from $\mathcal{V}$ to $\mathcal{F}$ forms a vector space over $\mathcal{F}$.

Because this is a particular situation, rather than general, we shall introduce special terminology and notation.

Definition 3.8. Let $\mathcal{V}$ be a vector space over $\mathcal{F}$. A linear transformation from $\mathcal{V}$ into $\mathcal{F}$ is called a *linear functional;* linear functionals will be denoted by small Latin letters, usually in boldface type. The vector space of all linear functionals on $\mathcal{V}$ is called the *dual space* of $\mathcal{V}$ and is denoted by $\mathcal{V}'$.

Examples of Linear Functionals

Several important examples of linear functionals on infinite-dimensional spaces are familiar from our study of elementary analysis.

(a) Let $\mathcal{V}$ be the space of all real-valued functions integrable for $a \leq t \leq b$, and let $\mathbf{j}$ be the functional defined by $f\mathbf{j} = \int_a^b f(t)\, dt$ for each $f \in \mathcal{V}$. Thus $\mathbf{j}$ is a linear mapping which assigns to each integrable function f a real number $f\mathbf{j}$, called the integral of f on the interval $a \leq t \leq b$. More generally, if ϕ is a fixed function which is integrable for $a \leq t \leq b$, then $\mathbf{h}$ is a linear functional where

$$f\mathbf{h} = \int_a^b f(t)\phi(t)\, dt.$$

(b) Let $\mathcal{P}$ be the space of all real polynomials, and let $\mathbf{d}_a$ be defined for each $P \in \mathcal{P}$ by

$$P\mathbf{d}_a = P'(a),$$

where P' denotes the derivative of P. Then $\mathbf{d}_a$ is a linear functional.

(c) Let $\mathcal{C}$ denote the space of all convergent sequences of real numbers. A linear functional is obtained by associating with each sequence the real number to which it converges.

(d) If $\mathcal{V}$ is any n-dimensional space over $\mathcal{F}$ and if $\xi \in \mathcal{V}$, let $\xi = \sum_{i=1}^n x_i\alpha_i$.

where $\{\alpha_1, \ldots, \alpha_n\}$ is any fixed basis. Let $\gamma = \sum_{i=1}^{n} c_i \alpha_i$ be any fixed vector of $\mathcal{V}$. The mapping $\mathbf{f}_\gamma$, defined by

$$\xi \mathbf{f}_\gamma = c_1 x_1 + c_2 x_2 + \cdots + c_n x_n,$$

is a linear functional on $\mathcal{V}$.

The last example reveals the nature of linear functionals on $\mathcal{V}_n$ so completely that we repeat a description of the ideas involved. We begin with any basis $\{\alpha_1, \ldots, \alpha_n\}$ for $\mathcal{V}_n$; each fixed $\gamma \in \mathcal{V}_n$ determines a linear functional $\mathbf{f}_\gamma$ on $\mathcal{V}_n$. The scalar value $\xi \mathbf{f}_\gamma$ which is assigned to the vector ξ by the linear functional $\mathbf{f}_\gamma$ is a fixed linear combination of the coordinates of ξ (relative to the α-basis), and the coefficients of that linear combination are the coordinates of γ (relative to the α-basis). As γ is varied, we obtain various linear functionals. In particular, if $\gamma = \theta$, then $\mathbf{f}_\theta$ maps each ξ onto 0; if $\gamma = \alpha_1$, $\mathbf{f}_\gamma$ maps each ξ into its first α-coordinate, and so on. We consider, therefore, the n linear functionals $\{\mathbf{f}_{\alpha_1}, \ldots, \mathbf{f}_{\alpha_n}\}$ which correspond in this manner to the vectors of the chosen basis, and we investigate the role they play in the dual space $\mathcal{V}'$.

To begin with, $\mathbf{f}_{\alpha_j}$ maps α_j into 1 and α_i into 0 if $i \neq j$. Hence

$$\alpha_i \mathbf{f}_{\alpha_j} = \delta_{ij}, \qquad \text{for } i, j = 1, \ldots, n,$$

where the symbol δ_{ij} is called the *Kronecker delta* and is defined by

$$\delta_{ij} = \begin{cases} 1 & \text{if } i = j, \\ 0 & \text{if } i \neq j, \text{ for } i, j = 1, 2, \ldots, n. \end{cases}$$

Next we show that $\{\mathbf{f}_{\alpha_1}, \ldots, \mathbf{f}_{\alpha_n}\}$ forms a basis for $\mathcal{V}'$. Clearly the zero element of $\mathcal{V}'$ is the linear functional $\mathbf{f}_\theta$ which maps each ξ into 0. To verify that the $\mathbf{f}_{\alpha_i}$ are linearly independent, we suppose that

$$\sum_{k=1}^{n} c_k \mathbf{f}_{\alpha_k} = \mathbf{f}_\theta.$$

Then for $i = 1, \ldots, n$,

$$0 = \alpha_i \mathbf{f}_\theta = \alpha_i \sum_{k=1}^{n} c_k \mathbf{f}_{\alpha_k} = \sum_{k=1}^{n} c_k \alpha_i \mathbf{f}_{\alpha_k} = \sum_{k=1}^{n} c_k \delta_{ik} = c_i.$$

To verify that the $\mathbf{f}_{\alpha_i}$ span $\mathcal{V}'$, we let $\mathbf{f}$ be any element of $\mathcal{V}'$, and let $a_i \in \mathfrak{F}$ be defined by

$$a_i = \alpha_i \mathbf{f} \qquad \text{for } i = 1, \ldots, n.$$

Then

$$\alpha_i \mathbf{f} = a_i = \sum_{j=1}^{n} a_j \delta_{ij} = \sum_{j=1}^{n} a_j (\alpha_i \mathbf{f}_{\alpha_j})$$

$$= \alpha_i \left(\sum_{j=1}^{n} a_j \mathbf{f}_{\alpha_j} \right).$$

Hence both $\mathbf{f}$ and $\sum_{j=1}^{n} a_j \mathbf{f}_{\alpha_j}$ are linear functionals on $\mathcal{V}$, whose values coincide on the basis $\{\alpha_1, \ldots, \alpha_n\}$. Linearity then implies that these values coincide on all of $\mathcal{V}$; that is, they are equal elements of $\mathcal{V}'$. We have therefore proved the following theorem.

Theorem 3.11. Let $\{\alpha_1, \ldots, \alpha_n\}$ be a basis for $\mathcal{V}_n$, and let $\mathbf{f}_j$ be the linear functional defined on $\mathcal{V}_n$ by prescribing

$$\alpha_i \mathbf{f}_j = \delta_{ij} \qquad \text{for } i = 1, 2, \ldots, m.$$

Then $\{\mathbf{f}_1, \ldots, \mathbf{f}_n\}$ is a basis for $\mathcal{V}_n'$. Hence $\mathcal{V}_n'$ is n-dimensional.

The basis for $\mathcal{V}'$ which is described in Theorem 3.11 is called the *dual basis* of $\{\alpha_1, \ldots, \alpha_n\}$.

Theorem 3.12. If ξ is any nonzero vector of $\mathcal{V}_n$, there exists a linear functional $\mathbf{f} \in \mathcal{V}_n'$ such that $\xi\mathbf{f} \neq 0$.

P R O O F : Let $\{\alpha_1, \ldots, \alpha_n\}$ be any basis for $\mathcal{V}_n$, and let $\{\mathbf{f}_1, \ldots, \mathbf{f}_n\}$ be its dual basis for $\mathcal{V}_n'$. Let $\xi = \sum_{i=1}^n x_i\alpha_i$. If $\xi \neq \theta$, there exists at least one index j for which $x_j \neq 0$. Then $\xi\mathbf{f}_j \neq 0$.

It follows immediately that if $\xi \neq \eta$ in $\mathcal{V}_n$, then for some $\mathbf{f} \in \mathcal{V}_n'$ $\xi\mathbf{f} \neq \eta\mathbf{f}$; we shall make use of this observation in Theorem 3.13.

But first we return to the general case in which $\mathcal{V}$ is not specifically assumed to be finite-dimensional. Since $\mathcal{V}'$ is a vector space, it has a dual space of its own which is denoted $(\mathcal{V}')'$ or simply $\mathcal{V}''$. $\mathcal{V}''$ is called the *second dual space* or the *bidual space* of $\mathcal{V}$. Thus any element $\mathbf{f}$ of $\mathcal{V}'$ can be given two interpretations; sometimes we wish to regard it as a linear mapping from $\mathcal{V}$ to $\mathcal{F}$, while at other times we wish to regard it as a vector which is mapped into $\mathcal{F}$ by each element of $\mathcal{V}''$. In order to distinguish between these two roles of the elements of $\mathcal{V}'$, we shall modify our notation slightly, writing $\mathbf{f}$ for an element of $\mathcal{V}'$ regarded as a mapping from $\mathcal{V}$ to $\mathcal{F}$, but writing f for the same element of $\mathcal{V}'$ regarded as a vector which is mapped into $\mathcal{F}$ by an element of $\mathcal{V}''$. An element of $\mathcal{V}''$ will be denoted by $\mathbf{x}$. Thus we have $\xi \in \mathcal{V}$, $\mathbf{f}$ or $f \in \mathcal{V}'$, and $\mathbf{x} \in \mathcal{V}''$; then $\xi\mathbf{f} \in \mathcal{F}$ and $f\mathbf{x} \in \mathcal{F}$.

Now we turn our attention to an important correspondence between the elements of a vector space $\mathcal{V}$ and some of the elements of its bidual space, $\mathcal{V}''$. Let ξ be a fixed vector of $\mathcal{V}$. For each $\mathbf{f} \in \mathcal{V}'$, $\xi\mathbf{f} \in \mathcal{F}$; this means that ξ can be used to attach a scalar value to each $\mathbf{f} \in \mathcal{V}'$—in other words, ξ determines a mapping from $\mathcal{V}'$ into $\mathcal{F}$. Furthermore, that mapping is linear on $\mathcal{V}'$, because

$$\xi(a\mathbf{f}_1 + b\mathbf{f}_2) = a\xi\mathbf{f}_1 + b\xi\mathbf{f}_2.$$

Thus with each $\xi \in \mathcal{V}$ we associate the linear functional $\mathbf{x}_\xi \in \mathcal{V}''$ which is defined by

$$f\mathbf{x}_\xi = \xi f \qquad \text{for each } \mathbf{f} \in \mathcal{V}'.$$

Furthermore, this correspondence or mapping from $\mathcal{V}$ to $\mathcal{V}''$ is linear (a vector space homomorphism), since if ξ_1 corresponds to $\mathbf{x}_1$ and ξ_2 to $\mathbf{x}_2$, then for each $\mathbf{f} \in \mathcal{V}'$ and all $a, b \in \mathfrak{F}$,

$$(a\xi_1 + b\xi_2)\mathbf{f} = a\xi_1\mathbf{f} + b\xi_2\mathbf{f} = a f\mathbf{x}_1 + b f\mathbf{x}_2 = f[a\mathbf{x}_1 + b\mathbf{x}_2].$$

Hence $\mathcal{V}$ is homomorphic to a subspace of $\mathcal{V}''$. We naturally wonder whether the homomorphism is an isomorphism (that is, whether the mapping from $\mathcal{V}$ to $\mathcal{V}''$ is one-to-one), and if so whether $\mathcal{V}$ is isomorphic to the full space $\mathcal{V}''$ (that is, whether the mapping is onto $\mathcal{V}''$ rather than into $\mathcal{V}''$). The answers to these questions are that the mapping *is* an isomorphism whether $\mathcal{V}$ is finite-dimensional or not, but the mapping is onto $\mathcal{V}''$ if and only if $\mathcal{V}$ is finite-dimensional. However, we shall prove these assertions only for the finite-dimensional case.

Theorem 3.13. Let $\mathcal{V}$ be an n-dimensional vector space. Each $\xi \in \mathcal{V}$ determines a mapping $\mathbf{x}_\xi$ from $\mathcal{V}'$ into $\mathfrak{F}$, defined by $f\mathbf{x}_\xi = \xi\mathbf{f}$ for all $\mathbf{f} \in \mathcal{V}'$. Then $\mathbf{x}_\xi \in \mathcal{V}''$, and the correspondence $\xi \longrightarrow \mathbf{x}_\xi$ is an isomorphism of $\mathcal{V}$ onto $\mathcal{V}''$.

P R O O F : Our previous remarks show that the given correspondence is a homomorphism of $\mathcal{V}$ onto a subspace $\mathcal{W}'' \subseteq \mathcal{V}''$. By Theorem 3.12, if $\xi_1 \neq \xi_2$ in $\mathcal{V}$, then for some $\mathbf{f} \in \mathcal{V}'$, $\xi_1\mathbf{f} \neq \xi_2\mathbf{f}$; thus $f\mathbf{x}_1 \neq f\mathbf{x}_2$, and $\mathbf{x}_1 \neq \mathbf{x}_2$ in $\mathcal{V}''$. By Theorem 3.11, $\mathcal{V}'$ is n-dimensional, and therefore so is $\mathcal{V}''$. If $\{\alpha_1, \ldots, \alpha_n\}$ is a basis for $\mathcal{V}$ and if $\alpha_i \longrightarrow \mathbf{x}_i$, then $\{\mathbf{x}_1, \ldots, \mathbf{x}_n\}$ is a basis for $\mathcal{W}''$, so $\mathcal{W}'' = \mathcal{V}''$.

Exercises

1. Given $c \neq 0$ in $\mathfrak{F}$ and $\mathbf{f} \neq \theta$ in $\mathcal{V}'$, show that there exists $\xi \neq \theta$ in $\mathcal{V}$ such that $\xi\mathbf{f} = c$.

2. In $\mathcal{E}_3$ the scalar or dot product of two vectors $\alpha = (a_1, a_2, a_3)$ and $\beta = (b_1, b_2, b_3)$ is defined by

$$\alpha \cdot \beta = a_1 b_1 + a_2 b_2 + a_3 b_3.$$

(i) Given any linear functional $\mathbf{f}$ on $\mathcal{E}_3$, let $\beta_\mathbf{f} = (\epsilon_1\mathbf{f}, \epsilon_2\mathbf{f}, \epsilon_3\mathbf{f})$. Show that $\alpha\mathbf{f} = \alpha \cdot \beta_\mathbf{f}$ for every $\alpha \in \mathcal{E}_3$.

(ii) Conversely, given any $\beta \in \mathcal{E}_3$, let $\mathbf{f}_\beta$ be the linear functional defined by $\epsilon_i\mathbf{f}_\beta = b_i$, $i = 1, 2, 3$. Show that $\alpha\mathbf{f}_\beta = \alpha \cdot \beta$ for every $\alpha \in \mathcal{E}_3$, and that $\mathbf{f}_\beta = \theta$ in $\mathcal{E}_3'$ if and only if $\beta = \theta$ in $\mathcal{E}_3$.

3. In $\mathcal{E}_3$ the following vectors form a basis:

$$\alpha_1 = (0, 1, 1),$$
$$\alpha_2 = (1, 0, 1),$$
$$\alpha_3 = (1, 1, 0).$$

Determine a basis $\{\mathbf{f}_1, \mathbf{f}_2, \mathbf{f}_3\}$ for $\mathcal{E}_3'$ which is dual to $\{\alpha_1, \alpha_2, \alpha_3\}$, and compute $(x_1, x_2, x_3)\mathbf{f}_i$ for each i.

4. Let $\mathcal{V}$ be a vector space over $\mathcal{F}$ and let S be any subset of $\mathcal{V}$. The *annihilator* S^0 of S is defined to be the set of all linear functionals on $\mathcal{V}$ which map each vector of S into 0:

$$S^0 = \{\mathbf{f} \in \mathcal{V}' \mid \sigma\mathbf{f} = 0 \text{ for each } \sigma \in S\}.$$

Prove the following properties of annihilators.

(i) If $S \subseteq T$ in $\mathcal{V}$, then $T^0 \subseteq S^0$ in $\mathcal{V}'$.

(ii) If $\mathfrak{M}$ is a subspace of $\mathcal{V}$, $\mathfrak{M}^0$ is a subspace of $\mathcal{V}'$. Furthermore, if $\mathcal{V}$ has dimension n and $\mathfrak{M}$ has dimension m, then $\mathfrak{M}^0$ has dimension $n - m$.

(iii) If $\mathcal{V}$ is finite-dimensional, the mapping of Theorem 3.13 is an isomorphism from $\mathfrak{M}$ to $(\mathfrak{M}^0)^0$.

(iv) If $\mathcal{V}$ is finite-dimensional and if $\mathfrak{M}$ and $\mathfrak{N}$ are subspaces of $\mathcal{V}$, then

$$(\mathfrak{M} \cap \mathfrak{N})^0 = \mathfrak{M}^0 + \mathfrak{N}^0,$$

$$(\mathfrak{M} + \mathfrak{N})^0 = \mathfrak{M}^0 \cap \mathfrak{N}^0.$$

5. Let $\mathcal{V}_n$ be a vector space over $\mathcal{F}$, and let $\mathbf{f}$ be a fixed, nonzero linear functional on $\mathcal{V}_n$. Show that $\mathcal{K} = \{\xi \in \mathcal{V}_n \mid \xi\mathbf{f} = 0\}$ is an $(n - 1)$-dimensional subspace of $\mathcal{V}_n$. [In geometric language any $(n - 1)$-dimensional subspace of an n-dimensional space is called a *hyperplane*.]

6. Let $\mathcal{P}$ be the infinite-dimensional space of all polynomials with real coefficients, and let $\mathcal{S}$ be the infinite-dimensional space of all infinite sequences of real numbers. With each real sequence $\{c_i\}$ we associate the mapping $\mathbf{f} \in \mathcal{P}'$, which is defined from $\mathcal{P}$ to the real numbers by specifying that $\mathbf{f}$ is linear and that $x^k\mathbf{f} = c_k$ for $k = 0, 1, 2, \ldots$. Show that $\mathcal{P}'$ is isomorphic to $\mathcal{S}$. (Theorem 3.11 shows that $\mathcal{V}$ and $\mathcal{V}'$ are isomorphic when $\mathcal{V}$ is finite-dimensional. This example shows that the corresponding result is not valid for infinite-dimensional spaces, since it is known that $\mathcal{P}$ and $\mathcal{S}$ are not isomorphic.)

§3.5. *Transpose of a Linear Transformation*

Next we shall show that each linear transformation $\mathbf{T}$ from a vector space $\mathcal{V}$ to a vector space $\mathcal{W}$ is associated in a natural way with a linear transformation $\mathbf{T}'$ from the dual space $\mathcal{W}'$ to the dual space $\mathcal{V}'$, as indicated in Figure 3.4. $\mathbf{T}'$ is defined as the transformation from $\mathcal{W}'$ to $\mathcal{V}'$ which maps each linear functional g on $\mathcal{W}$ into the linear functional $g\mathbf{T}'$ on $\mathcal{V}$, the value of $g\mathbf{T}'$ for each $\alpha \in \mathcal{V}$ being the scalar $(\alpha\mathbf{T})g$. Thus in $\mathcal{F}$

$$\alpha(g\mathbf{T}') = (\alpha\mathbf{T})g \qquad \text{for each } \alpha \in \mathcal{V} \text{ and each } g \in \mathcal{W}'.$$

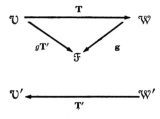

Figure 3.4

This condition can be expressed as an equation in υ':

$$g\mathbf{T}' = \mathbf{T}g \qquad \text{for each } \mathbf{g} \in \mathcal{W}'.$$

Since $\mathbf{T}$ is a linear mapping from υ to $\mathcal{W}$ and $\mathbf{g}$ is a linear mapping from $\mathcal{W}$ to $\mathcal{F}$, the composite mapping $\mathbf{T}g$ is linear from υ to $\mathcal{F}$. Hence $g\mathbf{T}' \in \upsilon'$ for each $g \in \mathcal{W}'$, and $\mathbf{T}'$ is indeed a mapping from $\mathcal{W}'$ to υ'. As an exercise you may verify that $\mathbf{T}'$ is linear.

Definition 3.9. Let υ and $\mathcal{W}$ be vector spaces over $\mathcal{F}$, and let $\mathbf{T}$ be a linear transformation from υ to $\mathcal{W}$. The *transpose* $\mathbf{T}'$ of $\mathbf{T}$ is the linear mapping from $\mathcal{W}'$ into υ', which is defined by

$$g\mathbf{T}' = \mathbf{T}g \qquad \text{for each } g \in \mathcal{W}'.$$

As another exercise you may verify that $\mathbf{I}' = \mathbf{I}$, $(c\mathbf{T})' = c\mathbf{T}'$ for each $c \in \mathcal{F}$, and $(\mathbf{S} + \mathbf{T})' = \mathbf{S}' + \mathbf{T}'$ if both $\mathbf{S}$ and $\mathbf{T}$ are linear transformations from υ to $\mathcal{W}$. The equation $\mathbf{I}' = \mathbf{I}$ is interpreted as meaning that if $\mathbf{I}$ is the identity mapping on υ, then $\mathbf{I}'$ is the identity mapping on υ'.

Theorem 3.14. Let $\mathbf{T}$ be a linear transformation from υ to $\mathcal{W}$ and $\mathbf{S}$ a linear transformation from $\mathcal{W}$ to $\mathcal{Y}$. Then

$$(\mathbf{TS})' = \mathbf{S}'\mathbf{T}'.$$

PROOF: Since $\mathbf{TS}$ is a mapping from υ to $\mathcal{Y}$, $(\mathbf{TS})'$ is a mapping from $\mathcal{Y}'$ to υ'; $\mathbf{S}'$ is a mapping from $\mathcal{Y}'$ to $\mathcal{W}'$ and $\mathbf{T}'$ a mapping from $\mathcal{W}'$ to υ'. For each $h \in \mathcal{Y}'$,

$$\begin{aligned}
h(\mathbf{TS})' &= (\mathbf{TS})h \\
&= \mathbf{T}(\mathbf{S}h) \\
&= \mathbf{T}(h\mathbf{S}') \\
&= (h\mathbf{S}')\mathbf{T}' \\
&= h(\mathbf{S}'\mathbf{T}').
\end{aligned}$$

The key observation in the preceding proof is that $h\mathbf{S}' \in \mathcal{W}'$, say $h\mathbf{S}' = g$. Then, by the definition of $\mathbf{T}'$,

$$\mathbf{T}(h\mathbf{S}') = \mathbf{T}g = g\mathbf{T}' = (h\mathbf{S}')\mathbf{T}'.$$

By applying Theorem 3.14 to the case in which $\mathbf{T} = \mathbf{S}^{-1}$, you may prove that if $\mathbf{S}$ is nonsingular, then $\mathbf{S}'$ is nonsingular and

$$(\mathbf{S}')^{-1} = (\mathbf{S}^{-1})'.$$

Theorem 3.15. Let $\mathbf{T}$ be a linear transformation from $\mathcal{V}_m$ to $\mathcal{W}_n$. Then $\mathbf{T}$ and $\mathbf{T}'$ have the same rank.

P R O O F : Let $\rho(\mathbf{T}) = k$; then $\mathcal{R}_{\mathbf{T}}$ is a k-dimensional subspace of $\mathcal{W}_n$. By Exercise 4(ii), § 3.4, the annihilator $\mathcal{R}_{\mathbf{T}}^0$ of $\mathcal{R}_{\mathbf{T}}$ is a subspace of $\mathcal{W}_n'$, of dimension $n - k$.
Then we have

$$f \in \mathcal{R}_{\mathbf{T}}^0 \text{ if and only if } \eta f = 0 \text{ for every } \eta \in \mathcal{R}_{\mathbf{T}},$$
$$\text{if and only if } (\xi\mathbf{T})f = 0 = \xi(f\mathbf{T}') \text{ for every } \xi \in \mathcal{V}_m,$$
$$\text{if and only if } f\mathbf{T}' = \theta \text{ in } \mathcal{V}_m',$$
$$\text{if and only if } f \in \mathfrak{N}_{\mathbf{T}'}.$$

Thus $\mathcal{R}_{\mathbf{T}}^0 = \mathfrak{N}_{\mathbf{T}'}$ and $\nu(\mathbf{T}') = n - k$. Since $\mathbf{T}'$ is a linear mapping of $\mathcal{W}_n'$, $\rho(\mathbf{T}') = k = \rho(\mathbf{T})$.

Exercises

1. Prove that the transpose of a linear mapping is linear.
2. Prove that $\mathbf{I}' = \mathbf{I}$, $(c\mathbf{T})' = c\mathbf{T}'$, and $(\mathbf{S} + \mathbf{T})' = \mathbf{S}' + \mathbf{T}'$.
3. Prove that if $\mathbf{S}$ is nonsingular, then $\mathbf{S}'$ is nonsingular and $(\mathbf{S}')^{-1} = (\mathbf{S}^{-1})'$.
4. If $\mathbf{T}$ is a linear transformation from $\mathcal{V}$ to $\mathcal{W}$, state precisely what is meant by $(\mathbf{T}')'$. If $\mathcal{V}$ and $\mathcal{W}$ are finite-dimensional, use Theorem 3.13 to interpret the equation $(\mathbf{T}')' = \mathbf{T}$, and then prove it.

§3.6. *Linear Algebras*

In § 3.1 we observed that a special situation arises when we consider the system $\mathcal{L}$ of all linear transformations of a vector space $\mathcal{V}$ into $\mathcal{V}$ itself. $\mathcal{L}$ is a vector space in which the "vectors" are linear mappings of $\mathcal{V}$ into $\mathcal{V}$; therefore, a product $\mathbf{S} \boxdot \mathbf{T}$ of "vectors" can be defined by means of the operation of successive mapping $\mathbf{ST}$. In general, a vector space over $\mathcal{F}$ in which a suitable product of vectors is defined is called an *algebra* over $\mathcal{F}$; there are various types of algebras, classified according to the properties of that product.

Definition 3.10. A *linear algebra* $\mathcal{L}$ over a field $\mathcal{F}$ is a system

$$\mathcal{L} = \{L, F; +, \cdot, \oplus, \odot, \boxdot\}$$

which satisfies the postulates:

(a) the system $\{L, F; +, \cdot, \oplus, \odot\}$ is a vector space over $\mathfrak{F}$,

(b) $\square$ is a binary operation on $\mathfrak{L}$ which is closed, associative, and bilinear.

This second postulate requires elaboration, but first we agree to dispense with the special notation. Then (b) simply asserts that for all $a, b \in \mathfrak{F}$ and all $\mathbf{T}_1, \mathbf{T}_2, \mathbf{T}_3 \in \mathfrak{L}$ the product operation is

Closed: $\mathbf{T}_1\mathbf{T}_2 \in \mathfrak{L}$,

Associative: $\mathbf{T}_1(\mathbf{T}_2\mathbf{T}_3) = (\mathbf{T}_1\mathbf{T}_2)\mathbf{T}_3$,

Bilinear: $\begin{cases} \mathbf{T}_1(a\mathbf{T}_2 + b\mathbf{T}_3) = a\mathbf{T}_1\mathbf{T}_2 + b\mathbf{T}_1\mathbf{T}_3, \\ (a\mathbf{T}_2 + b\mathbf{T}_3)\mathbf{T}_1 = a\mathbf{T}_2\mathbf{T}_1 + b\mathbf{T}_3\mathbf{T}_1. \end{cases}$

The *dimension* of $\mathfrak{L}$ is defined to be its dimension as a vector space.

Theorem 3.16. The system $\mathfrak{L}$ of all linear transformations from a vector space $\mathcal{U}$ over $\mathfrak{F}$ into $\mathcal{U}$ is a linear algebra over $\mathfrak{F}$. If $\mathcal{U}$ is of dimension n, then $\mathfrak{L}$ is of dimension n^2.

P R O O F : We have already verified that $\mathfrak{L}$ is a vector space over $\mathfrak{F}$ and that the product of linear mappings is linear and associative (Theorem 3.1 and Exercise 9 of § 3.1). Hence we need only show that the product is bilinear:

$$\alpha[\mathbf{T}_1(a\mathbf{T}_2 + b\mathbf{T}_3)] = (\alpha\mathbf{T}_1)(a\mathbf{T}_2 + b\mathbf{T}_3)$$
$$= (\alpha\mathbf{T}_1)(a\mathbf{T}_2) + (\alpha\mathbf{T}_1)(b\mathbf{T}_3)$$
$$= a(\alpha\mathbf{T}_1)\mathbf{T}_2 + b(\alpha\mathbf{T}_1)\mathbf{T}_3$$
$$= a(\alpha\mathbf{T}_1\mathbf{T}_2) + b(\alpha\mathbf{T}_1\mathbf{T}_3)$$
$$= \alpha(a\mathbf{T}_1\mathbf{T}_2) + \alpha(b\mathbf{T}_1\mathbf{T}_3)$$
$$= \alpha(a\mathbf{T}_1\mathbf{T}_2 + b\mathbf{T}_1\mathbf{T}_3).$$

A similar calculation verifies the second condition of bilinearity. Thus $\mathfrak{L}$ is a linear algebra. To prove that the dimension of $\mathfrak{L}$ is n^2 we use Theorem 2.14 to represent $\mathcal{U}_n$ as n-tuples of elements of $\mathfrak{F}$, and define the n^2 linear transformations $\mathbf{T}_{ij}$, where $i, j = 1, \ldots, n$, by

$$(x_1, \ldots, x_n)\mathbf{T}_{ij} = (0, \ldots, 0, x_i, 0, \ldots, 0)$$

where the jth component of the image vector is x_i, and all other components are zero. It can be shown that the $\mathbf{T}_{ij}$ are linearly independent linear transformations which span $\mathfrak{L}$. However this fact is more readily seen in terms of matrices, so the completion of this proof is deferred until § 4.3.

One additional remark is of interest here. An abstract linear algebra may or may not have an identity of multiplication. However, it can be shown that *any* linear algebra with an identity and of dimension k is isomorphic to a subalgebra of the algebra of all linear transformations on $\mathcal{V}_k$. This fact provides a concrete representation of any such abstract linear algebra and a striking illustration of the generality of linear transformations and their importance in linear algebra.

Exercises

1. Let $\mathcal{A}$ be a linear algebra over $\mathcal{F}$ and let $\{\alpha_1, \ldots, \alpha_m\}$ be a basis for $\mathcal{A}$. The product of any two elements of $\mathcal{A}$ is an element of $\mathcal{A}$ and hence is a linear combination of the α_i. Hence each pair α_i, α_j of basis vectors determines m scalars c_{ijk}, $k = 1, \ldots, m$ such that

$$\alpha_i \alpha_j = \sum_{k=1}^{m} c_{ijk} \alpha_k \qquad \text{for all } i, j = 1, \ldots, m.$$

(i) Show that the product of any two elements of $\mathcal{A}$ is determined by the m^3 scalars c_{ijk}.

(ii) Find a necessary and sufficient condition on the scalars c_{ijk} that the algebra be commutative ($\xi\eta = \eta\xi$ for all $\xi, \eta \in \mathcal{A}$).

(iii) Show that any finite-dimensional vector space can be made into a linear algebra by defining the trivial product in which $c_{ijk} = 0$ for all i, j, k.

2. An important example of a linear algebra of dimension four, given a century ago by Hamilton, was a forerunner of the study of matrices. The elements of the algebra are called *quaternions*, and the scalars are the real numbers. In a notation similar to that of the complex numbers, a quaternion is an expression of the form

$$a_1 1 + a_2 i + a_3 j + a_4 k.$$

Equality, sum, and scalar multiple are defined component by component; quaternion product is defined by bilinearity and the following multiplication table for the basis elements, wherein the product xy appears in the row labeled x at the left and in the column labeled y at the top:

	1	i	j	k
1	1	i	j	k
i	i	-1	k	$-j$
j	j	$-k$	-1	i
k	k	j	$-i$	-1

(i) Verify that this product is closed. All other postulates of a linear algebra are also satisfied.

(ii) Show that every quaternion except $0 + 0i + 0j + 0k$ has an inverse relative to this product; that is,

$$(a_1 + a_2i + a_3j + a_4k)(b_1 + b_2i + b_3j + b_4k) = 1 + 0i + 0j + 0k$$

for suitable b_1, b_2, b_3, b_4.

(iii) Is the product commutative?

From this we conclude that the quaternions form a noncommutative "division algebra." An important theorem of Frobenius proves that the quaternions form the *only* noncommutative division algebra over the real numbers.

§3.7. *Specific Form of a Linear Transformation*

Finally we approach the bridge which connects linear transformations and matrices. Let $\mathbf{T}$ be a linear transformation from $\mathcal{V}_m$ into $\mathcal{W}_n$. We choose any basis $\{\alpha_1, \ldots, \alpha_m\}$ for $\mathcal{V}_m$ and any basis $\{\beta_1, \ldots, \beta_n\}$ for $\mathcal{W}_n$, and then consider the images $\alpha_i \mathbf{T}$ of the basis vectors of $\mathcal{V}_m$, expressed in terms of the basis vectors of $\mathcal{W}_n$. Since $\alpha_i \mathbf{T} \in \mathcal{W}_n$ for each i, there is a *unique* representation for $\alpha_i \mathbf{T}$ as a linear combination of the vectors in the β-basis; that is,

$$\alpha_i \mathbf{T} = a_{i1}\beta_1 + a_{i2}\beta_2 + \cdots + a_{in}\beta_n$$

$$= \sum_{j=1}^{n} a_{ij}\beta_j, \qquad \text{for each } i = 1, 2, \ldots, m.$$

This set of m linear equations describes the effect of $\mathbf{T}$ on the vectors of the α-basis. But any vector $\xi \in \mathcal{V}_m$ can be represented uniquely as a linear combination of the vectors in the α-basis:

$$\xi = \sum_{i=1}^{m} x_i \alpha_i.$$

Hence

$$\xi\mathbf{T} = \left(\sum_{i=1}^{m} x_i \alpha_i\right)\mathbf{T} = \sum_{i=1}^{m} x_i(\alpha_i \mathbf{T})$$

$$= \sum_{i=1}^{m} x_i\left(\sum_{j=1}^{n} a_{ij}\beta_j\right) = \sum_{i=1}^{m}\left(\sum_{j=1}^{n} x_i a_{ij}\beta_j\right)$$

$$= \sum_{j=1}^{n}\left(\sum_{i=1}^{m} x_i a_{ij}\right)\beta_j.$$

Therefore the effect of $\mathbf{T}$ on any vector ξ is described in terms of the scalars x_i (which represent ξ in terms of the α-basis) and the scalars a_{ij} (which describe the effect of $\mathbf{T}$ on the vectors of the α-basis, expressed in terms of the β-basis).

This representation of $\mathbf{T}$ is so vital in our future work that we repeat, for emphasis, the idea involved. Given a linear transformation $\mathbf{T}$ from $\mathcal{V}_m$

to $\mathcal{W}_n$ we choose a basis for $\mathcal{V}_m$ and a basis for $\mathcal{W}_n$. The image of each of the m basis vectors of $\mathcal{V}_m$ is described by n scalars which depend upon $\mathbf{T}$ and *upon the basis for* $\mathcal{W}_m$. Furthermore, these mn scalars describe $\mathbf{T}$ completely since the image of any given vector can be determined from the mn scalars.

Conversely, *with respect to a fixed choice of bases for* $\mathcal{V}_m$ *and* $\mathcal{W}_n$, any mn scalars determine a linear transformation; given a_{ij}, $i = 1, 2, \ldots, m$ and $j = 1, 2, \ldots, n$, let $\mathbf{T}$ be the linear transformation defined by the equations

$$\alpha_1 \mathbf{T} = a_{11}\beta_1 + a_{12}\beta_2 + \cdots + a_{1n}\beta_n$$
$$\alpha_2 \mathbf{T} = a_{21}\beta_1 + a_{22}\beta_2 + \cdots + a_{2n}\beta_n$$
$$\vdots$$
$$\alpha_m \mathbf{T} = a_{m1}\beta_1 + a_{m2}\beta_2 + \cdots + a_{mn}\beta_n.$$

Since a linear transformation is determined by its effect on any basis (Exercise 7, § 3.1), $\xi \mathbf{T}$ is defined for all $\xi \in \mathcal{V}$. These results are summarized in the following theorem.

Theorem 3.17. Let $\mathbf{T}$ be a linear transformation from $\mathcal{V}_m$ to $\mathcal{W}_n$, both over $\mathfrak{F}$. With respect to a chosen pair of bases, $\mathbf{T}$ determines a set of mn scalars, arranged in a rectangular array of m rows and n columns. Conversely, each such array of mn scalars determines uniquely (using the convention just described) a linear transformation from $\mathcal{V}_m$ to $\mathcal{W}_n$.

In the next chapter we shall consider rectangular arrays of scalars, calling each such array a matrix. Theorem 3.17 tells us that every linear transformation determines an array of this type, relative to fixed bases, and every array determines a linear transformation, again with fixed bases being used to define the transformation. In order that these arrays be useful in representing facts about linear transformations, we shall define operations on matrices in such a way as to imitate the corresponding operations on linear transformations.

For linear transformations which map $\mathcal{V}$ into itself, only one basis is needed. To illustrate, let us consider the representation of the product of two linear transformations $\mathbf{T}$ and $\mathbf{S}$ from $\mathcal{V}$ to $\mathcal{V}$. Let $\{\alpha_1, \ldots, \alpha_n\}$ be a basis for $\mathcal{V}$. Then, using the method just described, we obtain n^2 scalars a_{ik} which represent $\mathbf{T}$ and n^2 scalars b_{kj} which represent $\mathbf{S}$, both in terms of the α-basis:

$$\alpha_i \mathbf{T} = \sum_{k=1}^{n} a_{ik}\alpha_k, \qquad i = 1, \ldots, n,$$

$$\alpha_k \mathbf{S} = \sum_{j=1}^{n} b_{kj}\alpha_j, \qquad k = 1, \ldots, n.$$

To find a representation of **TS** we calculate as follows:

$$\alpha_i(\mathbf{TS}) = (\alpha_i\mathbf{T})\mathbf{S} = \left(\sum_{k=1}^{n} a_{ik}\alpha_k\right)\mathbf{S} = \sum_{k=1}^{n} a_{ik}(\alpha_k\mathbf{S})$$

$$= \sum_{k=1}^{n} a_{ik}\left(\sum_{j=1}^{n} b_{kj}\alpha_j\right)$$

$$= \sum_{k=1}^{n}\left(\sum_{j=1}^{n} a_{ik}b_{kj}\alpha_j\right)$$

$$= \sum_{j=1}^{n}\left(\sum_{k=1}^{n} a_{ik}b_{kj}\alpha_j\right)$$

$$= \sum_{j=1}^{n}\left(\sum_{k=1}^{n} a_{ik}b_{kj}\right)\alpha_j.$$

The last form of the equation can be written

$$\alpha_i(\mathbf{TS}) = \left(\sum_{k=1}^{n} a_{ik}b_{k1}\right)\alpha_1 + \left(\sum_{k=1}^{n} a_{ik}b_{k2}\right)\alpha_2 + \cdots + \left(\sum_{k=1}^{n} a_{ik}b_{kn}\right)\alpha_n$$

for $i = 1, \ldots, n$. Hence the n^2 scalars which represent **TS** relative to the α-basis are

$$\sum_{k=1}^{n} a_{ik}b_{kj}, \qquad i, j = 1, 2, \ldots, n.$$

This observation is precisely what guides us in the next chapter, where the product of matrices is defined formally.

We now return to the simpler case of representing a single transformation relative to a chosen basis. To illustrate how the a_{ij} depend on the chosen basis as well as on **T**, let us consider the rotation of the plane through an angle of 90°. Referring to the usual coordinates, choose $\epsilon_1 = (1, 0)$ and $\epsilon_2 = (0, 1)$ as a basis. Then

$$\epsilon_1\mathbf{T} = (1, 0)\mathbf{T} = \quad(0, 1) = \quad 0\epsilon_1 + 1\epsilon_2,$$
$$\epsilon_2\mathbf{T} = (0, 1)\mathbf{T} = (-1, 0) = -1\epsilon_1 + 0\epsilon_2,$$

and the four scalars which represent **T** are

$$a_{11} = \quad 0 \qquad a_{12} = 1$$
$$a_{21} = -1 \qquad a_{22} = 0.$$

Now let us choose a different basis, say $\alpha_1 = (1, 1)$ and $\alpha_2 = (-1, 0)$. Then

$$\alpha_1\mathbf{T} = \quad(1, 1)\mathbf{T} = (-1, 1) = \quad 1\alpha_1 + \quad 2\,\alpha_2,$$
$$\alpha_2\mathbf{T} = (-1, 0)\mathbf{T} = (0, -1) = -1\alpha_1 + (-1)\alpha_2,$$

and the four scalars which represent **T** with respect to the new basis are

$$b_{11} = 1 \qquad b_{12} = 2$$
$$b_{21} = -1 \qquad b_{22} = -1.$$

In our thinking about linear transformations we have hitherto used the phrase "image of α under **T**" to describe α**T**. Using the plane for simplicity, the geometric picture we have of **T** is that **T** performs a rearrangement of the vectors (points) of the plane. Each point is moved by **T** into a new position (which might happen to coincide with the old one). In case **T** is nonsingular, a second means of interpreting **T** is sometimes convenient. If **T** is nonsingular, the image of a basis is again a basis. But in Chapter 2 we saw that each basis determines a coordinate system, so a change of basis is nothing more than a change of coordinates. Thus we may picture the points of the plane not being moved about by **T** but remaining fixed and acquiring a new set of coordinates.

To summarize, a nonsingular transformation may be interpreted in two ways:

Dynamic (Alibi). **T** moves each point P into a point P**T** in such a way that if $P \neq Q$ then P**T** $\neq Q$**T**.

Static (Alias). **T** assigns new coordinates to each point in such a way that if the old coordinates of P and Q are different, then the new coordinates of P and Q also differ.

For the example given above, the dynamic interpretation is illustrated by Figure 3.5. Alternately, in the static interpretation we consider the four pairs

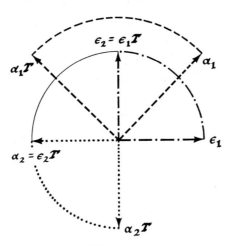

Figure 3.5

of vectors as defining four coordinate systems in the plane. If a point P has coordinates (a, b) in the ϵ_1, ϵ_2 basis, then by direct computation P has coordinates

$(b, -a)$ in the $\epsilon_1 \mathbf{T}, \epsilon_2 \mathbf{T}$ basis,
$(b, b - a)$ in the α_1, α_2 basis,
$(-a, -a - b)$ in the $\alpha_1 \mathbf{T}, \alpha_2 \mathbf{T}$ basis.

Exercises

1. A linear transformation $\mathbf{T}$ of the plane is known to carry the point $P(1, 1)$ into the point $P'(-2, 0)$ and to carry $Q(0, 1)$ into $Q'(-1, 1)$.

(i) Choose $\{\epsilon_1, \epsilon_2\}$ as a basis, and determine $\epsilon_1 \mathbf{T}$ and $\epsilon_2 \mathbf{T}$.

(ii) What scalars represent $\mathbf{T}$ relative to $\{\epsilon_1, \epsilon_2\}$?

(iii) What is the image under $\mathbf{T}$ of an arbitrary point $R(a, b)$?

(iv) Choose the basis vectors $\{\beta_1, \beta_2\}$ to be the points P and Q. What scalars represent $\mathbf{T}$ relative to $\{\beta_1, \beta_2\}$?

(v) Show that $\mathbf{T}$ is nonsingular, and find scalars which represent $\mathbf{T}^{-1}$ relative to $\{\epsilon_1, \epsilon_2\}$.

2. Let $\alpha_1 = \epsilon_1 + 2\epsilon_2$, $\alpha_2 = -\epsilon_1 + \epsilon_2$, and let $\mathbf{S}$ be the linear transformation determined by this change of basis; that is, $\epsilon_1 \mathbf{S} = \alpha_1$, $\epsilon_2 \mathbf{S} = \alpha_2$.

(i) What scalars represent $\mathbf{S}$ relative to $\{\epsilon_1, \epsilon_2\}$?

(ii) What scalars represent $\mathbf{S}$ relative to $\{\alpha_1, \alpha_2\}$?

(iii) What scalars represent $\mathbf{S}^{-1}$ relative to $\{\epsilon_1, \epsilon_2\}$?

(iv) Find the image under $\mathbf{S}$ of the vector $a\epsilon_1 + b\epsilon_2$.

3. Referring to Exercises 1 and 2 for the definitions of $\mathbf{S}$ and $\mathbf{T}$, consider the product transformations $\mathbf{TS}$ and $\mathbf{ST}$.

(i) What scalars represent $\mathbf{TS}$ relative to $\{\epsilon_1, \epsilon_2\}$? Answer in two ways: first by determining $\epsilon_1 \mathbf{TS}$ and $\epsilon_2 \mathbf{TS}$, and second by applying the formula $c_{ij} = \sum_{k=1}^{n} a_{ik} b_{kj}$ of § 3.5.

(ii) Similarly, calculate the scalars which represent $\mathbf{ST}$ relative to $\{\epsilon_1, \epsilon_2\}$.

(iii) Find the images of the point (a, b) under the transformations $\mathbf{TS}$ and $\mathbf{ST}$.

4. Consider a linear transformation $\mathbf{T}$ of $\mathcal{V}_m$ onto $\mathcal{W}_n$ and a linear transformation $\mathbf{S}$ of $\mathcal{W}_n$ onto $\mathcal{Y}_p$. Choose bases $\{\alpha_1, \ldots, \alpha_m\}$ for $\mathcal{V}_m$, $\{\beta_1, \ldots, \beta_n\}$ for $\mathcal{W}_n$, and $\{\gamma_1, \ldots, \gamma_p\}$ for $\mathcal{Y}_p$. Then $\mathbf{T}$ is represented relative to the α-basis for $\mathcal{V}_m$ and the β-basis for $\mathcal{W}_n$ by the mn scalars a_{ik}, where

$$\alpha_i \mathbf{T} = \sum_{k=1}^{n} a_{ik} \beta_k, \qquad i = 1, \ldots, m.$$

Likewise, $\mathbf{S}$ is represented relative to the β-basis for $\mathcal{W}_n$ and the γ-basis for $\mathcal{Y}_p$ by the np scalars b_{kj}, where

$$\beta_k \mathbf{S} = \sum_{j=1}^{p} b_{kj}\gamma_j, \qquad k = 1, \ldots, n.$$

Show that the product transformation $\mathbf{TS}$ of $\mathcal{V}_m$ onto $\mathcal{Y}_p$ is represented relative to the α-basis for $\mathcal{V}_m$ and the γ-basis for $\mathcal{Y}_p$ by mp scalars:

$$c_{ij} = \sum_{k=1}^{n} a_{ik}b_{kj} \qquad \text{for } i = 1, \ldots, m \text{ and } j = 1, \ldots, p.$$

5. (i) Prove that $\mathbf{T}$ is idempotent if and only if $\eta\mathbf{T} = \eta$ for every $\eta \in \mathcal{R}_\mathbf{T}$.

(ii) Prove that if $\mathbf{T}$ is idempotent, there exists a basis for $\mathcal{V}$ such that $\alpha_i\mathbf{T} = \alpha_i$ for $1 \le i \le \rho(\mathbf{T})$ and $\alpha_i\mathbf{T} = \theta$ for $\rho(\mathbf{T}) < i \le n$.

(iii) What array of scalars represents an idempotent transformation relative to the basis described in (ii)?

CHAPTER 4

Matrices

§4.1. *Matrices and Matrix Operations*

The considerations of the last section show that each linear transformation **T** from $\mho_m$ to $\mathcal{W}_n$ determines an array of mn scalars which describe **T** completely. The determination of these scalars requires the choice of a basis for $\mho_m$ and a basis for $\mathcal{W}_n$, and various choices of bases lead to different sets of scalars, each set representing **T** relative to a suitable pair of bases. A fundamental method of linear algebra is to investigate the nature of **T** by observing properties of an array of scalars which represent **T**, and vice versa.

Let $\mho_m$ be a vector space with an arbitrary but fixed basis $\{\alpha_1, \ldots, \alpha_m\}$. Let **T** be a linear transformation of $\mho_m$ into a vector space $\mathcal{W}_n$, and let $\{\beta_1, \ldots, \beta_n\}$ be any fixed basis for $\mathcal{W}_n$. For each $i = 1, 2, \ldots, m$, $\alpha_i \mathbf{T}$ is a uniquely determined vector of $\mathcal{W}_n$ and hence is uniquely represented as a linear combination of the $\beta_j, j = 1, 2, \ldots, n$:

$$
\begin{aligned}
\alpha_1 \mathbf{T} &= a_{11}\beta_1 + a_{12}\beta_2 + \cdots + a_{1n}\beta_n, \\
\alpha_2 \mathbf{T} &= a_{21}\beta_1 + a_{22}\beta_2 + \cdots + a_{2n}\beta_n, \\
&\ \vdots \\
\alpha_m \mathbf{T} &= a_{m1}\beta_1 + a_{m2}\beta_2 + \cdots + a_{mn}\beta_n.
\end{aligned}
$$

(*4.1*)

Notice the meaning of the subscripts: the first subscript i of a_{ij} means that a_{ij} is one of the coefficients of the representation of the vector $\alpha_i \mathbf{T}$ relative to the β-basis, and the second subscript j of a_{ij} means that a_{ij} is the coefficient of β_j in that representation. Relative to the two bases, **T** is completely determined by the mn scalars a_{ij}, together with this interpretation of the meaning of the subscripts. This means not only that we have selected bases for $\mho_m$ and $\mathcal{W}_n$, but that we have written the basis vectors in a specific order in each case, and we tacitly agree to observe this order. If we were to interchange the order, say of α_1 and α_2, then we would merely interchange the first two lines of (4.1), whereas an interchange of β_1 and β_2 would interchange the first two columns on the right hand side. The mn scalars representing **T** would be the same, but they would be written in a different arrangement from that of (4.1). To avoid ambiguity, therefore, we agree to pay attention to the order of the basis vectors.

With this convention understood, we can dispense with writing the α_i and β_j, and represent **T** by the rectangular array of scalars,

$$\begin{pmatrix} a_{11} & a_{12} & \ldots & a_{1n} \\ a_{21} & a_{22} & \ldots & a_{2n} \\ \cdot & \cdot & & \cdot \\ \cdot & \cdot & & \cdot \\ \cdot & \cdot & & \cdot \\ a_{m1} & a_{m2} & \ldots & a_{mn} \end{pmatrix}.$$

This array of m rows and n columns of field elements is denoted more compactly by (a_{ij}), $i = 1, \ldots, m$ and $j = 1, \ldots, n$. The component a_{ij} is the scalar in the ith row and the jth column, so the first index i is called the *row index*, and the second index j is called the *column index*.

Before we proceed it is appropriate to emphasize that we have agreed to represent **T** by the set of scalars arranged *exactly* as they appear as coefficients in (4.1). This convention is adopted in order that the algebraic properties of such arrays reflect corresponding properties of the linear transformations which they represent, and it is closely related to our earlier decision to use right-hand notation for linear transformations. Had we chosen to use left-hand notation, writing $T(\xi)$ instead of ξT, we would represent **T** by a different array of scalars, namely

$$\begin{pmatrix} a_{11} & a_{21} & \ldots & a_{m1} \\ a_{12} & a_{22} & \ldots & a_{m2} \\ \cdot & \cdot & & \cdot \\ \cdot & \cdot & & \cdot \\ \cdot & \cdot & & \cdot \\ a_{1n} & a_{2n} & \ldots & a_{mn} \end{pmatrix}.$$

This new array is obtained by interchanging the roles of rows and columns in the previous array. That is, in left-hand notation the first *column* of scalars specifies the coefficients of the vector $T(\alpha_1)$, the second column those of $T(\alpha_2)$, and so on. In right-hand notation the first *row* specifies the coefficients of $\alpha_1 T$, the second row those of $\alpha_2 T$, and so on.

Definition 4.1. A rectangular array containing m rows and n columns of elements of a field $\mathcal{F}$ is called an $m \times n$ *matrix* over $\mathcal{F}$.

More completely, a matrix is an element of an abstract system for which several relations and operations are defined, and a study of this system comprises matrix theory. In defining relations and operations for matrices we shall be guided by the principle that if matrices are to be used to represent linear transformations, their algebraic properties must reflect those of linear transformations.

First let us consider equality; two linear transformations are equal if and only if they have exactly the same effect on each vector, and therefore if and only if they have the same effect on each vector of a basis. The latter means that two equal linear transformations have identical matrix representations relative to a fixed choice of ordered bases for $\mathcal{V}_m$ and $\mathcal{W}_n$.

Definition 4.2. Two $m \times n$ matrices $A = (a_{ij})$ and $B = (b_{ij})$ are *equal* if and only if $a_{ij} = b_{ij}$ for every $i = 1, 2, \ldots, m$ and every $j = 1, 2, \ldots, n$.

The matrix representations of the transformations $\mathbf{T} + \mathbf{S}$ and $c\mathbf{T}$, expressed in terms of the representations of $\mathbf{T}$ and $\mathbf{S}$, provide the motivation for the following two definitions.

Definition 4.3. The *sum* of two $m \times n$ matrices $A = (a_{ij})$ and $B = (b_{ij})$ is the $m \times n$ matrix $C = (c_{ij})$, where

$$c_{ij} = a_{ij} + b_{ij}$$

for every $i = 1, 2, \ldots, m$ and every $j = 1, 2, \ldots, n$.

Definition 4.4. The *scalar multiple* of an $m \times n$ matrix $A = (a_{ij})$ by a scalar c is the $m \times n$ matrix $C = (c_{ij})$, where

$$c_{ij} = ca_{ij}$$

for every $i = 1, 2, \ldots, m$ and every $j = 1, 2, \ldots, n$.

Notice in particular that equality, sum, and scalar multiple are all defined component by component. Also note that equality and sum are defined only for matrices of the same dimensions. An example for 2×3 matrices will make the definitions clear. Let

$$A = \begin{pmatrix} 1 & -2 & 0 \\ 0 & 1 & 2 \end{pmatrix}, \quad B = \begin{pmatrix} 0 & 2 & 1 \\ 0 & -1 & -1 \end{pmatrix}.$$

Then

$$A + B = \begin{pmatrix} 1+0 & -2+2 & 0+1 \\ 0+0 & 1-1 & 2-1 \end{pmatrix} = \begin{pmatrix} 1 & 0 & 1 \\ 0 & 0 & 1 \end{pmatrix}$$

and

$$3A = \begin{pmatrix} 3 & -6 & 0 \\ 0 & 3 & 6 \end{pmatrix}.$$

Since addition and scalar multiplication of matrices are defined in terms of the field operations, we may expect certain properties of the field operations to be inherited by matrices. For example, matrix addition is associative and commutative, and scalar multiplication is distributive over matrix addition. These properties, and others listed below, may be proved as exercises.

1. $A + B = B + A$.
2. $(A + B) + C = A + (B + C)$.
3. $c(A + B) = cA + cB$.
4. $(c + d)A = cA + dA$.

In particular, the $m \times n$ matrix Z, all of whose components are zero, is the identity of addition for all $m \times n$ matrices.

5. $A + Z = A$.
6. $A + (-1)A = Z$.
7. $0(A) = Z$.

Next consider how matrix multiplication should be defined in order to simulate the product of linear transformations. The product **TS** was defined as a successive mapping, and this is possible only when **T** maps $\mathcal{V}_m$ into $\mathcal{W}_n$ and **S** maps $\mathcal{W}_n$ into $\mathcal{Y}_p$. The corresponding matrix product AB should be defined whenever the number of columns of A equals the number of rows of B, since each represents the dimension of $\mathcal{W}_n$. The exact form of the multiplication is indicated by Exercise 4, § 3.7, which calculates the representation of **TS** in terms of bases for $\mathcal{V}_m$, $\mathcal{W}_n$, and $\mathcal{Y}_p$.

Definition 4.5. If $A = (a_{ik})$ is an $m \times n$ matrix and if $B = (b_{kj})$ is an $n \times p$ matrix, the *product* AB is the $m \times p$ matrix $C = (c_{ij})$, where

$$c_{ij} = \sum_{k=1}^{n} a_{ik}b_{kj}$$

for every $i = 1, 2, \ldots, m$ and every $j = 1, 2, \ldots, p$.

Some of the time we shall be concerned with transformations of a space into itself. The corresponding matrices will be square, n rows and n columns, if n is the dimension of the space. Thus if A and B are square matrices of the same dimension, then AB and BA are both defined, but not necessarily equal.

We refer to Definition 4.5 to learn a technique for matrix multiplication. Each element in the product AB of an $m \times n$ matrix A by an $n \times p$ matrix B is the sum of n products of scalars. To find the element c_{ij} which is in the ith row and jth column of AB we multiply each element in the ith row of A by the corresponding element in the jth column of B, and then add:

$$c_{ij} = a_{i1}b_{1j} + a_{i2}b_{2j} + \cdots + a_{in}b_{nj}:$$

In practice we can perform this computation easily by the technique of using the left index finger to run across the ith row of the left-hand matrix and simultaneously using the right index finger to run down the jth column of the right-hand matrix, multiplying elements in corresponding positions and adding successively the products obtained. An example may help to clarify the procedure.

$$A = \begin{pmatrix} 1 & 0 & -1 \\ 2 & 4 & 7 \\ 5 & 3 & 0 \end{pmatrix}, \quad B = \begin{pmatrix} 6 & 1 \\ 0 & 4 \\ -2 & 3 \end{pmatrix};$$

$$AB = \begin{pmatrix} (1)(6) + (0)(0) + (-1)(-2) & (1)(1) + (0)(4) + (-1)(3) \\ (2)(6) + (4)(0) + (7)(-2) & (2)(1) + (4)(4) + (7)(3) \\ (5)(6) + (3)(0) + (0)(-2) & (5)(1) + (3)(4) + (0)(3) \end{pmatrix}$$

$$= \begin{pmatrix} 8 & -2 \\ -2 & 39 \\ 30 & 17 \end{pmatrix}.$$

Exercises

1. Verify properties 1 through 7, page 77, for addition and scalar multiples of matrices. Deduce that the set of all $m \times n$ matrices over a field $\mathfrak{F}$ forms a commutative group relative to addition.

2. Compute AB, AC, B^2, BC, CA, given that

$$A = \begin{pmatrix} 1 & 0 & -1 \\ 0 & 2 & 3 \end{pmatrix}, \quad B = \begin{pmatrix} 2 & -1 & 4 \\ 1 & 0 & -2 \\ 0 & 3 & 1 \end{pmatrix}, \quad C = \begin{pmatrix} 0 & 2 \\ -1 & 0 \\ 3 & 1 \end{pmatrix}.$$

Are any other binary products possible for these three matrices?

3. Referring to Example (c) of § 3.1, recall that $\{\epsilon_1, \epsilon_2\}$ is the basis chosen for $\mathcal{E}_2$.

(i) Find the matrices A, B, and C which represent T_1, T_2, and T_3, respectively.

(ii) Calculate AB, BC, CB, and A^2, and from the results deduce statements for matrices which are analogous to the statements observed in the discussion of these linear transformations.

4.   (i) Relative to the preferred basis $\{\epsilon_1, \epsilon_2, \ldots, \epsilon_n\}$ for $\mathcal{E}_n$, find the matrix E_{ij} which represents the linear transformation $\mathbf{T}_{ij}$ which was defined in the proof of Theorem 3.1.

(ii) Show that any $n \times n$ matrix is a linear combination of the matrices E_{ij}, for $i, j = 1, \ldots, n$.

(iii) Show that if a linear combination of the matrices E_{ij} equals Z then each coefficient of that linear combination is zero.

5. Show that the system of all 1×1 matrices over a field $\mathfrak{F}$, together with matrix addition and multiplication, is a field which is isomorphic to $\mathfrak{F}$.

6. Prove that the set of all real 2×2 matrices of the form

$$\begin{pmatrix} a & b \\ -b & a \end{pmatrix}$$

forms a system which is isomorphic to the field of complex numbers.

7. Prove that the set of all complex 2×2 matrices of the form

$$\begin{pmatrix} a + ib & c + id \\ -c + id & a - ib \end{pmatrix}, \qquad i^2 = -1,$$

forms a system which is isomorphic to the algebra of quaternions as described in Exercise 2, § 3.6.

8. Read "What is a Matrix?" by C. C. MacDuffee, *American Mathematical Monthly*, volume 50 (1943), pp. 360–365.

§4.2. *Special Types of Matrices*

Before proceeding with a general study of matrix operations, we shall consider certain classes of matrices which play an important role in matrix theory. The few calculations we have made in the examples and exercises have warned us to expect the unexpected; from Exercise 3, § 4.1, we see that matrix multiplication is not commutative (even when both AB and BA are defined) and also that a product of nonzero matrices can equal the zero matrix.

Identity matrix. We seek a matrix I such that $IX = XI = X$ for every matrix X. But if X is $m \times n$, I must have m columns in order that IX be defined and n rows in order that XI be defined. But then IX is $n \times n$, XI is $m \times m$, and X is $m \times n$. Hence m and n must be equal, so X must be square, say $n \times n$, and I must be likewise. Thus we must speak of the *identity matrix of dimension n*, which is easily seen to be

$$I = (\delta_{ij}) = \begin{pmatrix} 1 & 0 & 0 & \ldots & 0 \\ 0 & 1 & 0 & \ldots & 0 \\ 0 & 0 & 1 & \ldots & 0 \\ & \cdot & \cdot & & \cdot \\ & \cdot & \cdot & & \cdot \\ & \cdot & \cdot & & \cdot \\ 0 & 0 & 0 & \ldots & 1 \end{pmatrix},$$

where δ_{ij} is the *Kronecker delta*, defined in § 3.4.

Scalar matrices. Although matrix multiplication is not commutative, the $n \times n$ identity matrix commutes with every $n \times n$ matrix. Are there other square matrices $A = (a_{ij})$ which have the property that $AX = XA$ for every $n \times n$ matrix $X = (x_{ij})$? A straightforward approach would be to determine scalars a_{ij} which satisfy the n^2 equations,

$$\sum_{k=1}^{n} a_{ik}x_{kj} = \sum_{k=1}^{n} x_{ik}a_{kj}, \qquad i, j = 1, 2, \ldots, n.$$

This is a somewhat fearful task. Instead, we argue as follows: let E_{rs} be the $n \times n$ matrix with $e_{rs} = 1$ and $e_{ij} = 0$ if $i \neq r$ or $j \neq s$. If A commutes with all $n \times n$ matrices, then in particular we must have

$$AE_{rs} = \begin{pmatrix} 0 & \ldots & a_{1r} & \ldots & 0 \\ 0 & \ldots & a_{2r} & \ldots & 0 \\ \cdot & & \cdot & & \cdot \\ \cdot & & \cdot & & \cdot \\ 0 & \ldots & a_{nr} & \ldots & 0 \end{pmatrix} = \begin{pmatrix} 0 & 0 & \ldots & 0 \\ \cdot & & & \cdot \\ \cdot & & & \cdot \\ a_{s1} & a_{s2} & \ldots & a_{sn} \\ \cdot & & & \cdot \\ \cdot & & & \cdot \\ 0 & 0 & \ldots & 0 \end{pmatrix} = E_{rs}A,$$

where every element not in column s of the first matrix is zero, and every element not in row r of the second matrix is zero. Hence we have $a_{rr} = a_{ss}$, $a_{ir} = 0$ if $i \neq r$, and $a_{sj} = 0$ if $j \neq s$. Thus if A commutes with all the E_{rs} matrices, A must have the same element k in every position of the *main diagonal* and zeros elsewhere:

$$a_{ij} = k\delta_{ij}, \qquad i, j = 1, 2, \ldots, n,$$

$$A = \begin{pmatrix} k & 0 & \cdot & \cdot & 0 \\ 0 & k & \cdot & \cdot & 0 \\ \cdot & \cdot & & & \cdot \\ \cdot & \cdot & & & \cdot \\ 0 & 0 & \cdot & \cdot & k \end{pmatrix} = kI.$$

Such a matrix is called a *scalar matrix*, being merely a scalar multiple of I. Clearly, a scalar matrix commutes with every matrix, so the question is answered completely.

Diagonal matrices. Scalar matrices form a subclass of the class of *diagonal matrices*, which are defined by the property that $a_{ij} = 0$ if $i \neq j$. Thus zeros appear everywhere except possibly on the main diagonal. Clearly, the sum of diagonal matrices is diagonal; so is the product, for if A and B are diagonal and $AB = C$, then

$$c_{ij} = \sum_{k=1}^{n} a_{ik}b_{kj} = a_{ii}b_{ij} = \begin{cases} a_{ii}b_{ii} & \text{if } j = i, \\ 0 & \text{if } j \neq i. \end{cases}$$

$$\begin{pmatrix} a_{11} & 0 & \ldots & 0 \\ 0 & a_{22} & \ldots & 0 \\ \cdot & \cdot & & \cdot \\ \cdot & \cdot & & \cdot \\ \cdot & \cdot & & \cdot \\ 0 & 0 & \ldots & a_{nn} \end{pmatrix} \begin{pmatrix} b_{11} & 0 & \ldots & 0 \\ 0 & b_{22} & \ldots & 0 \\ \cdot & \cdot & & \cdot \\ \cdot & \cdot & & \cdot \\ \cdot & \cdot & & \cdot \\ 0 & 0 & \ldots & b_{nn} \end{pmatrix} = \begin{pmatrix} c_{11} & 0 & \ldots & 0 \\ 0 & c_{22} & \ldots & 0 \\ \cdot & \cdot & & \cdot \\ \cdot & \cdot & & \cdot \\ \cdot & \cdot & & \cdot \\ 0 & 0 & \ldots & c_{nn} \end{pmatrix}.$$

Triangular matrices. A still more inclusive class of square matrices is that for which $a_{ij} = 0$ whenever $i > j$. Such a matrix is called (upper) *triangular* because all the nonzero elements lie on or above the main diagonal:

$$\begin{pmatrix} a_{11} & a_{12} & \ldots & a_{1n} \\ 0 & a_{22} & \ldots & a_{2n} \\ \cdot & \cdot & & \cdot \\ \cdot & \cdot & & \cdot \\ \cdot & \cdot & & \cdot \\ 0 & 0 & \ldots & a_{nn} \end{pmatrix}.$$

A triangular matrix for which $a_{ii} = 0$ for $i = 1, \ldots, n$ is called *strictly triangular*. Clearly, any triangular matrix is the sum of a strictly triangular matrix and a diagonal matrix.

Idempotent matrices. A matrix A is said to be *idempotent* if and only if $A^2 = A$. An example other than Z and I is $\begin{pmatrix} 1 & -1 \\ 0 & 0 \end{pmatrix}$.

Nilpotent matrices. A matrix A is said to be *nilpotent* of index p if $A^p = Z$ but $A^{p-1} \neq Z$. Any strictly triangular matrix is nilpotent. (See Exercise 5.)

Nonsingular matrices. This special type of matrix is of great importance, since it corresponds to nonsingular linear transformations. We recall from Theorem 3.6 that a nonsingular linear transformation $\mathbf{T}$ from $\mathcal{U}$ into $\mathcal{W}$ is simply a one-to-one linear mapping of $\mathcal{U}$ onto $\mathcal{R}_{\mathbf{T}}$. Hence, by regarding $\mathbf{T}$ as a linear transformation from $\mathcal{U}$ to $\mathcal{R}_{\mathbf{T}}$, we can represent $\mathbf{T}$ by a square matrix.

> **Definition 4.6.** An $n \times n$ matrix A is said to be *nonsingular* if and only if a matrix B exists such that
>
> $$AB = I.$$
>
> Otherwise A is said to be *singular*.

First we point out the formal similarity of Definition 4.6 to Definition 3.7 which concerned nonsingular linear transformations. For transformations we proved in Theorem 3.7 that if $\mathbf{TT^*} = \mathbf{I}$ then $\mathbf{T^*T} = \mathbf{I}$. Is the corresponding result valid for matrices? We would like to prove that if $AB = I$, then $BA = I$. In terms of matrix multiplication we would have to prove that if

$$\sum_{k=1}^{n} a_{ik}b_{kj} = \delta_{ij}, \qquad i, j = 1, 2, \ldots, n,$$

then

$$\sum_{k=1}^{n} b_{ik}a_{kj} = \delta_{ij}, \qquad i, j = 1, 2, \ldots, n,$$

which is true but by no means obvious. However, after the discussion of the following section we prove this result merely by pointing to Theorem 3.7. Anticipating this proof, we call B the *inverse of* A, denoted A^{-1}. Thus nonsingular matrices are those which possess a multiplicative inverse.

For the next two types of matrices considered here, we need the notion of the transpose of A, which is simply the matrix obtained by reflecting A across its main diagonal.

Definition 4.7. Let $A = (a_{ij})$ be any $m \times n$ matrix. The *transpose* of A, denoted A', is the $n \times m$ matrix defined by

$$A' = (b_{rs}),$$

where $b_{rs} = a_{sr}$.

Theorem 4.1. Let $\{\alpha_1, \ldots, \alpha_m\}$ be a basis for $\mathcal{U}_m$ and $\{\beta_1, \ldots, \beta_n\}$ be a basis for $\mathcal{W}_n$; let $\{\mathbf{f}_1, \ldots, \mathbf{f}_m\}$ and $\{\mathbf{g}_1, \ldots, \mathbf{g}_n\}$ be the corresponding dual bases for $\mathcal{U}_m'$ and $\mathcal{W}_n'$, respectively. If a linear transformation $\mathbf{T}$ from $\mathcal{U}_m$ to $\mathcal{W}_n$ is represented relative to the α, β bases by a matrix A, then the transpose transformation $\mathbf{T}'$ from $\mathcal{W}_n'$ to $\mathcal{U}_m'$ is represented relative to the $\mathbf{g}$, $\mathbf{f}$ bases by the transpose matrix A'.

P R O O F : From § 3.4 we recall that the dual basis for $\mathcal{U}_m'$ is defined by $\alpha_i \mathbf{f}_k = \delta_{ik}$ for $i, k = 1, 2, \ldots, m$; similarly, the dual basis for $\mathcal{W}_n'$ is defined by $\beta_k \mathbf{g}_j = \delta_{kj}$ for $k, j = 1, 2, \ldots, n$. The transpose $\mathbf{T}'$ of the transformation $\mathbf{T}$ is the linear mapping from $\mathcal{W}_n'$ to $\mathcal{U}_m'$ defined in § 3.5 by

$$g_j\mathbf{T}' = \mathbf{T}g_j, \qquad j = 1, 2, \ldots, n.$$

Relative to the $\mathbf{g}$, $\mathbf{f}$ bases, $\mathbf{T}'$ is represented by the $n \times m$ matrix $B = (b_{jk})$, determined by the equations

$$g_j\mathbf{T}' = \sum_{k=1}^{m} b_{jk}\mathbf{f}_k, \qquad j = 1, 2, \ldots, n.$$

Thus,

$$\alpha_i g_j \mathbf{T}' = (\alpha_i \mathbf{T})\mathbf{g}_j = \left(\sum_{k=1}^{n} a_{ik}\beta_k\right)\mathbf{g}_j$$

$$= \sum_{k=1}^{n} a_{ik}(\beta_k \mathbf{g}_j) = \sum_{k=1}^{n} a_{ik}\delta_{kj} = a_{ij}.$$

However,

$$\alpha_i g_j \mathbf{T}' = \alpha_i \left(\sum_{k=1}^{m} b_{jk}\mathbf{f}_k\right) = \sum_{k=1}^{m} b_{jk}(\alpha_i \mathbf{f}_k)$$

$$= \sum_{k=1}^{m} b_{jk}\delta_{ik} = b_{ji}.$$

Hence $b_{ji} = a_{ij}$, so $B = A'$.

In Exercise 7 you may prove that $(A')' = A$, $(A + B)' = A' + B'$, and $(AB)' = B'A'$. Notice in particular that the transpose of a product of matrices is the product of the transposes *in the reverse order*.

Symmetric matrices. An $n \times n$ matrix A is said to be *symmetric* if and only if $A = A'$. Obviously any diagonal matrix is symmetric.

Skew-symmetric matrices. An $n \times n$ matrix A is said to be *skew-symmetric* (or simply *skew*) if and only if $A' = -A$. This implies of course that if $1 + 1 \neq 0$ in the base field, then every diagonal element of a skew matrix is zero. We exclude from our consideration any field in which $1 + 1 = 0$. (See § 1.6.)

Now let A be any square matrix. If $1 + 1 \neq 0$ in $\mathfrak{F}$,

$$A = \tfrac{1}{2}(A + A') + \tfrac{1}{2}(A - A').$$

Since $A + A'$ is symmetric and $A - A'$ is skew (see Exercise 8), this expresses A as a sum of two matrices, the first of which is symmetric and the second skew.

Row vectors and column vectors. Relative to a fixed basis, every vector of $\mathcal{U}_n$ has a unique representation as an n-tuple of scalars, $(a_1, \ldots, a_n)$. Except for the presence of commas, this is formally the same as a matrix of one row and n columns. Accordingly, a $1 \times n$ matrix is called a *row vector*. The transpose of a row vector is an $n \times 1$ matrix, of n rows and one column, and is called a *column vector*. If A is a row vector, where $A = (a_1\, a_2 \ldots a_n)$, and if B' is a column vector, where $B = (b_1\, b_2 \ldots b_n)$, then both AB' and $B'A$ are defined:

$$AB' = (a_1\ a_2\ \cdots\ a_n)\begin{pmatrix} b_1 \\ b_2 \\ \cdot \\ \cdot \\ \cdot \\ b_n \end{pmatrix} = (a_1b_1 + a_2b_2 + \cdots + a_nb_n),$$

which is a 1×1 matrix, or by Exercise 5, § 4.1, a scalar:

$$B'A = \begin{pmatrix} b_1 \\ b_2 \\ \cdot \\ \cdot \\ \cdot \\ b_n \end{pmatrix}(a_1\ a_2\ \cdots\ a_n) = \begin{pmatrix} b_1a_1 & b_1a_2 & \ldots & b_1a_n \\ b_2a_1 & b_2a_2 & \ldots & b_2a_n \\ \cdot & \cdot & & \cdot \\ \cdot & \cdot & & \cdot \\ \cdot & \cdot & & \cdot \\ b_na_1 & b_na_2 & \ldots & b_na_n \end{pmatrix},$$

which is an $n \times n$ matrix.

Exercises

1. Prove that $IA = AI = A$ for every square matrix A.

2. Show that for each n the set of all $n \times n$ scalar matrices over $\mathfrak{F}$ forms a field which is isomorphic to $\mathfrak{F}$.

3. (i) Prove that all $n \times n$ diagonal matrices commute.

   (ii) Prove that if A commutes with all $n \times n$ diagonal matrices, then A is diagonal.

4. Prove that the set of all $n \times n$ triangular matrices is closed under matrix sum and product. Deduce that the set of all nonsingular $n \times n$ triangular matrices forms a multiplicative group.

5. Show that any 4×4 strictly triangular matrix is nilpotent. How would you generalize your proof for the $n \times n$ case?

6. Prove that if A is idempotent and $A \neq I$, then A is singular.

7. Prove that

   (i) $(A')' = A$,

   (ii) $(A + B)' = A' + B'$,

   (iii) $(AB)' = B'A'$ if AB is defined.

8. Prove for every square matrix A that

   (i) AA' is symmetric,

   (ii) $A + A'$ is symmetric,

   (iii) $A - A'$ is skew.

9. Prove that A^2 is symmetric if either A is symmetric or A is skew.

10. If A and B are both symmetric, prove that

    (i) $A + B$ is symmetric,

    (ii) AB is symmetric if and only if A and B commute.

11. If A and B are skew, prove that $A + B$ is skew.
12. Prove $(A')^{-1} = (A^{-1})'$ if A is nonsingular.
13. Let $\{\alpha_1, \alpha_2, \alpha_3\}$ be a basis for $\mathcal{V}_3$, and let

$$\beta_1 = \alpha_1 - 2\alpha_2,$$
$$\beta_2 = \alpha_1 + \alpha_2 + \alpha_3,$$
$$\beta_3 = \alpha_2 - \alpha_3.$$

(i) Prove $\{\beta_1, \beta_2, \beta_3\}$ is a basis, and express each α_i as a linear combination of the β_j.

(ii) If $\mathbf{T}$ is defined by $\alpha_i\mathbf{T} = \beta_i$, find the matrix A which represents $\mathbf{T}$ relative to the α-basis.

(iii) If $\mathbf{S}$ is defined by $\beta_i\mathbf{S} = \alpha_i$, find the matrix B which represents $\mathbf{S}$ relative to the β-basis.

(iv) Prove by matrix calculations that $AB = I$.

§4.3. *Fundamental Isomorphism Theorem*

We might expect that the next step in our development of the theory of matrices would be to establish various properties of matrix operations. This is correct, but instead of verifying such properties directly we prove a theorem which clarifies the connection between matrices and linear transformations. This connection is an isomorphism, and therefore we can obtain properties of matrices from theorems already proved about linear transformations. Not only does this method avoid duplication of effort, but it substitutes geometric insight for involved arithmetic calculations.

From Theorem 3.16 we know that the set of all linear transformations on an n-dimensional vector space over $\mathfrak{F}$ forms a linear algebra

$$\mathcal{L} = \{L, F; +, \cdot, \oplus, \odot, \square\}$$

over $\mathfrak{F}$. We wish to show that the set of all $n \times n$ matrices, together with the matrix operations, form a linear algebra $\mathfrak{M}$ which is isomorphic to $\mathcal{L}$. Since a linear algebra is a vector space on which is defined a suitable multiplication of vectors, the concept of isomorphism of linear algebras is defined to be a vector space isomorphism which also preserves the multiplication of vectors.

Theorem 4.2. Let $\mathcal{V}$ be an n-dimensional vector space over $\mathfrak{F}$. The set of all $n \times n$ matrices over $\mathfrak{F}$ forms a linear algebra $\mathfrak{M}$ which is isomorphic to the linear algebra $\mathcal{L}$ of all linear transformations on $\mathcal{V}$.

PROOF: Fix a basis $\{\alpha_1, \ldots, \alpha_n\}$ for $\mathcal{V}$. Let $A = (a_{ij})$ be any $n \times n$

matrix over $\mathfrak{F}$. With A we associate the linear transformation $\mathbf{T}$ of $\mathcal{V}$ into $\mathcal{V}$ defined by

$$\alpha_i\mathbf{T} = \sum_{j=1}^{n} a_{ij}\alpha_j, \qquad i = 1, \ldots, n.$$

It was established in Theorem 3.17 that this correspondence is one-to-one, provided we regard a fixed ordering of the basis vectors. We next show that the correspondence preserves the three operations of scalar multiplication, matrix addition, and matrix multiplication. The matrix $kA = (ka_{ij})$ determines the linear transformation $\mathbf{S}_1$ defined by

$$\alpha_i\mathbf{S}_1 = \sum_{j=1}^{n} (ka_{ij})\alpha_j = k\sum_{j=1}^{n} a_{ij}\alpha_j = k\alpha_i\mathbf{T} = \alpha_i(k\mathbf{T}),$$

so if A corresponds to $\mathbf{T}$, kA corresponds to $k\mathbf{T}$. Let $A = (a_{ij})$ correspond to $\mathbf{T}$, and let $B = (b_{ij})$ correspond to $\mathbf{U}$. Then $A + B = (a_{ij} + b_{ij})$ corresponds to the transformation $\mathbf{S}_2$ defined by

$$\alpha_i\mathbf{S}_2 = \sum_{j=1}^{n} (a_{ij} + b_{ij})\alpha_j = \sum_{j=1}^{n} a_{ij}\alpha_j + \sum_{j=1}^{n} b_{ij}\alpha_j$$

$$= \alpha_i\mathbf{T} + \alpha_i\mathbf{U} = \alpha_i(\mathbf{T} + \mathbf{U}),$$

so $A + B$ corresponds to $\mathbf{T} + \mathbf{U}$. Finally, the matrix $AB = (c_{ij})$, where $c_{ij} = \sum_{k=1}^{n} a_{ik}b_{kj}$, corresponds to the transformation $\mathbf{S}_3$ defined by

$$\alpha_i\mathbf{S}_3 = \sum_{j=1}^{n} \left(\sum_{k=1}^{n} a_{ik}b_{kj}\right)\alpha_j = \sum_{k=1}^{n}\sum_{j=1}^{n} a_{ik}b_{kj}\alpha_j$$

$$= \sum_{k=1}^{n} a_{ik}\left(\sum_{j=1}^{n} b_{kj}\alpha_j\right)$$

$$= \sum_{k=1}^{n} a_{ik}(\alpha_k\mathbf{U}) = \left(\sum_{k=1}^{n} a_{ik}\alpha_k\right)\mathbf{U}$$

$$= \alpha_i\mathbf{T}\mathbf{U}.$$

Hence AB corresponds to $\mathbf{T}\mathbf{U}$, and the correspondence is an isomorphism. Theorem 3.16 showed that $\mathcal{L}$ is a linear algebra; hence $\mathfrak{M}$, the set of all $n \times n$ matrices over $\mathfrak{F}$, forms a linear algebra (since $\mathfrak{M}$ and $\mathcal{L}$ are isomorphic), and the proof is complete.

Recall that Theorem 3.16 stated that $\mathcal{L}$ is of dimension n^2, but we deferred the proof that the n^2 linear transformations $\mathbf{T}_{ij}$ form a basis for $\mathcal{L}$. $\mathbf{T}_{ij}$ was defined by

$$(x_1, \ldots, x_n)\mathbf{T}_{ij} = (0, \ldots, 0, x_i, 0, \ldots, 0),$$

where the jth component is x_i. Now the matrix corresponding to $\mathbf{T}_{ij}$ is the matrix E_{ij} in which every element is zero except the element in the ith row and jth column, which is 1. It is clear that any matrix is a linear combination of the E_{ij}, $i, j = 1, \ldots, n$, and that the E_{ij} are linearly independent (see Exercise 4, § 4.1). Hence they form a basis for $\mathfrak{M}$, and by the isomorphism the $\mathbf{T}_{ij}$ form a basis for $\mathfrak{L}$. This completes the proof of Theorem 3.16.

The argument of the preceding paragraph indicates the power and usefulness of Theorem 4.2. To prove a result about linear transformations we may, if convenient, prove the corresponding result about matrices, and vice versa. In the next section we list a number of theorems about matrices which have already been proved in the language of linear transformations.

However, we note that Theorem 4.2 concerns only $n \times n$ matrices; for the corresponding theorem for $m \times n$ matrices we recall from Theorem 3.17, that a linear transformation from $\mathcal{V}_m$ to $\mathcal{W}_n$ is represented, relative to a pair of bases, by an $m \times n$ matrix. Also, from Theorem 3.1, the set of all linear transformations from $\mathcal{V}_m$ to $\mathcal{W}_n$ forms a vector space. It is not difficult to verify that the dimension of this vector space is mn, and that the set of all $m \times n$ matrices forms a vector space isomorphic to it.

Exercises

1. Describe the linear transformation on $\mathcal{E}_2$ which is represented by the scalar matrix aI in case

    (i) $a > 1$,
    (ii) $0 < a < 1$,
    (iii) $a < 0$.

2. Describe the linear transformation on $\mathcal{E}_2$ which is represented by each of the following matrices:

    (i) $\begin{pmatrix} 1 & 0 \\ 0 & -1 \end{pmatrix}$,

    (ii) $\begin{pmatrix} 0 & -1 \\ -1 & 0 \end{pmatrix}$,

    (iii) $\begin{pmatrix} 0 & 1 \\ 0 & 0 \end{pmatrix}$,

    (iv) $\begin{pmatrix} 2 & 0 \\ 0 & 3 \end{pmatrix}$,

    (v) $\begin{pmatrix} 2 & 4 \\ -1 & -2 \end{pmatrix}$.

3. (i) Determine all possible 2×2 real matrices which represent idempotent linear transformations on $\mathcal{E}_2$.

    (ii) Determine all possible 2×2 real matrices which represent nilpotent linear transformations of index 2 on $\mathcal{E}_2$.

4. Prove that the set of all $m \times n$ matrices over $\mathfrak{F}$ forms a vector space

of dimension mn which is isomorphic to the space of all linear transformations from $\mathcal{U}_m$ to $\mathcal{W}_n$.

§4.4. *Rank of a Matrix*

Referring now to § 4.1, we see that properties 1 through 7 of matrices all follow by the isomorphism theorem from the corresponding properties of linear transformations. (See Exercise 1, § 4.1, which asked for direct matrix proofs.) In the same way, other properties of matrices can be derived from the corresponding properties of linear transformations. Before doing this we introduce the notion of the *rank* of a matrix.

First recall that the vector $\xi = \sum_{i=1}^{m} x_i \alpha_i$ can be represented relative to the α-basis as $\xi = (x_1, \ldots, x_m)$. This representation defines a $1 \times m$ matrix (row vector) $X = (x_1 \cdots x_m)$. If $A = (a_{ij})$ is $m \times n$, then the product XA is defined, and

$$XA = (y_1 \cdots y_n), \qquad \text{where } y_j = \sum_{i=1}^{m} x_i a_{ij}.$$

Let $\eta = \sum_{j=1}^{n} y_j \beta_j$, and let $\mathbf{T}$ be the transformation which corresponds to A, relative to the fixed bases $\{\alpha_1, \ldots, \alpha_m\}$ and $\{\beta_1, \ldots, \beta_n\}$. Then

$$\xi\mathbf{T} = \left(\sum_{i=1}^{m} x_i \alpha_i \right) \mathbf{T} = \sum_{i=1}^{m} x_i (\alpha_i \mathbf{T})$$

$$= \sum_{i=1}^{m} x_i \left(\sum_{j=1}^{n} a_{ij} \beta_j \right) = \sum_{j=1}^{n} \left(\sum_{i=1}^{m} x_i a_{ij} \right) \beta_j = \sum_{j=1}^{n} y_j \beta_j$$

$$= \eta.$$

Hence *if X represents the vector ξ and A represents the transformation $\mathbf{T}$, then XA represents the vector $\xi\mathbf{T}$.* This is a generalization of the observation that the image $\alpha_j\mathbf{T}$ of the jth vector of the basis is represented relative to the β-basis by the row vector which is the jth row of the matrix A.

Had we chosen left-hand notation for linear transformations, the situation would be different. (See the remarks following Definition 3.1 and those preceding Definition 4.1.) Relative to the α, β bases the vector ξ would be represented by the column vector X'; $\mathbf{T}$ would be represented by the $n \times m$ matrix A'; $\mathbf{T}(\alpha_i)$ would be represented by the ith column vector of A'; and $\mathbf{T}(\xi)$ would be represented by $A'X' = (XA)'$. Thus one is able to pass from one notation to the other simply by taking transposes of appropriate matrices. The simplicity of representing $\mathbf{T}$ by the array of scalars as they stand in the arrangement (4.1) is one reason for preferring right-hand notation.

Definition 4.9. The *rank* of a matrix A, denoted $\rho(A)$, is the maximal number of linearly independent row vectors of A.

An immediate question is the following: What is the relation (if any) between the rank of a matrix and the rank of the linear transformation it represents relative to a chosen basis? Notice that $\rho(A)$ as defined is an intrinsic property of the matrix A and is independent of any bases we choose in order to represent A as a linear transformation. Likewise, the rank of a linear transformation is defined to be the dimension of its range space and thus is an intrinsic property of the transformation, independent of any choice of bases.

Theorem 4.3. Let $\mathbf{T}$ be the transformation corresponding to the $m \times n$ matrix A relative to chosen bases. Then

$$\rho(\mathbf{T}) = \rho(A).$$

P R O O F : Let $\{\alpha_1, \ldots, \alpha_m\}$ be any basis for $\mathcal{V}_m$. Any vector in $\mathcal{R}_\mathbf{T}$ is a linear combination of the row vectors of A, since if $\xi = \sum_{i=1}^{k} c_i \alpha_i$, $\xi \mathbf{T} = \sum_{i=1}^{k} c_i (\alpha_i \mathbf{T})$. Hence any maximal independent subset of the row vectors of A is a basis for $\mathcal{R}_\mathbf{T}$.

Theorem 4.4. For any matrix A, $\rho(A) = \rho(A')$.

P R O O F : Given an $m \times n$ matrix A, choose vector spaces $\mathcal{V}_m$ and $\mathcal{W}_n$ and a pair of bases, and let $\mathbf{T}$ be the linear mapping from $\mathcal{V}_m$ to $\mathcal{W}_n$ represented by A relative to that pair of bases. By Theorem 4.1, the transpose transformation $\mathbf{T}'$ from $\mathcal{W}'_n$ to $\mathcal{V}'_m$ is represented by A' relative to the corresponding pair of dual bases. By Theorem 4.3, we have $\rho(\mathbf{T}) = \rho(A)$ and $\rho(\mathbf{T}') = \rho(A')$, and by Theorem 3.15, $\rho(\mathbf{T}) = \rho(\mathbf{T}')$. Hence any matrix and its transpose have the same rank; this means that in any matrix the number of linearly independent row vectors equals the number of linearly independent column vectors.

We conclude this section with a list of theorems, all of which are readily proved by the isomorphism theorem and a corresponding theorem for linear transformations.

Theorem 4.5. Matrix multiplication is associative and bilinear.

Theorem 4.6. If A and B are $n \times n$ matrices such that $AB = I$, then $BA = I$.

Theorem 4.7. The following are equivalent for an $n \times n$ matrix A:
(a) A is nonsingular,
(b) $\rho(A) = n$,
(c) The row vectors of A are linearly independent.

Theorem 4.8. If A is a nonsingular $n \times n$ matrix, B an $m \times n$ matrix, and C an $n \times p$ matrix, then $\rho(BA) = \rho(B)$ and $\rho(AC) = \rho(C)$.

Theorem 4.9. Let A and B be $n \times n$ matrices. AB is nonsingular if and only if A and B are both nonsingular. If AB is nonsingular, then $(AB)^{-1} = B^{-1}A^{-1}$.

Exercises

1. Using the isomorphism theorem and appropriate theorems for linear transformations, prove Theorems 4.5–4.9.

2. Prove directly by matrix calculations that

$$A(bB + cC) = bAB + cAC$$

for all $n \times n$ matrices A, B, C.

3. Prove that a triangular matrix is nonsingular if and only if every diagonal element is different from zero.

4. Let $\xi \in \mathcal{V}_n$, $\xi \neq \theta$. Prove that the set of all linear transformations $\mathbf{T}$ on $\mathcal{V}_n$ such that $\xi \mathbf{T} = \theta$ forms a linear algebra whose dimension is $n^2 - n$.

5. Let A, B be $n \times n$ matrices. What statements can you make about $\rho(A + B)$ and $\rho(AB)$?

6. State as a theorem for matrices the assertion of Theorem 3.6, statements (a), (b), and (c).

7. State as a theorem for matrices the assertion of Exercise 7, § 3.2.

8. An $n \times n$ Markov matrix is defined to be any $n \times n$ real matrix $A = (a_{ij})$ which satisfies the two properties

$$0 \leq a_{ij} \leq 1,$$

$$\sum_{j=1}^{n} a_{ij} = 1 \qquad \text{for } i = 1, 2, \ldots, n.$$

Prove that the product of two Markov matrices is a Markov matrix. Do such matrices form a multiplicative group?

9. A Markov (stochastic) matrix is called *doubly stochastic* if the sum of the elements in each column is unity. Is the product of two doubly stochastic matrices doubly stochastic?

10. If M is a Markov matrix, show that the value of every element of column j of M^2 is between the values of the minimal and maximal elements of column j of M.

11. In quantum mechanics the Pauli theory of electron spin makes use of linear transformations $\mathbf{T}_x$, $\mathbf{T}_y$, $\mathbf{T}_z$, whose complex matrices in the preferred coordinate system are, respectively,

$$X = \begin{pmatrix} 0 & 1 \\ 1 & 0 \end{pmatrix},$$

$$Y = \begin{pmatrix} 0 & -i \\ i & 0 \end{pmatrix}, \quad \text{where } i^2 = -1,$$

$$Z = \begin{pmatrix} 1 & 0 \\ 0 & -1 \end{pmatrix}.$$

(i) Show that $X^2 = Y^2 = Z^2 = I$, and therefore that each is non-singular.

(ii) Form a multiplication table of the four matrices I, X, Y, Z, and observe that any product of these matrices is a scalar times one of these matrices.

(iii) List the elements of the smallest multiplicative group which contains X and Y.

12. In the special theory of relativity, use is made of the Lorentz transformation,

$$x' = b(x - vt),$$

$$t' = b\left(-\frac{vx}{c^2} + t\right),$$

where $|v|$ represents the speed of a moving object, c the speed of light, and $b = c(c^2 - v^2)^{-1/2}$. The corresponding matrix is

$$L(v) = b \begin{pmatrix} 1 & -v \\ \dfrac{-v}{c^2} & 1 \end{pmatrix}.$$

(i) Show that $L(v)$ is nonsingular for $|v| < c$.

(ii) Show that the set of all $L(v)$ for $|v| < c$ forms a multiplicative group. This group is called the Lorentz group.

§4.5. *Block Multiplication of Matrices*

Although our emphasis in this book is on the theory of matrices rather than on the practical problems which arise in applications, it would be misleading to pretend that such problems do not exist. For example, the form of the product of two matrices may be unfamiliar to a beginner, but it is conceptually simple. In the product of an $m \times n$ matrix and an $n \times p$ matrix there are mp terms to be calculated, and each term requires n binary products and $n - 1$ sums. Hence, there are altogether mpn products and $mp(n - 1)$ sums to be performed. For square matrices, this reduces to n^3 products and $n^3 - n^2$ sums.

In matrices which arise from experimental work the individual entries are decimal numbers which are seldom integral, so that multiplication is considerably more tedious than addition. For this reason the amount of work required for a matrix calculation is usually expressed in terms of the number of multiplications involved. Since the product of two $n \times n$ matrices requires n^3 multiplications, it is clear that a tremendous amount of computation is required when n is large. Even for $n = 10$ the work is sufficiently long to discourage mental computation. The recent development of high-speed computers has reduced this problem considerably, and thereby has opened to solution by matrix methods many applied problems for which theoretical solutions were known but were computationally unfeasible. But even a large electronic computer has a limited storage space, and the practical question of computational technique remains.

We now indicate a device, known as *block multiplication* of matrices, which can be used to decompose the product of two large matrices into numerous products of smaller matrices. Let A be $m \times n$ and B be $n \times p$. Write $n = n_1 + n_2 + \cdots + n_k$, where each n_i is a positive integer; partition the *columns* of A by putting the first n_1 columns in the first block, the next n_2 columns in the second block, and so on. Partition the *rows* of B in exactly the same way. Then

$$A = (A_1|A_2|\cdots|A_k), \qquad B = \begin{pmatrix} B_1 \\ \hline B_2 \\ \cdot \\ \cdot \\ \cdot \\ \hline B_k \end{pmatrix},$$

where A_i is the $m \times n_i$ matrix consisting of columns of A beginning with column $n_1 + \cdots + n_{i-1} + 1$ and ending with column $n_1 + \cdots + n_i$, and where B_j is the $n_j \times p$ matrix consisting of rows of B beginning with row $n_1 + \cdots + n_{j-1} + 1$ and ending with row $n_1 + \cdots + n_j$. Then the method of block multiplication asserts that

$$AB = A_1B_1 + A_2B_2 + \cdots + A_kB_k.$$

More generally, suppose that having partitioned the columns of A and the rows of B as described above, we partition the *rows* of A in any manner and the *columns* of B in any manner. We obtain

$$A = \begin{pmatrix} A_{11} & A_{12} & \ldots & A_{1k} \\ A_{21} & A_{22} & \ldots & A_{2k} \\ \cdot & \cdot & & \cdot \\ \cdot & \cdot & & \cdot \\ \cdot & \cdot & & \cdot \\ A_{r1} & A_{r2} & \ldots & A_{rk} \end{pmatrix}, \qquad B = \begin{pmatrix} B_{11} & B_{12} & \ldots & B_{1s} \\ B_{21} & B_{22} & \ldots & B_{2s} \\ \cdot & \cdot & & \cdot \\ \cdot & \cdot & & \cdot \\ \cdot & \cdot & & \cdot \\ B_{k1} & B_{k2} & \ldots & B_{ks} \end{pmatrix},$$

where A_{it} is a matrix (rectangular array) having r_i rows and n_t columns and B_{tj} is a matrix having n_t rows and s_j columns. Then for fixed i, j the product $A_{it}B_{tj}$ is defined and yields an $r_i \times s_j$ matrix; therefore $\sum_{t=1}^{k} A_{it}B_{tj}$ is an $r_i \times s_j$ matrix. The method of block multiplication asserts that

$$AB = \begin{pmatrix} C_{11} & C_{12} \ldots & C_{1s} \\ C_{21} & C_{22} \ldots & C_{2s} \\ \cdot & \cdot & \cdot \\ \cdot & \cdot & \cdot \\ \cdot & \cdot & \cdot \\ C_{r1} & C_{r2} \ldots & C_{rs} \end{pmatrix},$$

where $C_{ij} = \sum_{t=1}^{k} A_{it}B_{tj}$.

This is in the same form as the element-by-element definition of the product of matrices in which each element is considered as a 1×1 block. The important thing to remember in block multiplication of AB is that the column partition of A must coincide with the row partition of B, in order that all the matrix products $A_{it}B_{tj}$ be defined. Since matrix multiplication is noncommutative, it is essential that the proper order be maintained in forming products of blocks.

The proof of this result is not difficult, but it does require care in choosing notation and manipulating indices. Since we do not require the result for the development of theory, a general proof is omitted. To understand the application of block multiplication to the problem of large-scale computations, consider two 50×50 matrices. There are 2500 elements in each matrix; the multiplication of two such matrices requires 125,000 multiplications and almost as many additions. One method of performing such calculations on a computer whose storage capacity is exceeded by the magnitude of the problem would be to partition each of the matrices into smaller matrices, perhaps into four 25×25 blocks,

$$A = \left(\begin{array}{c|c} A_{11} & A_{12} \\ \hline A_{21} & A_{22} \end{array} \right), \qquad B = \left(\begin{array}{c|c} B_{11} & B_{12} \\ \hline B_{21} & B_{22} \end{array} \right).$$

If the blocks are suitably small, the machine can successively compute the products $A_{11}B_{11}, A_{11}B_{12}, A_{12}B_{21}, A_{12}B_{22}$, and so on, record the results on punched cards to clear the machine storage for the next block of calculations, and finally compute $C_{11} = A_{11}B_{11} + A_{12}B_{21}$, and so on.

Even for human calculators, block multiplication is useful in case special patterns appear in the matrix. For example, let

$$A = \left(\begin{array}{cc|ccc} 2 & 0 & 0 & 0 & 0 \\ 0 & 2 & 0 & 0 & 0 \\ \hline 1 & 0 & a & b & c \\ 0 & 1 & d & e & f \end{array} \right) = \left(\begin{array}{cc} 2I & Z \\ I & A_0 \end{array} \right),$$

and let
$$B = \begin{pmatrix} B_0 \\ C_0 \end{pmatrix},$$
where B_0 has two rows and C_0 has three rows. Then
$$AB = \begin{pmatrix} 2B_0 \\ B_0 + A_0 C_0 \end{pmatrix}.$$
Hence the only nontrivial computation required for AB is the product of the 2×3 matrix A_0 with the $3 \times p$ matrix C_0.

To observe that it is sometimes possible to introduce convenient patterns in a matrix by judicious selection of bases, consider a linear transformation $\mathbf{T}$ from $\mathcal{V}_m$ to $\mathcal{W}_n$. Choose a basis for $\mathfrak{N}_\mathbf{T}$ and extend it to a basis $\{\alpha_1, \ldots, \alpha_m\}$ for $\mathcal{V}_m$, numbered so that the basis $\{\alpha_{m-\nu+1}, \ldots, \alpha_m\}$ for $\mathfrak{N}_\mathbf{T}$ appears last. Now in $\mathcal{W}_n$ choose any basis $\{\beta_1, \ldots, \beta_{m-\nu}\}$ for $\mathfrak{R}_\mathbf{T}$ and extend it to a basis $\{\beta_1, \ldots, \beta_n\}$ for $\mathcal{W}_n$. Then relative to these bases $\mathbf{T}$ is represented by an $m \times n$ matrix A of the block form
$$A = \begin{pmatrix} B & Z_1 \\ Z_2 & Z_3 \end{pmatrix},$$
where B is $(m-\nu) \times (m-\nu)$, and Z_1, Z_2, Z_3 are zero matrices of dimensions $(m-\nu) \times (n-m+\nu)$, $\nu \times (m-\nu)$, and $\nu \times (n-m+\nu)$, respectively.

In particular, $\mathbf{T}$ is nonsingular if and only if $\nu = 0$. In that case we have
$$A = (B|Z_1).$$
The $m \times m$ matrix B is nonsingular since its m rows represent the linearly independent vectors $\alpha_i \mathbf{T}, i = 1, \ldots, m$. Let C be the $n \times m$ matrix defined by
$$C = \begin{pmatrix} B^{-1} \\ Z_4 \end{pmatrix},$$
where Z_4 is the $(n-m) \times m$ zero matrix. Then we compute
$$AC = I_m,$$
$$CA = \begin{pmatrix} I_m & Z \\ Z & Z \end{pmatrix}.$$

These calculations should help to make clear the distinction between our definition of nonsingular linear mappings and that of nonsingular matrices. If $\mathbf{T}$ is a nonsingular linear transformation from $\mathcal{V}_m$ to $\mathcal{W}_n$, then $m \leq n$, and $\mathbf{T}$ can be represented by a rectangular matrix consisting of an $m \times m$ block which is a nonsingular matrix and an $m \times (n-m)$ block of zeros.

Exercises

1. Prove the first of the two assertions of the text concerning block multiplication: If $A = (A_1|\cdots|A_k)$ and

$$B = \begin{pmatrix} \overline{B_1} \\ \cdot \\ \cdot \\ \cdot \\ \overline{B_k} \end{pmatrix},$$

then $AB = A_1B_1 + \cdots + A_kB_k$.

2. Calculate AB in three ways: directly without partition; with the partition indicated; with a different partition of your own choosing.

$$A = \left(\begin{array}{cc|c|cc} 2 & 3 & 4 & 0 & 0 \\ 3 & 1 & 0 & 0 & 0 \\ \hline 1 & 0 & 1 & 0 & 4 \\ \hline -1 & 0 & 0 & 1 & 0 \\ 0 & -1 & 4 & 0 & 1 \end{array}\right),$$

$$B = \left(\begin{array}{c|cc} 1 & 0 & 0 \\ 3 & 0 & 0 \\ \hline 0 & 2 & 1 \\ \hline -1 & 0 & 0 \\ -1 & 0 & 0 \end{array}\right).$$

3. Suppose an $n \times n$ matrix A is of the form

$$A = \left(\begin{array}{c|c} A_1 & Z \\ \hline A_3 & A_4 \end{array}\right),$$

where Z is a $k \times (n - k)$ block of zeros.

(i) Consider the linear transformation **T** determined by A relative to a chosen basis $\{\alpha_1, \ldots, \alpha_n\}$. What is the geometric meaning of the block of zeros?

(ii) Suppose an $n \times n$ matrix B is also of the form described above for the matrix A. Prove by block multiplication that AB has this same property.

(iii) Prove the result of (ii) by a geometric argument.

CHAPTER 5

Linear Equations and Determinants

§5.1. *Systems of Linear Equations*

One of the most frequent applications of matrices to modern science arises from the need to solve a system of linear equations:

$$
\begin{aligned}
a_{11}\,x_1 + a_{12}\,x_2 + \cdots + a_{1n}\,x_n &= y_1 \\
a_{21}\,x_1 + a_{22}\,x_2 + \cdots + a_{2n}\,x_n &= y_2 \\
&\;\;\vdots \\
a_{m1}x_1 + a_{m2}x_2 + \cdots + a_{mn}x_n &= y_m.
\end{aligned}
$$

(5.1)

Here we consider the mn scalars a_{ij} and the m scalars y_i as fixed. By a *solution* of the system (5.1) we mean an n-tuple of scalars x_j, $j = 1, \ldots, n$, for which each of the m equations is satisfied. To *solve* the system means to find *all* solutions.

The system can be written in compact form by using matrix notation; let

$$
A = \begin{pmatrix} a_{11} & a_{12} & \ldots & a_{1n} \\ a_{21} & a_{22} & \ldots & a_{2n} \\ \cdot & \cdot & & \cdot \\ \cdot & \cdot & & \cdot \\ \cdot & \cdot & & \cdot \\ a_{m1} & a_{m2} & \ldots & a_{mn} \end{pmatrix}, \quad X = \begin{pmatrix} x_1 \\ x_2 \\ \cdot \\ \cdot \\ \cdot \\ x_n \end{pmatrix}, \quad Y = \begin{pmatrix} y_1 \\ y_2 \\ \cdot \\ \cdot \\ \cdot \\ y_m \end{pmatrix}.
$$

Then the system is represented by the single matrix equation,

(5.2) $$AX = Y.$$

By taking the transpose of each side we obtain

(5.3) $$X'A' = Y',$$

which is in the form we have adopted for linear transformations: X' is a row
vector of n components, A' an $n \times m$ matrix, and Y' a row vector of m compo-
nents. Therefore, if we choose $\{\beta_1, \ldots, \beta_n\}$ as a basis for $\mathcal{W}_n$ and $\{\alpha_1, \ldots, \alpha_m\}$
as a basis for $\mathcal{V}_m$, then A' represents a linear transformation $\mathbf{T}$ from $\mathcal{W}_n$ to $\mathcal{V}_m$,
X' a vector ξ in $\mathcal{W}_n$, and Y' a vector η in $\mathcal{V}_m$:

$$(5.4) \qquad\qquad \xi\mathbf{T} = \eta.$$

In this section we shall develop the theory concerned with the existence
and uniqueness of solutions, deferring several observations concerning specific
methods of obtaining solutions until further properties of matrices are established. We remark first about notation; our choice of right-hand notation
for linear transformations has led to the necessity of considering transposes
of the natural arrangement of the scalars of a system of linear equations, in
order to reduce the system to right-hand matrix notation. Thus, while right-
hand notation seems preferable for the matrix representation of linear transformations, left-hand notation is more natural for the matrix representation
of systems of linear equations. This intrinsic difference is the underlying
reason for a lack of uniformity in notation for matrix representations. Since
the passage from either notation to the other is easily performed by means of
transposes, no real difficulty is encountered in consulting various references,
provided we remember to ascertain which notation is adopted in each case.

To return to the problem of solving a system of linear equations, we have
a given linear transformation $\mathbf{T}$ from $\mathcal{W}_n$ to $\mathcal{V}_m$, a given vector $\eta \in \mathcal{V}_m$, and
we seek to find all $\xi \in \mathcal{W}_n$ which are mapped by $\mathbf{T}$ into η:

$$\xi\mathbf{T} = \eta.$$

In solving this problem we shall consider separately the cases $\eta = \theta$ and
$\eta \neq \theta$; also, some of our conclusions will depend upon the relative magnitudes
of the three positive integers $m, n, \rho(A)$, where (5.1) is a system of m equations
in n unknowns whose matrix of coefficients has rank $\rho(A)$. Since $\rho(A) =
\rho(A') = \rho(\mathbf{T})$, $\rho(A)$ cannot exceed either m or n.

The homogeneous case. If $\eta = \theta$, or equivalently $y_1 = y_2 = \cdots = y_m = 0$,
the system is said to be *homogeneous*. In this case the set of all solutions ξ is
simply the null space $\mathfrak{N}_\mathbf{T}$, whose dimension is $\nu(\mathbf{T}) = n - \rho(\mathbf{T}) = n -
\rho(A) \geq 0$. The zero vector θ is always a solution, called the *trivial* solution.
There will exist nontrivial (nonzero) solutions if and only if $\nu(\mathbf{T}) > 0$. This
simple geometric argument has provided a full description of the solution of
a homogeneous system of linear equations.

Theorem 5.1. If $y_1 = y_2 = \cdots = y_m = 0$, the solutions of (5.1) form
a vector space of dimension $n - \rho(A)$. Nontrivial solutions exist if and

only if $n - \rho(A) > 0$. Thus, if $m = n = \rho(A)$, the trivial solution is unique.

For $n = 3$, the geometric interpretation is that either $x_1 = x_2 = x_3 = 0$ is the only solution, or that every point on a certain line through the origin is a solution, or that every point on a certain plane through the origin is a solution. (The case $\rho(A) = 0$ is not considered, since then $a_{ij} = 0$ for all i, j.)

The nonhomogeneous case. If $\eta \neq 0$ (or, equivalently, if some $y_j \neq 0$), the system is said to be *nonhomogeneous.* In this case the solution is the set of all vectors ξ which are mapped by $\mathbf{T}$ into η. Since $\mathbf{T}$ and η are fixed by the given scalars a_{ij} and y_j, there is no assurance that even one solution exists. Clearly, a solution will exist if and only if $\eta \in \Re_{\mathbf{T}}$. But $\Re_{\mathbf{T}}$ is spanned by the rows of A', which are the columns of A. Hence, a solution exists if and only if the column vector Y is a linear combination of the columns of A. Let us form a new matrix A_Y, called the *augmented* matrix of the system (5.1), by adjoining the column vector Y to the matrix A: in partitioned form,

$$A_Y = (A|Y).$$

By our previous remark, a solution to (5.1) exists if and only if Y is a linear combination of the columns of A. Taking transposes, Y' must then be a linear combination of the rows of A', so

$$\rho(A_Y) = \rho(A'_Y) = \rho(A') = \rho(A).$$

We have proved the following result.

Theorem 5.2. A solution of (5.1) exists if and only if $\rho(A_Y) = \rho(A)$, where A_Y is the augmented matrix

$$\begin{pmatrix} a_{11} & \cdots & a_{1n} & y_1 \\ a_{21} & \cdots & a_{2n} & y_2 \\ \cdot & & \cdot & \cdot \\ \cdot & & \cdot & \cdot \\ \cdot & & \cdot & \cdot \\ a_{m1} & \cdots & a_{mn} & y_m \end{pmatrix}.$$

Our next theorem describes the set of all solutions of the nonhomogeneous system.

Theorem 5.3. If ξ_0 is a solution of the nonhomogeneous system (5.4), then ξ is a solution if and only if

$$\xi = \xi_0 + \nu \quad \text{for some } \nu \in \Re_{\mathbf{T}}.$$

P R O O F : Let ξ and ξ_0 be solutions. Then $\xi\mathbf{T} = \eta = \xi_0\mathbf{T}$. Hence $\xi\mathbf{T} - \xi_0\mathbf{T} = (\xi - \xi_0)\mathbf{T} = \eta - \eta = 0$, so $\xi - \xi_0 \in \Re_{\mathbf{T}}$. Conversely, if

$$\xi = \xi_0 + \nu \quad \text{for some } \nu \in \mathfrak{N}_T,$$

then

$$\xi T = (\xi_0 + \nu)T = \xi_0 T + \nu T = \eta + \theta = \eta,$$

so ξ is a solution.

The geometric meaning of this theorem is interesting. There may be no solutions to (5.4). If one solution ξ_0 exists, then the set of all solutions is a translation by ξ_0 of the subspace $\mathfrak{N}_T$ of all solutions of the associated homogeneous system. Hence, the solution set for $n = 3$ is void, a single point P, a line through P, or a plane through P. These are not subspaces in the nonhomogeneous case, because then P is not the origin.

It is appropriate to comment further about Theorem 5.2. The condition that the rank of A equal the rank of the augmented matrix A_Y is called the *consistency condition,* and a system which satisfies this condition is said to be *consistent.* Thus a consistent system is simply one which has a solution. This is equivalent to saying that any linear dependence of the rows of A produces an identical dependence of the components of Y. More precisely, if γ_i denotes the ith row of A,

$$\sum_{i=1}^{m} c_i \gamma_i = \theta \quad \text{only if} \quad \sum_{i=1}^{m} c_i y_i = 0.$$

We conclude with a uniqueness theorem which is valid for both homogeneous and nonhomogeneous systems.

Theorem 5.4. If $m = n = \rho(A)$, there is a unique solution of (5.1).

P R O O F : By hypothesis, A is a square matrix which is nonsingular. Clearly, $X_0 = A^{-1}Y$ is a solution to (5.2), and for any solution X, $AX = Y$, so $X = A^{-1}Y = X_0$.

Exercises

1. Find a necessary and sufficient condition on $\rho(A)$ that the system (5.2) have a solution for all possible choices of Y. Prove your result.

2. (i) Describe geometrically the solutions of the single equation

$$a_{i1}x_1 + x_{i2}x_2 + a_{i3}x_3 = y_i.$$

What if $y_i = 0$?

(ii) Describe geometrically the solutions of a system of two equations ($i = 1, 2$) of the type in (i). Need solutions exist? Discuss fully.

(iii) In the nonhomogeneous case with $m = n = 3$, discuss the geometric meaning of $\rho(A) = 1, 2, 3$, including in your discussion both consistency and nonconsistency for each value of $\rho(A)$.

3. Solve the system

$$
\begin{aligned}
x_1 - x_2 + x_3 - x_4 + x_5 &= 1, \\
2x_1 - x_2 + 3x_3 \qquad\quad + 4x_5 &= 2, \\
3x_1 - 2x_2 + 2x_3 + x_4 + x_5 &= 1, \\
x_1 \qquad\quad + x_3 + 2x_4 + x_5 &= 0.
\end{aligned}
$$

4. Solve the system

$$
\begin{aligned}
x_1 + 2x_2 + x_3 &= -1, \\
6x_1 + x_2 + x_3 &= -4, \\
2x_1 - 3x_2 - x_3 &= 0, \\
-x_1 - 7x_2 - 2x_3 &= 7, \\
x_1 - x_2 \qquad &= 1.
\end{aligned}
$$

5. Solve the system

$$
\begin{aligned}
2x_1 + x_2 + 5x_3 &= 4, \\
3x_1 - 2x_2 + 2x_3 &= 2, \\
5x_1 - 8x_2 - 4x_3 &= 1.
\end{aligned}
$$

§5.2. *Determinants*

It is quite likely that you have encountered determinants in your previous study of the solution of a system of n linear equations in n unknowns, particularly for the cases $n = 2, 3$. If so, your estimate of their efficiency as a computational device may be unrealistically high, for while determinants are manageable enough for low values of n, they become quite unwieldy as n increases. Since more economical methods of solving linear equations are available, determinants actually have little value as a general technique computation. However, they do possess definite value as a theoretical tool, and for this reason we include a self-contained exposition of the basic properties of a determinant.

Our point of departure may appear at first to be outrageously abstract, but we shall soon see that this abstraction pays handsome dividends in the simplicity of the proofs of the properties of $n \times n$ determinants. This will be especially apparent to anyone who has worked through an inductive definition of determinants.

In formulating any definition abstractly we usually are guided by some knowledge of a special system which we wish to generalize. Here it suffices to consider the determinant of a 2×2 matrix,

$$
\begin{vmatrix} a & b \\ c & d \end{vmatrix} = ad - bc.
$$

First we recognize that a 2×2 determinant associates a field element with each 2×2 matrix, so this determinant is a function whose domain is the set of all 2×2 matrices over a field and whose range is a subset of the field. This function has many properties: of these we mention four, which are easily verified.

1. $\begin{vmatrix} a & kb \\ c & kd \end{vmatrix} = k \begin{vmatrix} a & b \\ c & d \end{vmatrix}.$

2. $\begin{vmatrix} a & b + e \\ c & d + f \end{vmatrix} = \begin{vmatrix} a & b \\ c & d \end{vmatrix} + \begin{vmatrix} a & e \\ c & f \end{vmatrix}.$

3. $\begin{vmatrix} a & a \\ c & c \end{vmatrix} = 0.$

4. $\begin{vmatrix} 1 & 0 \\ 0 & 1 \end{vmatrix} = 1$

Since all of these properties, except the last, are assertions about columns, we shall agree to write A_i for the ith column vector of an $n \times n$ matrix; also, to make clear the separation between columns, we insert commas:

$$A = (A_1, \ldots, A_n).$$

We are now ready to give an axiomatic definition of determinant.

Definition 5.1. A function "det" whose domain is the set of all $n \times n$ matrices over $\mathfrak{F}$ and whose range is a subset of $\mathfrak{F}$ is called a *determinant*, provided det satisfies three conditions:

(a) det is a linear function of each column; that is, for any $k = 1, 2, \ldots, n$ and all $b, c \in \mathfrak{F}$, if $A_k = bB_k + cC_k$, then

$$\det(A_1, \ldots, bB_k + cC_k, \ldots, A_n)$$
$$= b \det(A_1, \ldots, B_k, \ldots, A_n) + c \det(A_1, \ldots, C_k, \ldots, A_n);$$

(b) if two adjacent columns of A are equal, $\det A = 0$;

(c) $\det I = 1$, where I is the identity matrix and 1 is the unity element of $\mathfrak{F}$.

Notice that (a) combines the first two properties listed for the 2×2 example. It is a remarkable fact that we are able to derive most of the essential properties of determinants from the first and second axioms of Definition 5.1. The third axiom is a normalizing assumption which guarantees that det is uniquely defined, for we must prove that such a function is unique, and even that a function with these properties exists. Three problems are of immediate concern: to prove that det exists, to prove that det is uniquely determined, and to derive properties of det. We shall consider these problems in the reverse order.

Theorem 5.5. If det is a function with properties (a) and (b) of Definition 5.1, then

(a) $\det(A_1, \ldots, cA_k, \ldots, A_n) = c \det(A_1, \ldots, A_k, \ldots, A_n)$,

(b) $\det(A_1, \ldots, B_k + C_k, \ldots, A_n)$
$$= \det(A_1, \ldots, B_k, \ldots, A_n) + \det(A_1, \ldots, C_k, \ldots, A_n),$$

(c) if $A_k = \theta$, then $\det A = 0$,

(d) $\det(A_1, \ldots, A_k, \ldots, A_n) = \det(A_1, \ldots, A_k + cA_{k+1}, \ldots, A_n)$,

(e) $\det(A_1, \ldots, A_k, A_{k+1}, \ldots, A_n) = -\det(A_1, \ldots, A_{k+1}, A_k, \ldots, A_n)$,

(f) if $A_j = A_k$ for any $j \neq k$, then $\det A = 0$,

(g) $\det A = \det(A_1, \ldots, A_k + cA_j, \ldots, A_n)$ for any $j \neq k$,

(h) $\det(A_1, \ldots, A_i, \ldots, A_j, \ldots, A_n)$
$$= -\det(A_1, \ldots, A_j, \ldots, A_i, \ldots, A_n).$$

P R O O F : Before proving each statement, we translate it into words to emphasize its meaning.

(a) *A common factor of each element of a fixed column may be factored out as a multiplicative constant.* Let $b = 0$ in Definition 5.1 (a).

(b) *If a fixed column of A is written as the sum of two column vectors, the determinant of A is the sum of the two determinants as indicated.* Let $b = c = 1$ in Definition 5.1 (a).

(c) *If any column of A consists entirely of zeros, then* $\det A = 0$. Use (a) to factor out 0.

(d) *Any scalar multiple of a column may be added to an adjacent column without changing the value of the determinant.* Use (b) to expand the altered determinant into the sum of two determinants. One of these two is $\det A$; the other is $\det(A_1, \ldots, cA_{k+1}, A_{k+1}, \ldots, A_n) = 0$, since c factors out and then Definition 5.1 (b) may be applied.

(e) *If two adjacent columns are interchanged, the value of the determinant merely changes sign.* First add A_{k+1} to A_k, using (d); then subtract the new kth column from A_{k+1}. This gives

$$\det A = \det(A_1, \ldots, A_k + A_{k+1}, - A_k, \ldots, A_n)$$
$$= \det(A_1, \ldots, A_{k+1}, - A_k, \ldots, A_n)$$
$$= -\det(A_1, \ldots, A_{k+1}, A_k, \ldots, A_n).$$

The interchange of two adjacent columns is called a *transposition*.

(f) *If any two columns are equal, the determinant is zero.* Use (e) repeatedly to bring the equal columns into adjacent position, changing the sign of the determinant at each transposition. Then apply Definition 5.1 (b).

(g) *Any constant multiple of a column may be added to any other column without changing the value of the determinant.* Transpose one of the two columns repeatedly until it is adjacent to the other, and apply (d). Then transpose the moving column back to its original position. The number of transpositions needed to do all of this is even, so the result follows from (e).

(h) *If any two columns are interchanged, the determinant merely changes sign.* Transpose A_j repeatedly until it replaces A_k. If this requires p transpositions, then A_k can be moved from its new position (adjacent to its old one) to the original position of A_j in $p - 1$ transpositions. The interchange can be accomplished in an odd number of adjacent interchanges, and (e) may be applied.

Exercises

1. Consider Definition 5.1 for $n = 2$. Let A, B be any 2×2 matrices.

   (i) Calculate $\det(BA)$, using *only* the properties proved in Theorem 5.5, to obtain an answer in the form $k \det B$, for some scalar k which is a combination of the entries of A.

   (ii) Specialize the result in (i) to the case $B = I$, thus showing that the specific form stated in the text for 2×2 matrices is actually a consequence of Definition 5.1.

2. Show that in $\mathcal{E}_2$ the absolute value of $\det A$ is the area of the parallelogram determined by the row vectors of A.

3. If not all of a, b, c, d are zero, consider the system of equations

$$ax + by = e,$$
$$cx + dy = f.$$

   (i) Express the consistency condition in determinant form.
   (ii) Express the solution, assuming existence and uniqueness, in determinant form.

§5.3. *An Explicit Form for det A*

We continue with the program declared in the last section—to investigate properties of det, and particularly to show that such a function exists and is uniquely defined by Definition 5.1. The first step is to obtain an explicit form for det A. For any $n \times n$ matrix B let $C = BA$; then the kth column of C is given by $C_k = \sum_{j=1}^{n} B_j a_{jk}$, where B_j is the jth column of B. Hence

$$\det C = \det(C_1, \ldots, C_n) = \det \left(\sum_{j=1}^{n} B_j a_{j1}, \ldots, \sum_{j=1}^{n} B_j a_{jn} \right),$$

where each index of summation runs independently of the others. Each column is the sum of n columns, and we may use Definition 5.1 (a) on each column in succession to expand det C to a sum of n^n determinants:

$$\det C = \sum \det(B_{j_1}a_{j_11}, B_{j_2}a_{j_22}, \ldots, B_{j_n}a_{j_nn}),$$

where the summation is extended over all possible values of the indices, each running from 1 to n. By Theorem 5.5 (f), the only nonzero determinants of this sum are the ones in which $j_1, \ldots, j_n$ are all different—in other words, the subscripts of the various B's form a permutation of $1, \ldots, n$. Hence

$$\det C = \sum \det(B_{p(1)}a_{p(1)1}, \ldots, B_{p(n)}a_{p(n)n})$$
$$= \sum [a_{p(1)1} \cdots a_{p(n)n} \det(B_{p(1)}, \ldots, B_{p(n)})],$$

since, for each j, $a_{p(j)j}$ factors out of the jth column. Here the summation is extended over all permutations p of $1, \ldots, n$. It is well known (see References, 1 or 2) that each permutation p can be classified as even or odd according to whether p can be represented as a product of an even or an odd number of transpositions. But each transposition of columns of B produces a change in the sign of det B. Hence

$$\det(B_{p(1)}, \ldots, B_{p(n)}) = \pm\det B,$$

where the $+$ sign is used if p is an even permutation and the $-$ sign is used if p is odd. Then we have

(5.5) $$\det C = \det B \cdot \sum_{\text{all } p} [\pm a_{p(1)1} \cdots a_{p(n)n}].$$

Now *for the first time* we use property (c) of Definition 5.1. Since equation (5.5) is true for all $n \times n$ matrices A and B, we may specify $B = I$. Then $C = IA = A$, and det $B = \det I = 1$, yielding an expression for det A in terms of the elements of A.

We have proved several important results, which we now state explicitly.

Theorem 5.6. If a function det exists with the properties of Definition 5.1, then for every square matrix A,

$$\det A = \sum_p \pm [a_{p(1)1}a_{p(2)2} \cdots a_{p(n)n}],$$

where the sum is extended over all permutations p of the integers $1, 2, \ldots, n$ and where a $+$ or $-$ sign is affixed to each product according to whether p is even or odd.

Thus det A is an algebraic sum of all products of n terms which can be formed by selecting exactly one term from each row and each column of A.

Theorem 5.7. If A' is the transpose of A, then

$$\det A' = \det A.$$

Theorem 5.7 follows from the representation of det A as a sum of signed products of elements of A, each product containing exactly one element from each row and each column. Hence in Theorem 5.5 the statements about columns are valid for rows.

Theorem 5.8. $\det(AB) = (\det A)(\det B) = \det(BA)$.

P R O O F : Exercise.

Theorem 5.6 is a uniqueness theorem because it states that any function det which satisfies Definition 5.1 must assign to A a value det A which is completely described by the elements of A. But we have not yet proved that a function exists which has the properties assumed for det. One way to settle the existence question is to verify that the specific function described by Theorem 5.6 satisfies the three properties of Definition 5.1. Such a proof is possible, but an alternative method is chosen here.

To prove that det exists for every n, we proceed by induction. For $n = 1$, $A = (a)$, and we let det $A = a$. This function trivially satisfies Definition 5.1. Now assume that such a function exists for square matrices of dimension $n - 1$. For an $n \times n$ matrix A, define

$$\det A = \sum_{j=1}^{n} a_{ij}|A_{ij}|,$$

where i is any fixed value $1, 2, \ldots, n$, and $|A_{ij}|$ is the $(n - 1) \times (n - 1)$ determinant obtained by deleting the ith row and the jth column of A and affixing the sign $(-1)^{i+j}$. Thus,

$$|A_{ij}| = (-1)^{i+j} \det \begin{pmatrix} a_{11} & \cdots & a_{1j} & \cdots & a_{1n} \\ & & \vdots & & \\ a_{i1} & \cdots & a_{ij} & \cdots & a_{in} \\ & & \vdots & & \\ a_{n1} & \cdots & a_{nj} & \cdots & a_{nn} \end{pmatrix}$$

We next verify that det has the three properties of Definition 5.1.

(a) First, suppose $A_k = bB_k + cC_k$. Then

$$A = (A_1, \ldots, A_k, \ldots, A_n).$$

Let

$$B = (A_1, \ldots, bB_k, \ldots, A_n)$$

and

$$C = (A_1, \ldots, cC_k, \ldots, A_n),$$

so that B and C coincide with A except in the kth column. If $j = k$,

$$a_{ik}|A_{ik}| = (bb_{ik} + cc_{ik})|A_{ik}| = bb_{ik}|B_{ik}| + cc_{ik}|C_{ik}|,$$

since $|A_{ik}| = |B_{ik}| = |C_{ik}|$. If $j \neq k$,

$$|A_{ij}| = (-1)^{i+j} \det \begin{pmatrix} a_{11} & \cdots & a_{1j} & \cdots & a_{1k} & \cdots & a_{1n} \\ \vdots & & \vdots & & \vdots & & \vdots \\ a_{i1} & \cdots & a_{ij} & \cdots & a_{ik} & \cdots & a_{in} \\ \vdots & & \vdots & & \vdots & & \vdots \\ a_{n1} & \cdots & a_{nj} & \cdots & a_{nk} & \cdots & a_{nn} \end{pmatrix}$$

where $a_{hk} = bb_{hk} + cc_{hk}$. By the induction hypothesis, an $(n-1) \times (n-1)$ determinant is a linear function of any column, so for $j \neq k$

$$a_{ij}|A_{ij}| = a_{ij}(b|B_{ij}| + c|C_{ij}|) = bb_{ij}|B_{ij}| + cc_{ij}|C_{ij}|.$$

Finally,

$$\det A = \sum_{j=1}^{n} a_{ij}|A_{ij}| = \sum_{j=1}^{n} (bb_{ij}|B_{ij}| + cc_{ij}|C_{ij}|) = b \det B + c \det C.$$

(b) Next, suppose $A_k = A_{k+1}$ for some k. If $j \neq k, j \neq k+1$, then $|A_{ij}| = 0$, since two adjacent columns of this determinant are equal. Hence

$$\det A = a_{ik}|A_{ik}| + a_{i,k+1}|A_{i,k+1}| = 0,$$

since $a_{ik} = a_{i,k+1}$ and $|A_{ik}| = -|A_{i,k+1}|$.

(c) Finally, if $A = I_n$,

$$\det I_n = \sum_{j=1}^{n} a_{ij}|A_{ij}| = |A_{ii}| = \det I_{n-1} = 1.$$

Thus a determinant function exists for all n.

While an existence proof is necessary for logical completeness, the fact that det exists does not surprise us. However, in the proof we have established a useful method of evaluating determinants. In the notation used above, $|A_{ij}|$ is called the *cofactor* of a_{ij}, and the equation

$$\det A = \sum_{j=1}^{n} a_{ij}|A_{ij}| \qquad \text{for fixed } i$$

is the rule for expanding det A according to the elements of the ith row. The corresponding result,

$$\det A = \sum_{i=1}^{n} a_{ij}|A_{ij}| \qquad \text{for fixed } j$$

holds for columns. These results are summarized below.

Definition 5.2. The *cofactor* $|A_{ij}|$ of a_{ij} in det A is $(-1)^{i+j}$ times the determinant of the matrix obtained by deleting the ith row and jth column of A.

Theorem 5.9.

(a) $$\det A = \sum_{j=1}^{n} a_{ij}|A_{ij}| \qquad \text{for fixed } i.$$

(b) $$\det A = \sum_{i=1}^{n} a_{ij}|A_{ij}| \qquad \text{for fixed } j.$$

Theorem 5.10.

$$\delta_{ik}\det A = \sum_{j=1}^{n} a_{ij}|A_{kj}|,$$

where δ_{ik} is the Kronecker delta.

P R O O F : Exercise.

The following example illustrates some of the properties discussed above. The common notation which replaces det A by $|A|$ is employed here.

$$
\begin{vmatrix} 3 & 1 & -2 & 4 \\ 2 & 0 & -5 & 1 \\ 1 & -1 & 2 & 6 \\ -2 & 3 & -2 & 3 \end{vmatrix}
\underset{\substack{\text{Add } R_1 \\ \text{to } R_3}}{=}
\begin{vmatrix} 3 & 1 & -2 & 4 \\ 2 & 0 & -5 & 1 \\ 4 & 0 & 0 & 10 \\ -2 & 3 & -2 & 3 \end{vmatrix}
$$

$$
\underset{\substack{\text{Add } -3R_1 \\ \text{to } R_4}}{=}
\begin{vmatrix} 3 & 1 & -2 & 4 \\ 2 & 0 & -5 & 1 \\ 4 & 0 & 0 & 10 \\ -11 & 0 & 4 & -9 \end{vmatrix}
\underset{\substack{\text{Expand by} \\ \text{elements of } C_2}}{=} (-1)
\begin{vmatrix} 2 & -5 & 1 \\ 4 & 0 & 10 \\ -11 & 4 & -9 \end{vmatrix}
$$

$$
\underset{\substack{\text{Add } -2C_3 \text{ to } C_1 \\ \text{and } 5C_3 \text{ to } C_2}}{=} (-1)
\begin{vmatrix} 0 & 0 & 1 \\ -16 & 50 & 10 \\ 7 & -41 & 9 \end{vmatrix}
\underset{\substack{\text{Expand by} \\ \text{elements of } R_1}}{=} (-1)
\begin{vmatrix} -16 & 50 \\ 7 & -41 \end{vmatrix}
$$

$$= -[(-16)(-41) - (50)(7)] = -306.$$

Exercises

1. Prove Theorem 5.8.
2. Prove Theorem 5.10.
3. Illustrate Theorem 5.10 by calculating $\sum_{j=1}^{3} a_{ij}|A_{kj}|$ for $i = 1$, $k = 2$, and for $i = 2$, $k = 2$, given

$$A = \begin{pmatrix} 1 & -1 & -2 \\ -2 & 3 & 1 \\ 2 & -2 & x \end{pmatrix}.$$

4. By applying the remark which immediately follows Theorem 5.6, show that if an $n \times n$ matrix can be partitioned in the form

$$A = \left(\begin{array}{c|c} E & Z \\ \hline G & H \end{array} \right),$$

where E is a square matrix and Z consists entirely of zeros, then det $A = $ (det E)(det H).

5.   (i) How many terms are involved in the representation of det A by the method of Theorem 5.6?

(ii) How many multiplications are required to evaluate det A by the method of Theorem 5.6?

(iii) How many multiplications are required to evaluate det A by the method of Theorem 5.9?

6. The Vandermonde matrix of order n is, by definition,

$$V(x_1,\ldots,x_n) = \begin{pmatrix} 1 & 1 & \ldots 1 \\ x_1 & x_2 & \ldots x_n \\ x_1^2 & x_2^2 & \ldots x_n^2 \\ \cdot & \cdot & \cdot \\ \cdot & \cdot & \cdot \\ \cdot & \cdot & \cdot \\ x_1^{n-1} & x_2^{n-1} & \ldots x_n^{n-1} \end{pmatrix}.$$

(i) For $n = 2,\ 3$ verify that det $V = \prod_{1 \le i < j \le n} (x_j - x_i)$, where $\prod$ denotes "product."

(ii) Prove this statement for all $n > 1$.

§5.4. *The Inverse of a Matrix: Adjoint Method*

One of the most useful properties of the determinant function is that it provides a simple characterization of nonsingular matrices. Furthermore, the cofactors of a nonsingular matrix can be used to calculate its inverse by a method which is inefficient for large n, but quite easy for $n \le 4$. Other methods for computing A^{-1} are described in the next chapter.

Theorem 5.11. A is nonsingular if and only if det $A \ne 0$. If A is nonsingular, $\det(A^{-1}) = (\det A)^{-1}$.

P R O O F : If A is singular, then its rows are linearly dependent, by Theorem 4.7. Using the results of Theorem 5.5 for rows instead of columns, we can obtain a row of zeros in a determinant whose value is det A. Hence det $A = 0$. Conversely, if A is nonsingular, A^{-1} exists and

$$\det A \det A^{-1} = \det (AA^{-1}) = \det I = 1,$$

so det $A \ne 0$.

The first method we describe for calculating A^{-1} is called the *adjoint method*. We now define the term *adjoint*.

Definition 5.3. The *adjoint* of an $n \times n$ matrix $A = (a_{ij})$ is the $n \times n$ matrix adj $A = (a_{ij}^*)$, where $a_{ij}^* = |A_{ji}| =$ cofactor of a_{ji} in det A.

We note in particular two things about the adjoint: first, the elements of adj A are determinants formed from A, each with a suitable sign attached (see Definition 5.2); second, the element in the (i, j) position of adj A is the cofactor of the element in the (j, i) position of A.

Theorem 5.12. If A is nonsingular, then
$$A^{-1} = [\det A]^{-1} \text{ adj } A.$$
P R O O F : We calculate A adj $A = (b_{ij})$, where
$$b_{ij} = \sum_{k=1}^{n} a_{ik} a_{kj}^* = \sum_{k=1}^{n} a_{ik} |A_{jk}|$$
$$= \delta_{ij} \det A \qquad \text{by Theorem 5.10.}$$
Hence A adj $A = (\delta_{ij} \det A) = (\det A)I$, from which the theorem follows.

Example

Let
$$A = \begin{pmatrix} -2 & 1 & 3 \\ 0 & -1 & 1 \\ 1 & 2 & 0 \end{pmatrix}.$$

Then $\det A = 8$. To compute a_{12}^* we find the cofactor of a_{21}:
$$|A_{21}| = (-1) \begin{vmatrix} 1 & 3 \\ 2 & 0 \end{vmatrix} = 6.$$

Similar computations yield
$$\text{adj } A = \begin{pmatrix} -2 & 6 & 4 \\ 1 & -3 & 2 \\ 1 & 5 & 2 \end{pmatrix},$$

and therefore
$$A^{-1} = \frac{\text{adj } A}{8} = \begin{pmatrix} -\frac{1}{4} & \frac{3}{4} & \frac{1}{2} \\ \frac{1}{8} & -\frac{3}{8} & \frac{1}{4} \\ \frac{1}{8} & \frac{5}{8} & \frac{1}{4} \end{pmatrix}.$$

It is simpler of course to leave $\frac{1}{8}$ factored in front of adj A.

Now let us return to the problem of solving a system of n linear equations in n unknowns. In the notation of § 5.1, $AX = Y$, where A is an $n \times n$ matrix which we here assume to be nonsingular. The unique solution is given by the column vector,
$$X = A^{-1}Y = (\det A)^{-1}(\text{adj } A)Y$$
Hence
$$x_i = (\det A)^{-1} \sum_{j=1}^{n} a_{ij}^* y_j = (\det A)^{-1} \sum_{j=1}^{n} |A_{ji}| y_j.$$

The terms under the summation sign are easily seen to be the terms of the expansion by elements of the ith column of the determinant

$$\det A_{Y(i)} = \det \begin{pmatrix} a_{11} & \cdots & a_{1,i-1} & y_1 & a_{1,i+1} & \cdots & a_{1n} \\ \cdot & & \cdot & & \cdot & & \cdot \\ \cdot & & \cdot & & \cdot & & \cdot \\ \cdot & & \cdot & & \cdot & & \cdot \\ a_{n1} & \cdots & a_{n,i-1} & y_n & a_{n,i+1} & \cdots & a_{nn} \end{pmatrix},$$

where $A_{Y(i)}$ agrees with A except in the ith column, where Y has replaced A_i. This result is known as Cramer's rule.

Theorem 5.13. If the determinant of coefficients of the system of linear equations

$$a_{11}x_1 + \cdots + a_{1n}x_n = y_1$$
$$\cdot \qquad\qquad \cdot \qquad \cdot$$
$$\cdot \qquad\qquad \cdot \qquad \cdot$$
$$\cdot \qquad\qquad \cdot \qquad \cdot$$
$$a_{n1}x_1 + \cdots + a_{nn}x_n = y_n$$

is not zero, then the unique solution is given by

$$x_i = \frac{\det(A_1, \ldots, A_{i-1}, Y, A_{i+1}, \ldots, A_n)}{\det(A_1, \ldots, A_{i-1}, A_i, A_{i+1}, \ldots, A_n)}, \qquad i = 1, 2, \ldots, n.$$

The amount of work involved in the solution of a linear system by Cramer's rule is the same as in solving by calculating A^{-1} by the adjoint method. Both methods are unnecessarily cumbersome for large n, and for small values of n the method of direct algebraic elimination is often simpler than either the adjoint method or Cramer's rule.

To underline the practical importance of these remarks, consider the problem of solving a system of 25 linear equations in 25 unknowns. Cramer's rule requires the evaluation of 26 determinants of order 25; if either Theorem 5.6 or Theorem 5.9 is used to evaluate these determinants, more than 26! multiplications are required, a number of the order 10^{26}. A computer which performs 1000 multiplications per second would require 10^{16} years for the calculation. However, by making use of other computational techniques, systems of more than 2000 equations have been solved recently. In the next section a method is described in which a system of n equations can be solved by means of only n^3 multiplications, and $n^3 < n!$ whenever $n > 5$.

Exercises

1. Solve the following system of equations,

$$2x_1 - x_2 + 3x_3 = 3,$$
$$x_2 \qquad\quad = -2,$$
$$2x_1 + x_2 + x_3 = 1,$$

  (i) by the adjoint method of calculating A^{-1},

  (ii) by Cramer's rule,

  (iii) by direct algebraic elimination.

2. Prove that every square skew-symmetric matrix of odd dimension is singular.

3. In $\mathcal{E}_3$, let $A(a_1, a_2, a_3)$, $B(b_1, b_2, b_3)$, $C(c_1, c_2, c_3)$ be three points, not all on the same line. Prove that an equation for the plane determined by A, B, and C is

$$\begin{vmatrix} x_1 & x_2 & x_3 & 1 \\ a_1 & a_2 & a_3 & 1 \\ b_1 & b_2 & b_3 & 1 \\ c_1 & c_2 & c_3 & 1 \end{vmatrix} = 0.$$

4. Prove that $\det(\operatorname{adj} A) = (\det A)^{n-1}$.

5. For what values of x is the following matrix singular?

$$\begin{pmatrix} 3 - x & 2 & 2 \\ 1 & 4 - x & 1 \\ -2 & -4 & -1 - x \end{pmatrix}$$

6. Show that A is nonsingular, where

$$A = \begin{pmatrix} 1^0 & 1^1 & \cdots & 1^{n-1} \\ 2^0 & 2^1 & \cdots & 2^{n-1} \\ \cdot & \cdot & & \cdot \\ \cdot & \cdot & & \cdot \\ \cdot & \cdot & & \cdot \\ (n-1)^0 & (n-1)^1 & \cdots & (n-1)^{n-1} \end{pmatrix}.$$

7. Show that the determinant of a triangular matrix is the product of its diagonal elements. Use this fact to solve Exercise 3, § 4.4.

8. Let A be a singular $n \times n$ matrix.

  (i) Prove that if $n = 1, 2$, then A^2 is proportional to A.

  (ii) Show that A^2 need not be proportional to A whenever $n > 2$.

  (iii) How are these results related to Exercise 7, § 3.2?

9. Read "Solving linear equations can be interesting," by G. E. Forsythe, *Bulletin of the American Mathematical Society*, vol. 59 (1953), pp. 299–329.

§5.5. *Operations on Linear Systems*

In spite of its apparent simplicity, the solution of a system of linear equations by direct algebraic elimination is of such fundamental importance that it deserves analysis here. When we first considered the system (*5.1*) or equivalently (*5.2*), we regarded the column vector Y as fixed and sought to determine all column vectors X for which $AX = Y$. In these terms the system represented m linear equations in n unknowns. Sometimes it is useful to regard the vector Y as variable, in which case we have a system of m linear homogeneous equations in $m + n$ variables:

$$-Y + AX = Z.$$

It is convenient to eliminate the minus sign by letting $V = -Y$, to obtain in block form

$$(I|A) \begin{pmatrix} V \\ X \end{pmatrix} = Z,$$

or, in extended form,

$$(5.6)\qquad \begin{aligned} v_1 &\quad + a_{11} x_1 + \cdots + a_{1n} x_n = 0, \\ v_2 &\quad + a_{21} x_1 + \cdots + a_{2n} x_n = 0, \\ &\qquad\qquad \vdots \\ v_m &+ a_{m1}x_1 + \cdots + a_{mn}x_n = 0. \end{aligned}$$

When any system of m linear equations in $m + n$ unknowns is written in the form (5.6), it is a trivial matter to solve for the v's in terms of the x's. However, the usual objective is to solve for as many as possible of the x_j in terms of the v's and the remaining x's. The idea which underlies most methods of solution is akin to horsetrading: to solve (5.6) we exchange this system for another system which has exactly the same solution but which is preferable in some sense, until we arrive at a system of the form

$$(5.7)\qquad \begin{aligned} x_{1'} &\quad + b_{11}x_{(r+1)'} + \cdots + b_{1s}x_{n'} + c_{11}v_1 + \cdots + c_{1m}v_m = 0, \\ &\qquad\qquad \vdots \\ x_{r'} &+ b_{r1}x_{(r+1)'} + \cdots + b_{rs}x_{n'} + c_{r1}v_1 + \cdots + c_{rm}v_m = 0, \\ &\quad\; 0x_{(r+1)'} + \cdots + \;\;0x_{n'} + c_{t1}v_1 + \cdots + c_{tm}v_m = 0, \\ &\qquad\qquad \vdots \\ &\quad\; 0x_{(r+1)'} + \cdots \qquad 0x_{n'} + c_{m1}v_1 + \cdots + c_{mm}v_m = 0, \end{aligned}$$

where $\{1', \ldots, n'\}$ is a permutation of $\{1, \ldots, n\}$, $r \le m$, $s = n - r$, and $t = r + 1$. Of course r is simply the rank of the matrix A of coefficients of (5.6), and any solution of (5.7) is obtained by assigning to the v's any set of values which satisfy the last $m - r$ equations and assigning arbitrary values to $x_{(r+1)'}, \ldots, x_{n'}$. In case the values of the v's are specified, (5.7) has a non-vacuous solution if and only if the last $m - r$ equations reduce to $0 = 0$.

Now let us formalize these ideas: Two systems of linear equations are said to be *equivalent* if and only if any solution of either system is a solution of the other. In manipulating equations we wish to be certain that any operations we perform will produce a system which is equivalent to the original system. What operations are permissible under this requirement? First, it is apparent that the solution is not affected by the order in which the equations are written. Hence any permutation of the arrangement of the equations will produce an equivalent system. Second, any equation may be replaced by a nonzero scalar multiple of itself. Since such a scalar has a reciprocal, the process can be reversed, and so the two systems are equivalent. Third, an equation can be replaced by the sum of itself and any other equation in the system. In summary, we consider three types of *elementary operations:*

P: permutation of any two equations,
M: multiplication of any equation by a nonzero scalar,
A: addition of one equation to another.

It will be noted that the three elementary operations correspond to row operations which are useful in evaluating determinants by replacing a given determinant by an equal determinant which is simpler. In this connection, "simpler" usually means that the new determinant contains more zeros, or at least a more useful arrangement of zeros. The effect of each of these operations on a determinant is described by Theorem 5.5 (h), (a), and (g), interpreted for rows instead of columns. The effect of each of these row operations on a matrix will be considered in some detail in the next chapter.

There is another general approach to the solution of (5.1) which leads us to a different type of operation on matrices and which has recently received recognition as being the essential arithmetic process of the simplex method for solving problems in linear programming. The forms of (5.6) and (5.7) show clearly that the process of solving a system of linear equations is simply to reverse the roles of the v's and some of the x's. This is so whether the v's are regarded as known scalars or as variables, and it can be done systematically, as in elementary algebra, by selecting an equation, solving that equation for one of the x_j in terms of the v's and the other x's, and substituting the resulting expression for x_j in all the other equations of the system.

Specifically, suppose that $a_{ij} \neq 0$ in (5.6). Then

$$(5.8) \quad x_j = -a_{ij}^{-1}[v_i + a_{i1}x_1 + \cdots + a_{i,j-1}x_{j-1} + a_{i,j+1}x_{j+1} + \cdots + a_{in}x_n].$$

A new system having the same solutions as (5.6) is obtained as follows: for $k \neq i$, equation k of the new system is the one obtained by substituting (5.8) for x_j in equation k of (5.6); equation i of the new system is (5.8). The new system can be written in the form

$$v_1 \qquad\qquad + b_{11}x_1 + \cdots + b_{ij}v_i + \cdots + b_{1n}x_n = 0$$

$$x_j \qquad\qquad b_{i1}x_1 + \cdots + b_{ij}v_i + \cdots + b_{in}x_n = 0$$

$$v_n + b_{m1}x_1 + \cdots + b_{mj}v_i + \cdots + b_{mn}x_n = 0.$$

Note that the roles of v_i and x_j have been interchanged; in matrix form the original system

$$(I|A) \begin{pmatrix} V \\ X \end{pmatrix} = Z$$

has been replaced by the new system

$$(I|B) \begin{pmatrix} V^* \\ X^* \end{pmatrix} = Z,$$

where V^* coincides with V except that x_j has replaced v_i in the ith component, and X^* coincides with X except that v_i has replaced x_j in the jth component. The entries of the matrix B are given by

$$b_{rs} = \begin{cases} a_{rs} - a_{ij}^{-1} a_{rj} a_{is} = a_{ij}^{-1} \det \begin{pmatrix} a_{rs} & a_{rj} \\ a_{is} & a_{ij} \end{pmatrix} & \text{if } r \neq i \text{ and } s \neq j, \\ -a_{ij}^{-1} a_{rj} & \text{if } r \neq i \text{ and } s = j, \\ a_{ij}^{-1} a_{is} & \text{if } r = i \text{ and } s \neq j, \\ a_{ij}^{-1} & \text{if } r = i \text{ and } s = j. \end{cases}$$

An operation of this type is called a *pivot operation* on the nonzero element a_{ij}. Since all steps are reversible, the new system has the same solutions as the original system. Whenever a succession of m pivot operations replaces all of the v's by x's, the system is solved. The calculations needed to perform one pivot operation can be arranged so as to require only one division and $mn - 1$ multiplications. In particular, if A is $n \times n$ and nonsingular, n pivot operations will suffice to find A^{-1} with at most n divisions and $n^3 - n$ multiplications. This shows that pivot operations form a relatively efficient method of computation, especially for large n.

Example

To illustrate the use of pivot operations in solving linear systems, we consider the example of Exercise 1, § 5.4:

$$\begin{aligned} 2x_1 - x_2 + 3x_3 &= 3, \\ x_2 &= -2, \\ 2x_1 + x_2 + x_3 &= 1. \end{aligned}$$

A pivot operation on a_{ij} interchanges v_i with x_j and replaces the matrix A with the matrix B. Hence we adopt a computational format which keeps track of all the essential information. A is written in table form with each column labeled by the corresponding x and each row by the corresponding v. Each pivot operation will produce a new table of coefficients and interchange the row and column labels corresponding to the pivot element:

	x_1	x_2	x_3
v_1	2	-1	3
v_2	0	1^*	0
v_3	2	1	1

where $v_1 = -3$, $v_2 = 2$, $v_3 = -1$. A pivot on the element marked with an asterisk solves for x_2 in terms of x_1, x_3, and v_2, and produces the following table:

	x_1	v_2	x_3
v_1	2	1	3
x_2	0	1	0
v_3	2	-1	1^*

A second pivot solves for x_3 in terms of x_1, v_2, and v_3 and produces the following table:

	x_1	v_2	v_3
v_1	-4^*	4	-3
x_2	0	1	0
x_3	2	-1	1

A final pivot solves for x_1 in terms of v_1, v_2, and v_3:

	v_1	v_2	v_3
x_1	$-\frac{1}{4}$	-1	$\frac{3}{4}$
x_2	0	1	0
x_3	$\frac{1}{2}$	1	$-\frac{1}{2}$

The solution is read from this table by writing

$$x_1 = -\tfrac{1}{4}v_1 - 1v_2 + \tfrac{3}{4}v_3,$$
$$x_2 = 0v_1 + 1v_2 + 0v_3,$$
$$x_3 = \tfrac{1}{2}v_1 + 1v_2 - \tfrac{1}{2}v_3.$$

Using the given values of the v_i, the solution is

$$x_1 = 2,$$
$$x_2 = -2,$$
$$x_3 = -1.$$

Further examples are suggested in Exercise 1 below.

Pivot operations can also be used to define an interesting relation between matrices, called combinatorial equivalence. However, since combinatorial equivalence is not used to develop the fundamental ideas of the next three chapters, its discussion is deferred to Chapter 9. Other equivalence relations are studied in Chapters 6 and 8.

One further comment should be made. The particular form for a pivot operation, derived above, is a consequence of our having started with a system of equations in the form *(5.6)*, or equivalently, in the form

$$(I|A) \begin{pmatrix} V \\ X \end{pmatrix} = Z.$$

Had we begun with equations in the form *(5.1)*,

$$(-I|A) \begin{pmatrix} Y \\ X \end{pmatrix} = Z,$$

which is obtained simply by making the substitution $V = -Y$, then a second form of pivot operation would be obtained. After a pivot on $a_{ij} \neq 0$, the system

$$(-I|A) \begin{pmatrix} Y \\ X \end{pmatrix} = Z$$

is replaced by the system

$$(-I|B^*) \begin{pmatrix} Y^* \\ X^* \end{pmatrix} = Z,$$

where (as before) Y^* coincides with Y except that x_j has replaced y_i in the ith component, and X^* coincides with X except that y_i has replaced x_j in the jth component. B^* can be obtained from the matrix B obtained in the pivot operation as originally defined by multiplying each element of row i and each element of column j by -1; this implies that $b_{ij}^* = b_{ij}$, but otherwise the minus signs that appeared in column j of B have been shifted to appear along row i of B^*.

Both forms of pivot operations appear in the literature; the only difference is in a few signs, and being aware of the existence of both forms you should have no difficulty in following both.

Exercises

1. Solve the following systems by the use of pivot operations:
    (i) Exercise 3, § 5.1,
    (ii) Exercise 4, § 5.1,
    (iii) Exercise 5, § 5.1.

2. Let A be an $n \times n$ matrix, let $a_{ij} \neq 0$, and let B be the matrix obtained from A by pivoting on a_{ij}. Prove that

$$\det B = a_{ij}^{-1} |A_{ij}|.$$

3. Given $A = \begin{pmatrix} 1 & -2 & -1 \\ 2 & 3 & 1 \\ 0 & 5 & -2 \end{pmatrix}$.

(i) Compute det A.

(ii) Pivot on $a_{11} = 1$ to obtain a matrix B, and verify the result of Exercise 2.

(iii) Pivot B on $b_{22} = 7$ to obtain a matrix C, and again verify the result of Exercise 2.

(iv) Pivot C on $c_{33} = -\frac{29}{7}$ to obtain a matrix D.

(v) Show that $D = A^{-1}$.

(vi) Show that det A equals the product of the pivots used in transforming A to A^{-1}.

4. Let A be an $n \times n$ matrix, let $a_{ij} \neq 0$, and let B be the $(n-1) \times (n-1)$ matrix obtained by pivoting A on a_{ij} and then deleting the ith row and jth column. Prove that

$$\det A = (-1)^{i+j} a_{ij} \det B.$$

5. Let A be an $n \times n$ matrix partitioned as follows:

$$A = \begin{pmatrix} A_1 & \beta \\ \gamma & d \end{pmatrix},$$

where A_1 is a $(n-1) \times (n-1)$ matrix, β is an $(n-1)$ column vector, γ is a $(n-1)$ row vector, and d is a nonzero scalar. Then in terms of matrix multiplication $\beta\gamma$ is an $(n-1) \times (n-1)$ matrix.

(i) Show that $\det A = d^{2-n} \det(dA_1 - \beta\gamma)$.

(ii) Show also that $dA_1 - \beta\gamma$ can be computed with at most $2(n-1)^2$ multiplications, and therefore by successive applications of this method det A can be computed by no more than $2n^3/3$ multiplications.

(iii) For what values of n does this method of evaluating det A require more multiplications than those of Theorem 5.6 and Theorem 5.9?

6. As discussed at the close of this section, begin with a system of the form

$$(-I | A) \begin{pmatrix} Y \\ X \end{pmatrix} = Z,$$

where $a_{ij} \neq 0$. Pivot on a_{ij} and verify that the resulting system is

$$(-I | B^*) \begin{pmatrix} Y^* \\ X^* \end{pmatrix} = Z,$$

as described in the text.

CHAPTER 6

Equivalence Relations on Matrices

§6.1. *Introduction*

In § 5.5 we skirmished tentatively with the central problem of matrix theory; we now need to describe the problem in more definite terms, because a major portion of the next three chapters will bear directly on its solution.

First we should recognize that we have already used matrices to describe two different mathematical entities: linear transformations and systems of linear equations. In Chapters 8 and 10 we shall see that matrices can represent still other mathematical structures, each of which has its own distinctive problems and methods, which in turn can be used to define corresponding matrix concepts.

For the case of linear transformations the matrix representation was made in terms of preselected bases which were fixed throughout the discussion. Presumably then, a different choice of bases would have resulted in a different matrix representation of the same transformation. But since a linear transformation is a vector space homomorphism, it is intrinsically independent of the coordinate systems (bases) of the spaces involved, and any matrix which represents a fixed linear transformation reflects the properties of that transformation. Therefore, as we vary the bases we can expect to obtain different representative matrices which share certain common properties. We wonder how such matrices are related to each other, and particularly how we can select a "simplest" matrix to represent that linear transformation.

Now let us return to the problem of solving a system of linear equations. As described in § 5.5, the general method is to exchange the given system for an equivalent system—that is, one with precisely the same solutions as the original. By so doing we exchange the given coefficient matrix for another matrix. Since a matrix reflects the properties of the system it represents, different matrices which represent equivalent systems must have certain properties in common. Again we wonder how such matrices are related to each other and how we can find a "simplest" representative matrix.

In order to deal effectively with such problems we need to use the concept of *equivalence relation*. Relations are discussed in § 1.3 and § A.2, and equivalence relations are treated in § A.9, but for convenience we summarize here some essential facts concerning equivalence relations. Let M denote any nonvoid set; as a specific example we might think of M as the set of all $m \times n$ matrices whose entries are elements of a field $\mathfrak{F}$. Let the symbol $\sim$ denote a relation between the elements of M. Then the relation $\sim$ is called an *equivalence relation* on M if and only if three properties are satisfied:

1. $\sim$ is *reflexive;* $A \sim A$ for every $A \in M$.
2. $\sim$ is *symmetric;* if $A \sim B$, then $B \sim A$.
3. $\sim$ is *transitive;* if $A \sim B$ and $B \sim C$, then $A \sim C$.

Any equivalence relation, $\sim$, on M separates M into disjoint subsets, called *equivalence classes*. Each equivalence class $[E]$ has the property that

$$\text{if } A \in [E], \text{ then } B \in [E] \text{ if and only if } B \sim A;$$

that is, all equivalent elements belong to the same equivalence class, and any two elements of the same class are equivalent.

As we shall see, many different equivalence relations arise naturally in the study of matrices. For each equivalence relation we shall want to describe the matrices which appear in each of the corresponding equivalence classes and, if possible, to find a simple standard form such that each equivalence class of M contains one and only one matrix which is in that form. Such a form is called *canonical*. Sometimes we are content to settle for less; namely, it might suffice to obtain a standard form such that each equivalence class contains more than one matrix in standard form, but if two matrices have the same standard form they must be in the same equivalence class.

Exercises

1. Determine which of the three properties of an equivalence relation are satisfied by each of the following relations.

    (i) Similarity of plane triangles.
    (ii) Parallelism of lines on a plane.
    (iii) Strong inequality of real numbers.

(iv) Divisibility of integers.

(v) Perpendicularity of lines on a plane.

2. Describe a simple canonical form for each of the equivalence relations defined in Exercise 1 (i) and (ii).

3. For fixed m and n, consider all real $m \times n$ matrices. We define $A \sim B$ to mean that A has the same rank as B.

(i) Verify that $\sim$ is an equivalence relation.

(ii) Describe the corresponding equivalence classes.

(iii) Describe a simple canonical form for this notion of equivalence.

4. A student waiter drops a plate, thereby separating it into a finite number of disjoint pieces. Describe how this act defines an equivalence relation on the molecules of the plate such that the pieces of the decomposition form the equivalence classes.

§6.2. *Elementary Matrices*

We now consider the matrix interpretation of the elementary operations which were introduced in § 5.5. There we were concerned with equivalent systems of linear equations, where two systems were considered equivalent if and only if they have the same solutions. Clearly, this defines an equivalence relation on the collection of all systems of linear equations with coefficients in a field $\mathfrak{F}$. Each such system determines a unique rectangular matrix A according to the representation of § 5.1. The elementary operations were so chosen that the application of each operation to a system produced a new system which was equivalent to the original. We shall see that a corresponding equivalence relation is induced on the matrices which represent the systems. For this purpose we focus our attention on three *elementary row operations* for matrices:

P: permutation of two rows,

M: multiplication of a row by a nonzero scalar,

A: addition of one row to another.

We first examine the effect of these operations on the identity matrix.

> **Definition 6.1.** An *elementary* matrix is any matrix which can be obtained by performing a single elementary row operation on the identity matrix.

There are three types of elementary matrices, one for each type of elementary row operation. To describe these we recall the notation of § 4.2; E_{rs} denotes the square matrix with $e_{ij} = 0$ if $i \neq r$ or $j \neq s$ and $e_{rs} = 1$.

P: Let P_{ij} denote the matrix obtained from I by permuting the ith and jth rows. Then
$$P_{ij} = I - E_{ii} + E_{ji} - E_{jj} + E_{ij}.$$

M: Let $M_i(c)$ denote the matrix obtained from I by multiplying the ith row by $c \neq 0$. $M_i(c)$ is obtained by adding $c - 1$ to the element in the (i, i) position, so
$$M_i(c) = I + (c - 1)E_{ii}.$$

A: Let A_{ij} denote the matrix obtained from I by adding row i to row j, where $i \neq j$. Clearly,
$$A_{ij} = I + E_{ji}.$$

The usefulness of the three elementary matrices P_{ij}, $M_i(c)$, and A_{ij} stems from the fact that an elementary row operation on an arbitrary rectangular matrix A may be performed by *premultiplying* A (i.e., multiplying A on the left) by the corresponding elementary matrix. But there is more to be said in order to make our meaning precise. Since there is an identity matrix of each dimension, there are three elementary matrices of each dimension. If A is $m \times n$, then any premultiplying matrix B must have m columns for BA to be defined.

Theorem 6.1. Any elementary row operation can be performed on an $m \times n$ matrix A by premultiplying A by the corresponding $m \times m$ elementary matrix.

P R O O F : Exercise.

Theorem 6.2. Every $m \times m$ elementary matrix is nonsingular.

P R O O F : Exercise. Show that each has m linearly independent rows.

Theorem 6.3. The inverse of an elementary matrix of type P or type M is an elementary matrix of the same type. The inverse of an elementary matrix of type A is the product of elementary matrices of type M and type A.

P R O O F : By expressing each of the elementary matrices in terms of the E_{rs} and using the results of Exercise 1, below, it is easy to verify that
$$P_{ij}^{-1} = P_{ji},$$
$$M_i^{-1}(c) = M_i(c^{-1}),$$
$$A_{ij}^{-1} = I - E_{ji} = M_i(-1)A_{ij}M_i(-1).$$

It should be observed that any type P elementary matrix is a product of elementary matrices of type M and type A (see Exercise 5, below). If we were interested in the most concise axiomatic treatment of row operations,

we would consider only the latter two types. However, once we have observed this relationship there is little to be gained by insisting upon using
it to replace the natural operation of interchanging rows.

Exercises

1. Prove that $E_{ik}E_{hj} = \delta_{kh}E_{ij}$, and therefore that each E_{ij} is either idempotent or nilpotent of index 2, according to whether $i = j$ or $i \neq j$.

2. Prove Theorem 6.1.

3. Prove Theorem 6.2.

4. Carry out the calculations which establish the statements made in the proof of Theorem 6.3.

5. Using Exercise 1, or otherwise, show that
$$P_{ij} = M_j(-1)A_{ij}M_i(-1)A_{ji}M_j(-1)A_{ij}.$$

6. Write a sequence of elementary row operations whose only effect on A is to add a constant multiple of the ith row of A to the jth row of A.

7. Calculate the determinant of each type of elementary matrix.

§6.3. *Row Equivalence*

The three types of elementary row operations were selected by a consideration of algebraic processes which lead from one system of linear equations to an equivalent system—that is, one with the same solutions as the original. While it is clear that elementary row operations transform any system into an equivalent system, the converse is not so obvious—that any two equivalent systems can be derived from each other by a finite sequence of these elementary row operations. Our investigation of this question will provide a non-trivial example of the general problem of equivalence and canonical forms, as discussed in § 6.1. As is often the case, side results of the investigation will prove to be more important than the answer to the original question.

Definition 6.2. An $m \times n$ matrix B is said to be *row equivalent* to an $m \times n$ matrix A if and only if B can be obtained by performing a finite number of elementary row operations on A.

The relation of row equivalence of $m \times n$ matrices is easily seen to be an equivalence relation. It is reflexive and transitive by its nature, and symmetric because if B can be obtained from A by elementary row operations, then the reversed sequence of inverse operations applied to B will yield A.

The collection of $m \times n$ matrices is thus partitioned into disjoint classes of row equivalent matrices.

Theorem 6.4. Row equivalent matrices have the same rank.

P R O O F : If B is row equivalent to A, then

$$B = E_k \ldots E_2 E_1 A,$$

where the E_i are elementary matrices and hence nonsingular. By Theorem 4.8, A and B have the same rank.

Now let $A = (a_{ij})$ be an m $\times$ n matrix and suppose that the qth column is the first column in which a nonzero element, say a_{pq}, appears. If we multiply row p by a_{pq}^{-1} and then interchange row p and row 1, we obtain a matrix with 1 in row 1 and column q. Then by adding suitable multiples of row 1 to the other rows we obtain a matrix of the following form which is row equivalent to A,

$$B = \begin{pmatrix} 0 \ldots 0 & 1 & *\ldots* \\ 0 \ldots 0 & 0 & \\ \cdot & \cdot & \\ \cdot & \cdot & R \\ \cdot & \cdot & \\ 0 \ldots 0 & 0 & \end{pmatrix}$$

where each $*$ denotes some scalar and where R is an $(m - 1) \times (n - q)$ matrix. We continue the process by operating with the last $m - 1$ rows of B. In R we find the first column in which nonzero element b_{rs} appears, and multiply row r by b_{rs}^{-1}. We then interchange row r of B with row 2 of B, and as before produce zeros in column s of every row below row 2. Eventually we obtain a matrix which is row equivalent to A and has the following properties:

1. The first k rows are nonzero; the other rows are zero.
2. The first nonzero element in each nonzero row is 1, and it appears in a column to the right of the first nonzero element of any preceding row.

An example of a matrix in this form, for $k = 4$, $m = 5$, $n = 8$, is

$$\begin{pmatrix} 0 & 1 & * & * & * & * & * & * \\ 0 & 0 & 1 & * & * & * & * & * \\ 0 & 0 & 0 & 0 & 1 & * & * & * \\ 0 & 0 & 0 & 0 & 0 & 0 & 0 & 1 \\ 0 & 0 & 0 & 0 & 0 & 0 & 0 & 0 \end{pmatrix}.$$

A matrix which satisfies properties 1 and 2 is said to be in *echelon form*. Suppose B is a matrix in echelon form, and consider any nonzero row. The first nonzero element of that row is $b_{ij} = 1$. In column j above b_{ij} there are elements which may or may not be zero. Below b_{ij} the jth column contains only zeros. Clearly, by a succession of row operations, the elements above b_{ij} in column j can be replaced by zeros, and the resulting matrix will still be in echelon form with the additional property,

3. The first nonzero element in each nonzero row is the only nonzero element in its column.

Any matrix which is in echelon form and also satisfies property 3 is said to be in *reduced echelon form*.

A reduced echelon form for the matrix of the preceding example is

$$\begin{pmatrix} 0 & 1 & 0 & * & 0 & * & * & 0 \\ 0 & 0 & 1 & * & 0 & * & * & 0 \\ 0 & 0 & 0 & 0 & 1 & * & * & 0 \\ 0 & 0 & 0 & 0 & 0 & 0 & 0 & 1 \\ 0 & 0 & 0 & 0 & 0 & 0 & 0 & 0 \end{pmatrix}.$$

Theorem 6.5. Any $m \times n$ matrix of rank k is row equivalent to a matrix in echelon form (also, reduced echelon form) with k nonzero rows.

PROOF : Our previous discussion established the row equivalences which the theorem asserts, so we need only prove the statement concerning rank. The rank of any matrix cannot exceed the number of nonzero rows in that matrix, and the nonzero rows of an echelon matrix are linearly independent. Hence its rank is the number of its nonzero rows, and by Theorem 6.4 any matrix row equivalent to it has the same rank.

We now apply the concept of row equivalence to give an independent proof of Theorem 4.4—a matrix and its transpose have the same rank. Let E be a matrix which is row equivalent to A and in reduced echelon form. If $\rho(A) = k$, consider the k column vectors whose only nonzero element is a 1 which is the first nonzero element of the row in which it appears. These k column vectors are linearly independent, and every other column vector is a linear combination of these. Since the columns of E are the rows of E', $\rho(E') = k = \rho(E) = \rho(A)$. Also, $E = E_p E_{p-1} \cdots E_1 A$, so $E' = A' E_1 E_2 \cdots E'_p$. Since the transpose of an elementary matrix is an elementary matrix, and therefore nonsingular, $\rho(A') = \rho(E')$. Hence $\rho(A') = \rho(A)$.

Theorem 6.6. The rank of any matrix is the dimension of its largest nonsingular submatrix.

PROOF : Exercise. (By a *submatrix* of A we mean the array which is obtained by deleting a set of rows and a set of columns from A.)

Theorem 6.7. An $n \times n$ matrix is nonsingular if and only if it is row equivalent to the identity matrix.

P R O O F : If A is row equivalent to I, then A must have rank n, and thus be nonsingular. Conversely, suppose that A is nonsingular. Then it is row equivalent to a matrix E in reduced echelon form and of rank n. Hence $E = I$.

Theorem 6.8. A square matrix is nonsingular if and only if it is the product of elementary matrices.

P R O O F : If A is nonsingular, then by Theorem 6.7

$$E_k \cdots E_2 E_1 A = I$$

for suitable elementary matrices. Hence $A = E_1^{-1} E_2^{-1} \cdots E_k^{-1}$. Since the inverse of each elementary matrix is the product of elementary matrices, A is a product of elementary matrices. The converse is trivial, since the product of nonsingular matrices is nonsingular.

The usefulness of this theorem actually lies in its proof, because we have

$$E_k \cdots E_2 E_1 I = A^{-1},$$

which gives us a second way of calculating the inverse of a nonsingular matrix. We determine the row operations needed to reduce A to I. Those same row operations when applied to I yield A^{-1}. A similar method of calculating A^{-1} is given in the next section.

Example

To calculate the inverse of

$$A = \begin{pmatrix} 1 & 2 & 3 \\ 2 & 3 & 0 \\ 0 & 1 & 2 \end{pmatrix},$$

we write the block form $(I|A)$ and perform on this 3×6 matrix a sequence of row operations which reduces A to I, yielding $(B|I)$. Then $B = A^{-1}$.

$$\begin{pmatrix} 1 & 0 & 0 & | & 1 & 2 & 3 \\ 0 & 1 & 0 & | & 2 & 3 & 0 \\ 0 & 0 & 1 & | & 0 & 1 & 2 \end{pmatrix} \xrightarrow{R_2 - 2R_1} \begin{pmatrix} 1 & 0 & 0 & | & 1 & 2 & 3 \\ -2 & 1 & 0 & | & 0 & -1 & -6 \\ 0 & 0 & 1 & | & 0 & 1 & 2 \end{pmatrix}$$

$$\xrightarrow{R_3 + R_2} \begin{pmatrix} 1 & 0 & 0 & | & 1 & 2 & 3 \\ -2 & 1 & 0 & | & 0 & -1 & -6 \\ -2 & 1 & 1 & | & 0 & 0 & -4 \end{pmatrix} \xrightarrow[-\frac{1}{4}R_3]{-1R_2;} \begin{pmatrix} 1 & 0 & 0 & | & 1 & 2 & 3 \\ 2 & -1 & 0 & | & 0 & 1 & 6 \\ \frac{1}{2} & -\frac{1}{4} & -\frac{1}{4} & | & 0 & 0 & 1 \end{pmatrix}$$

$$\xrightarrow{R_2 - 6R_3} \begin{pmatrix} 1 & 0 & 0 & | & 1 & 2 & 3 \\ -1 & \frac{1}{2} & \frac{3}{2} & | & 0 & 1 & 0 \\ \frac{1}{2} & -\frac{1}{4} & -\frac{1}{4} & | & 0 & 0 & 1 \end{pmatrix} \xrightarrow{R_1 - 2R_2 - 3R_3} \begin{pmatrix} \frac{3}{2} & -\frac{1}{4} & -\frac{9}{4} & | & 1 & 0 & 0 \\ -1 & \frac{1}{2} & \frac{3}{2} & | & 0 & 1 & 0 \\ \frac{1}{2} & -\frac{1}{4} & -\frac{1}{4} & | & 0 & 0 & 1 \end{pmatrix}.$$

Thus

$$A^{-1} = \tfrac{1}{4} \begin{pmatrix} 6 & -1 & -9 \\ -4 & 2 & 6 \\ 2 & -1 & -1 \end{pmatrix},$$

a result which should be checked by showing that $A^{-1}A = I$.

Theorem 6.9. B is row equivalent to A if and only if $B = PA$ for some nonsingular matrix P.

P R O O F : Exercise.

Finally we return to the question posed at the beginning of this section. Given any two systems of linear equations having the same solutions, are their corresponding matrices row equivalent? To answer this we first determine what meaning row equivalence of matrices has for the corresponding linear transformations. Let A, B be $m \times n$ matrices; choose a basis $\{\alpha_1, \ldots, \alpha_m\}$ for $\mathcal{V}_m$ and $\{\beta_1, \ldots, \beta_n\}$ for $\mathcal{W}_n$. Let $\mathbf{T}$ and $\mathbf{S}$ be the linear transformations from $\mathcal{V}_m$ to $\mathcal{W}_n$ determined by A and B relative to this choice of bases; that is, $\alpha_i\mathbf{T}$ and $\alpha_i\mathbf{S}$ are respectively represented in the β-basis by the ith rows of A and B, $i = 1, \ldots, m$.

Theorem 6.10. Relative to a pair of bases, let matrices A and B represent linear transformations $\mathbf{T}$ and $\mathbf{S}$. Then A and B are row equivalent if and only if $\mathcal{R}_{\mathbf{T}} = \mathcal{R}_{\mathbf{S}}$.

P R O O F : $\mathcal{R}_{\mathbf{T}}$ is the subspace of $\mathcal{W}_n$ which is spanned by the rows of A. If B is row equivalent to A, the rows of B are linear combinations of the rows of A. Hence $\mathcal{R}_{\mathbf{S}} \subseteq \mathcal{R}_{\mathbf{T}}$, and equality must hold since row equivalence is a symmetric relation. Conversely, if $\mathcal{R}_{\mathbf{T}} = \mathcal{R}_{\mathbf{S}}$, the row vectors of B are linear combinations of the row vectors of A, and each linear combination of rows can be performed by elementary row operations.

Theorem 6.11. Two matrices A and B in reduced echelon form are row equivalent if and only if $A = B$.

P R O O F : Equal matrices are row equivalent. Conversely, let A and B be row equivalent matrices, both in reduced echelon form; as above, A and B correspond to linear transformations $\mathbf{T}$ and $\mathbf{S}$. A and B have the same rank r, so the first r rows of A and B, and only those rows, are nonzero. For each $k = 1, 2, \ldots, r$ the first nonzero element of row k of A and of B must be 1; let t_k denote the column in which that element occurs in A, and s_k the column in which it occurs in B. From the form of a reduced echelon matrix we observe that

$$\text{if } j \neq k, \text{ then } t_j \neq t_k,$$
$$a_{kt_k} = 1$$
$$a_{it_k} = 0 \text{ for all } i \neq k,$$

with similar properties holding for B.

We assert that $s_k = t_k$ for each k. Suppose that for some index $p \leq r$, $s_p < t_p$ but that $s_k = t_k$ for $k < p$. Since $\mathfrak{R}_T = \mathfrak{R}_S$ by Theorem 6.10, there exist scalars $c_1, \ldots, c_r$, not all zero, such that

$$\alpha_p S = \sum_{i=1}^{r} c_i \alpha_i T = \sum_{i=1}^{r} c_i \left(\sum_{j=1}^{n} a_{ij} \alpha_j \right) = \sum_{j=1}^{n} \left(\sum_{i=1}^{r} c_i a_{ij} \right) \alpha_j$$

$$= \sum_{j=1}^{n} b_{pj} \alpha_j.$$

Hence for each $j = 1, 2, \ldots, n$,

$$b_{pj} = \sum_{i=1}^{r} c_i a_{ij}.$$

Thus in particular,

(6.1) $$b_{pt_p} = \sum_{i=1}^{r} c_i a_{it_p} = c_p,$$

and

$$b_{ps_p} = 1 = \sum_{i=1}^{r} c_i a_{is_p}.$$

But A is in reduced echelon form and $s_p < t_p$, so $a_{is_p} = 0$ for $i \geq p$. Hence for some $q < p$,

$$c_q a_{qs_p} \neq 0.$$

Then $t_q = s_q < s_p$ since B is in reduced echelon form. Thus $a_{qt_q} = 1$, $a_{it_q} = 0$ if $i \neq q$, and

$$b_{pt_q} = \sum_{i=1}^{r} c_i a_{it_q} = c_q \neq 0.$$

Since $t_q < s_p$, this contradicts the statement that row p of B has its first nonzero element in column s_p. Hence the assumption that $s_p < t_p$ is false. If $t_p < s_p$, we can repeat the entire argument, reversing the roles of A and B to obtain a similar contradiction. Hence $s_k = t_k$ for $k = 1, 2, \ldots, r$; it follows from the nature of the reduced echelon form that columns $t_1, t_2, \ldots, t_r$ of A and B are identical. Furthermore, from (6.1),

$$c_p = b_{pt_p} = 1.$$

Let $k \neq p$, $k \leq r$; we have

$$b_{pt_k} = \sum_{i=1}^{r} c_i a_{it_k} = c_k$$

$$= a_{pt_k} = 0,$$

since column t_k of B coincides with that of A. Thus, $c_p = 1$ and $c_k = 0$ if $k \neq p$. Therefore,

$$b_{pj} = \sum_{i=1}^{r} c_i a_{ij} = a_{pj}$$

for all $p \leq r$ and all j, so $A = B$.

From this theorem we draw two conclusions.

There is one and only one reduced echelon matrix which is row equivalent to a given matrix A; that is, the reduced echelon form is *canonical* with respect to row equivalence.

Two homogeneous systems of m linear equations in n unknowns are equivalent (have the same solutions) if and only if their coefficient matrices are row equivalent.

We note also that if row equivalence had been defined to include the trivial row operations of adding or deleting a zero row, then the latter statement above would be valid for any two homogeneous systems of linear equations in n unknowns.

Exercises

1. Use the method of this section to calculate the inverse of each of the following matrices:

(i)
$$\begin{pmatrix} -2 & 1 & 3 \\ 0 & -1 & 1 \\ 1 & 2 & 0 \end{pmatrix},$$

(ii)
$$\begin{pmatrix} 1 & -1 & 1 & -1 \\ 0 & 1 & 0 & 1 \\ 1 & 0 & -1 & 0 \\ 0 & 1 & 0 & -1 \end{pmatrix}.$$

2. Determine which of the following matrices are row equivalent:

$$A = \begin{pmatrix} 5 & 3 & 8 \\ 3 & 1 & 4 \\ -1 & 3 & 2 \end{pmatrix},$$

$$B = \begin{pmatrix} -1 & -3 & -2 \\ 5 & 7 & 2 \\ -3 & 1 & 4 \end{pmatrix},$$

$$C = \begin{pmatrix} -1 & 5 & 6 \\ 1 & 2 & 1 \\ -1 & -3 & -2 \end{pmatrix}.$$

3. Prove Theorem 6.6.

4. Prove Theorem 6.9.

5. Show in detail how the two statements at the end of this section follow from previous theorems.

6. Prove that if A is $m \times n$ and P_{ij} is $n \times n$, then AP_{ij} coincides with A except that columns i and j are interchanged.

7. (i) Let A be an $m \times (m + n)$ matrix of rank m, and let E be the reduced echelon form of A. Show that a permutation of the columns of E transforms E into block form $(I|B)$ where B is $m \times n$.

(ii) Using Exercise 6, or otherwise, show that there exist nonsingular matrices P and Q such that
$$PAQ = (I|B).$$

§6.4. *Equivalence*

If we consider matrices as rectangular arrays, without regard to any systems which they represent, it is as natural to perform elementary operations on *columns* as on rows. For this purpose we observe that a column operation on A is the same as a row operation on A'. Hence A may be transformed into B by a succession of elementary column operations if and only if A' can be transformed into B' by the same succession of row operations. That is, if
$$B' = PA',$$
then
$$B = (PA')' = AP' = AQ,$$
where Q is nonsingular, since Q is the transpose of the nonsingular matrix P. Hence column operations can be performed on A by *postmultiplying* A by a suitable nonsingular matrix.

We next propose to study the effect of changing A by both column operations and row operations. If B is the resulting matrix, then
$$B = PAQ,$$
where P is the nonsingular matrix which performs the row operations and Q is the nonsingular matrix which performs the column operations.

Definition 6.3. B is said to be *equivalent* to A if and only if B can be obtained from A by a finite number of elementary row and column operations.

Theorem 6.12. B is equivalent to A if and only if $B = PAQ$ for suitable nonsingular matrices P and Q.

P R O O F : See the remarks preceding Definition 6.3.

Theorem 6.13. Equivalence of matrices is an equivalence relation.

P R O O F : Exercise.

Theorem 6.14. An $m \times n$ matrix of rank k is equivalent to the $m \times n$ matrix B in which $b_{11} = b_{22} = \cdots = b_{kk} = 1$, and $b_{ij} = 0$ otherwise.

P R O O F : Let A be of rank k. If $k = 0$, then $A = Z$, and there is nothing to prove. Otherwise, by row operations we obtain the reduced echelon form of A, with k nonzero rows, the first nonzero element of each of which is 1, and it is the only nonzero element in its column. By permuting the columns we place these 1's in the first k diagonal positions, obtaining the block form

$$\begin{pmatrix} I_k & M \\ Z & Z \end{pmatrix}.$$

Column operations are then used to produce zeros in the last $n - k$ columns of the first k rows.

Theorem 6.15. Two $m \times n$ matrices are equivalent if and only if they have the same rank.

P R O O F : If A and B are equivalent, $\rho(A) = \rho(B)$ since $B = PAQ$. Conversely, if A and B have rank k, each is equivalent to the matrix described in Theorem 6.14.

From Theorem 6.15 we derive two immediate corollaries. The first is that the form described in Theorem 6.14 is *canonical* with respect to equivalence. The second we state formally.

Theorem 6.16. A square matrix is nonsingular if and only if it is equivalent to the identity matrix.

P R O O F : Apply Theorem 6.15.

Therefore, if A is nonsingular, there exist nonsingular matrices P and Q such that

$$I = PAQ,$$
$$P^{-1}Q^{-1} = A,$$
$$A^{-1} = QP.$$

Recall that P is obtained by performing on I the same row operations which were performed on A, and that Q is obtained by performing on I the same column operations which were performed on A, the combination of row and column operations transforming A into I. This gives us another method of computing A^{-1}, and the following scheme simplifies the calculation of P and Q. Write I to the left of A and below A:

$$\begin{array}{c|c} I & A \\ \hline & I \end{array}.$$

Perform row and column operations on A as needed to transform A into I. As each row operation is performed on A, perform the same row operation on the matrix at the upper left of the array. Similarly, as each column operation is performed on A, perform the same column operation on the lower right-hand matrix. Then the final array is

$$\frac{P \;\big|\; I}{\;\big|\; Q},$$

and $A^{-1} = QP$.

Example

Let

$$A = \begin{pmatrix} 2 & -1 & 0 \\ 1 & 2 & 1 \\ -1 & 0 & 3 \end{pmatrix}.$$

$$\left[\begin{array}{ccc|ccc}
1 & 0 & 0 & 2 & -1 & 0 \\
0 & 1 & 0 & 1 & 2 & 1 \\
0 & 0 & 1 & -1 & 0 & 3 \\ \hline
 & & & 1 & 0 & 0 \\
 & & & 1 & 1 & 0 \\
 & & & 0 & 0 & 1
\end{array}\right],$$

Interchange R_1 and R_2

$$\left[\begin{array}{ccc|ccc}
0 & 1 & 0 & 1 & 2 & 1 \\
1 & 0 & 0 & 2 & -1 & 0 \\
0 & 0 & 1 & -1 & 0 & 3 \\ \hline
 & & & 1 & 0 & 0 \\
 & & & 0 & 1 & 0 \\
 & & & 0 & 0 & 1
\end{array}\right],$$

$C_2 - 2C_1$; $C_3 - C_1$

$$\left[\begin{array}{ccc|ccc}
0 & 1 & 0 & 1 & 0 & 0 \\
1 & 0 & 0 & 2 & -5 & -2 \\
0 & 0 & 1 & -1 & 2 & 4 \\ \hline
 & & & 1 & -2 & -1 \\
 & & & 0 & 1 & 0 \\
 & & & 0 & 0 & 1
\end{array}\right],$$

$R_2 - 2R_1$; $R_3 + R_1$

$$\left[\begin{array}{ccc|ccc}
0 & 1 & 0 & 1 & 0 & 0 \\
1 & -2 & 0 & 0 & -5 & -2 \\
0 & 1 & 1 & 0 & 2 & 4 \\ \hline
 & & & 1 & -2 & -1 \\
 & & & 0 & 1 & 0 \\
 & & & 0 & 0 & 1
\end{array}\right],$$

$\tfrac{1}{2}R_3$; interchange R_2 and R_3

$$\left[\begin{array}{ccc|ccc}
0 & 1 & 0 & 1 & 0 & 0 \\
0 & \tfrac{1}{2} & \tfrac{1}{2} & 0 & 1 & 2 \\
1 & -2 & 0 & 0 & -5 & -2 \\ \hline
 & & & 1 & -2 & -1 \\
 & & & 0 & 1 & 0 \\
 & & & 0 & 0 & 1
\end{array}\right],$$

$C_3 - 2C_2$

$$\left[\begin{array}{ccc|ccc}
0 & 1 & 0 & 1 & 0 & 0 \\
0 & \tfrac{1}{2} & \tfrac{1}{2} & 0 & 1 & 0 \\
1 & -2 & 0 & 0 & -5 & 8 \\ \hline
 & & & 1 & -2 & 3 \\
 & & & 0 & 1 & -2 \\
 & & & 0 & 0 & 1
\end{array}\right],$$

$R_3 + 5R_2$

$$\left[\begin{array}{ccc|ccc}
0 & 1 & 0 & 1 & 0 & 0 \\
0 & \tfrac{1}{2} & \tfrac{1}{2} & 0 & 1 & 0 \\
1 & \tfrac{1}{2} & \tfrac{5}{2} & 0 & 0 & 8 \\ \hline
 & & & 1 & -2 & 3 \\
 & & & 0 & 1 & -2 \\
 & & & 0 & 0 & 1
\end{array}\right],$$

$\tfrac{1}{8}R_3$

$$\left[\begin{array}{ccc|ccc}
0 & 1 & 0 & 1 & 0 & 0 \\
0 & \tfrac{1}{2} & \tfrac{1}{2} & 0 & 1 & 0 \\
\tfrac{1}{8} & \tfrac{1}{16} & \tfrac{5}{16} & 0 & 0 & 1 \\ \hline
 & & & 1 & -2 & 3 \\
 & & & 0 & 1 & -2 \\
 & & & 0 & 0 & 1
\end{array}\right].$$

We have

$$P = \tfrac{1}{16}\begin{pmatrix} 0 & 16 & 0 \\ 0 & 8 & 8 \\ 2 & 1 & 5 \end{pmatrix} \quad \text{and} \quad Q = \begin{pmatrix} 1 & -2 & 3 \\ 0 & 1 & -2 \\ 0 & 0 & 1 \end{pmatrix},$$

and therefore

$$A^{-1} = QP = \tfrac{1}{16}\begin{pmatrix} 6 & 3 & -1 \\ -4 & 6 & -2 \\ 2 & 1 & 5 \end{pmatrix}.$$

This method of calculating A^{-1} is tedious to write, but all calculations are easy ones.

Exercises

1. Use the method of § 6.4 to calculate the inverse of each matrix of Exercise 1, § 6.3.

2. Prove Theorem 6.13.

3. Show that the form described by Theorem 6.14 is canonical for matrix equivalence.

4. Which of the matrices of Exercise 2, § 6.3, are equivalent?

5. Show that if A is a symmetric $n \times n$ matrix of complex numbers, then there exists a nonsingular matrix P such that PAP' is in canonical form for matrix equivalence.

6. If A and B are equivalent, determine whether or not each of the following pairs are equivalent:

    (i) A' and B',
    (ii) A^2 and B^2,
    (iii) AB and BA.

§6.5. *Similarity*

Thus far we have introduced two different equivalence relations for matrices which were suggested by processes for solving a system of linear equations. In this section we resume the study of linear transformations and their representative matrices. In so doing we discover an important interpretation of equivalence of matrices, a special case of which leads us to a third equivalence relation, called *similarity*. Other equivalence relations will be considered in Chapter 8, where matrices are used to represent still another mathematical structure.

In § 4.1 we derived the matrix representation of a linear transformation **T** under the agreement that our discussion pertained to a fixed basis $\{\alpha_1, \ldots, \alpha_m\}$

of the domain $\mathcal{V}_m$ of **T** and a fixed basis $\{\beta_1, \ldots, \beta_n\}$ of a space $\mathcal{W}_n$ which contained the range of **T**. With this understanding, **T** is represented uniquely by a matrix, but the matrix representation of **T** depends upon the choice of bases. Now we are ready to determine the relationship between two matrices, each of which represents the same **T** with respect to independent choices of bases for $\mathcal{V}_m$ and $\mathcal{W}_n$.

Let **T** be a linear transformation from $\mathcal{V}_m$ to $\mathcal{W}_n$. With respect to bases $\{\alpha_1, \ldots, \alpha_m\}$ and $\{\beta_1, \ldots, \beta_n\}$, **T** is represented by a uniquely determined matrix A. With respect to bases $\{\gamma_1, \ldots, \gamma_m\}$ and $\{\delta_1, \ldots, \delta_n\}$, **T** is represented by a matrix C. Thus

$$\alpha_i \mathbf{T} = \sum_{j=1}^{n} a_{ij}\beta_j,$$

$$\gamma_j \mathbf{T} = \sum_{k=1}^{n} c_{jk}\delta_k.$$

Let **R** be the linear transformation which maps γ_i onto α_i in $\mathcal{V}_m$. Since **R** maps a basis onto a basis, it is nonsingular, and relative to the γ-basis it is represented by a nonsingular matrix P, where

$$\alpha_i = \gamma_i \mathbf{R} = \sum_{j=1}^{m} p_{ij}\gamma_j.$$

Similarly, let **S** be the linear transformation which maps δ_j onto β_j in $\mathcal{W}_n$. **S** is represented relative to the δ-basis by a nonsingular matrix Q, where

$$\beta_j = \delta_j \mathbf{S} = \sum_{k=1}^{n} q_{jk}\delta_k.$$

The situation is represented graphically by the following scheme, where subscripts on the matrices indicate the bases concerned.

$$\mathcal{V}_m = [\alpha] \xrightarrow[A_{\alpha,\beta}]{\mathbf{T}} \mathcal{W}_n = [\beta]$$

$$\mathbf{R} \uparrow P_{\gamma,\gamma} \qquad Q_{\delta,\delta} \uparrow \mathbf{S}$$

$$\mathcal{V}_m = [\gamma] \xrightarrow[\mathbf{T}]{C_{\gamma,\delta}} \mathcal{W}_n = [\delta]$$

Figure 6.1

We compute the **T**-image of α_i in two ways:

$$\alpha_i \mathbf{T} = \sum_{j=1}^{n} a_{ij}\beta_j = \sum_{j=1}^{n} a_{ij}\left(\sum_{k=1}^{n} q_{jk}\delta_k\right) = \sum_{k=1}^{n}\left(\sum_{j=1}^{n} a_{ij}q_{jk}\right)\delta_k,$$

$$\alpha_i \mathbf{T} = \left(\sum_{j=1}^{m} p_{ij}\gamma_j\right)\mathbf{T} = \sum_{j=1}^{m} p_{ij}\left(\sum_{k=1}^{n} c_{jk}\delta_k\right) = \sum_{k=1}^{n}\left(\sum_{j=1}^{m} p_{ij}c_{jk}\right)\delta_k,$$

for $i = 1, 2, \ldots, m$. Since $\alpha_i \mathbf{T}$ is a unique linear combination of the δ_k,

$$\sum_{j=1}^{n} a_{ij} q_{jk} = \sum_{j=1}^{m} p_{ij} c_{jk}.$$

The left-hand side is the (i, k) element of AQ, and the right-hand side is the (i, k) element of PC. Hence

$$AQ = PC,$$
$$A = PCQ^{-1},$$

or, in a form which reminds us of the bases used to obtain each matrix,

$$A_{\alpha,\beta} = P_{\gamma,\gamma} C_{\gamma,\delta} Q_{\delta,\delta}^{-1}.$$

Theorem 6.17. Two $m \times n$ matrices A and C represent the same linear transformation from $\mathcal{V}_m$ to $\mathcal{W}_n$ relative to two pairs of bases if and only if A and C are equivalent.

P R O O F : Our previous discussion has shown that if A and C represent the same linear transformation, then

$$A = PCQ^{-1}$$

for some nonsingular $m \times m$ matrix P and some nonsingular $n \times n$ matrix Q. Hence A and C are equivalent. Conversely, if A and C are equivalent, then for suitable nonsingular matrices P, Q

$$A = PCQ^{-1}.$$

Choose any basis pair, $\{\gamma\}$ for $\mathcal{V}_m$ and $\{\delta\}$ for $\mathcal{W}_n$, and let $\mathbf{T}$ be the linear transformation represented by C relative to this choice of bases. Let $\mathbf{R}$ be the linear transformation on $\mathcal{V}_m$ defined by the matrix P relative to the γ-basis, and let $\mathbf{S}$ be the linear transformation on $\mathcal{W}_n$ defined by the matrix Q relative to the δ-basis.

Let $\alpha_i = \gamma_i \mathbf{R}$ and $\beta_j = \delta_j \mathbf{S}$. Since $PC = AQ$ we can reverse the order of the calculations which follow Figure 6.1 to obtain

$$\alpha_i \mathbf{T} = \sum_{k=1}^{n} \left(\sum_{j=1}^{m} p_{ij} c_{jk} \right) \delta_k = \sum_{k=1}^{n} \left(\sum_{j=1}^{n} a_{ij} q_{jk} \right) \delta_k = \sum_{j=1}^{n} a_{ij} \beta_j.$$

Hence A represents $\mathbf{T}$ relative to the α, β pair of bases.

Now let us reverse the roles of matrices and linear transformations in this discussion. Suppose we have a single $m \times n$ matrix A and two pairs of bases, α, β and γ, δ. Relative to each basis pair, A determines a linear transformation, say $\mathbf{T}_1$ and $\mathbf{T}_2$. How are these transformations related?

As before, we let $\mathbf{R}$ and $\mathbf{S}$ be the linear transformations defined by $\gamma_i \mathbf{R} = \alpha_i$ and $\delta_j \mathbf{S} = \beta_j$. We have

$$\gamma_i \mathbf{T}_2 = \sum_{j=1}^{n} a_{ij}\delta_j,$$

$$\alpha_i \mathbf{T}_1 = \sum_{j=1}^{n} a_{ij}\beta_j.$$

Hence

$$\gamma_i \mathbf{R}\mathbf{T}_1 = \alpha_i \mathbf{T}_1 = \sum_{j=1}^{m} a_{ij}\beta_j = \sum_{j=1}^{m} a_{ij}\delta_j \mathbf{S} = \gamma_i \mathbf{T}_2 \mathbf{S}.$$

Therefore

$$\mathbf{R}\mathbf{T}_1 = \mathbf{T}_2\mathbf{S},$$

$$\mathbf{T}_1 = \mathbf{R}^{-1}\mathbf{T}_2\mathbf{S}.$$

Conversely, suppose that there exist nonsingular transformations $\mathbf{R}$ on $\mathcal{V}_m$ and $\mathbf{S}$ on $\mathcal{W}_n$ such that $\mathbf{T}_1 = \mathbf{R}^{-1}\mathbf{T}_2\mathbf{S}$. Choose a pair of bases $\{\gamma\}$, $\{\delta\}$ for $\mathcal{V}_m$ and $\mathcal{W}_n$, and define $\alpha_i = \gamma_i\mathbf{R}$, $\beta_j = \delta_j\mathbf{S}$. Then $\{\alpha\}$, $\{\beta\}$ forms a pair of bases also. Let A be the matrix which represents $\mathbf{T}_2$ relative to the γ- and δ-bases. Then

$$\gamma_i \mathbf{R}\mathbf{T}_1 = \alpha_i \mathbf{T}_i = \gamma_i \mathbf{T}_2 \mathbf{S} = \left(\sum_{j=1}^{n} a_{ij}\delta_j\right)\mathbf{S} = \sum_{j=1}^{n} a_{ij}\beta_j,$$

so A represents $\mathbf{T}_1$ relative to the α- and β-bases. Now the pictorial scheme is especially helpful:

$$\begin{array}{ccc} \mathcal{V}_m = [\alpha] & \xrightarrow[A_{\alpha,\beta}]{\mathbf{T}_1} & \mathcal{W}_n = [\beta] \\ \mathbf{R}\uparrow & & \uparrow\mathbf{S} \\ \mathcal{V}_m = [\gamma] & \xrightarrow[\mathbf{T}_2]{A_{\gamma,\delta}} & \mathcal{W}_n = [\delta] \end{array}$$

Figure 6.2

$\mathbf{T}_1$ has the same effect on $\mathcal{V}_m$ as a change of coordinates in $\mathcal{V}_m$ ($\mathbf{R}^{-1}$ indicated by going against the arrow), followed by $\mathbf{T}_2$, followed by a change of coordinates $\mathbf{S}$ in $\mathcal{W}_n$. Notice that in Figure 6.1 a similar interpretation can be made only by considering the vertical arrows as being reversed. We have proved the following analogue of Theorem 6.17.

Theorem 6.18. Two linear transformations $\mathbf{T}_1$ and $\mathbf{T}_2$ from $\mathcal{V}_m$ to $\mathcal{W}_n$ are represented relative to two pairs of bases by the same matrix if and only if nonsingular linear transformations $\mathbf{R}$ on $\mathcal{V}_m$ and $\mathbf{S}$ on $\mathcal{W}_n$ exist such that $\mathbf{T}_2 = \mathbf{R}\mathbf{T}_1\mathbf{S}^{-1}$.

We now specialize our consideration to linear transformations of an n-dimensional space into itself; many of the important transformations of mathematics and physics are of this type. The matrices which represent such transformations will be square, say $n \times n$, and our work of the next four chapters will principally concern square matrices.

For the present discussion, if $\mathcal{U}_m = \mathcal{W}_n$ we can take the α- and β-bases to be the same, and the γ- and δ-bases to be the same. In this case the transformations $\mathbf{R}$ and $\mathbf{S}$ are equal, and the relation between the two matrices A and C which represent the same linear transformation relative to the α-basis and the γ-basis, respectively, is

$$A_\alpha = P_\gamma C_\gamma P_\gamma^{-1},$$

where P represents relative to the γ-basis the transformation which changes bases from γ to α. This relation between matrices exists only for square matrices and is a special type of equivalence wherein $Q = P^{-1}$.

Definition 6.4. Two $n \times n$ matrices A and C are said to be *similar* if and only if

$$A = PCP^{-1}$$

for some nonsingular matrix P.

Theorem 6.19. Two $n \times n$ matrices A and C are similar if and only if there exist two bases $\{\alpha\}$ and $\{\gamma\}$ for $\mathcal{U}_n$ and a linear transformation $\mathbf{T}$ on $\mathcal{U}_n$ such that A represents $\mathbf{T}$ relative to the α-basis and C represents $\mathbf{T}$ relative to the γ-basis.

P R O O F : This theorem may be regarded as a special case of Theorem 6.17 in which only one space is involved, and therefore only two bases rather than two *pairs* of bases are required. In the proof of Theorem 6.17 we let $m = n$, $\mathcal{U}_m = \mathcal{W}_n$, $\beta_i = \alpha_i$, and $\delta_i = \gamma_i$. Then $\mathbf{S} = \mathbf{R}$, $Q = P$, and the conclusions follow.

Theorem 6.20. Two linear transformations $\mathbf{T}_1$ and $\mathbf{T}_2$ on $\mathcal{U}_n$ are represented relative to two bases for $\mathcal{U}_n$ by the same matrix if and only if a nonsingular transformation $\mathbf{R}$ on $\mathcal{U}_n$ exists such that $\mathbf{T}_2 = \mathbf{R}\mathbf{T}_1\mathbf{R}^{-1}$.

P R O O F : Exercise.

It is important to distinguish clearly between the relations of equivalence and similarity. To begin with, equivalence is defined for $m \times n$ matrices, while similarity is defined only for $n \times n$ matrices. But in obtaining Theorems 6.19 and 6.20 as special cases of Theorems 6.17 and 6.18, the specialization occurred not only by choosing $m = n$ but also in the selection of bases. Although both equivalence and similarity are defined for $n \times n$ matrices, they are different relations; similar matrices are equivalent, but equivalent $n \times n$ matrices are not necessarily similar.

The notion of similarity is particularly important because of Theorem 6.19.

Since similar matrices represent the same linear transformation, they must share all properties of the transformation which are independent of any coordinate system. These are the intrinsic geometric properties of the transformation. A problem of special interest is to find a simple canonical form for every similarity class; this problem is the same as that of selecting a coordinate system in which a given linear transformation assumes a simple form which is determined by intrinsic geometric properties. The next chapter is concerned with its solution.

Exercises

1. Prove that similarity of matrices is an equivalence relation.
2. Prove that if A and B are similar, then

    (i) $\rho(A) = \rho(B)$,
    (ii) $\det A = \det B$.

3. Are AB and BA similar for all $n \times n$ matrices? What can be said if either A or B is nonsingular?

4. In the analysis of three-phase power systems, an impedance matrix often occurs in the form

$$C = \begin{pmatrix} z_1 & z_2 & z_3 \\ z_3 & z_1 & z_2 \\ z_2 & z_3 & z_1 \end{pmatrix},$$

where z_j is a complex number for $j = 1, 2, 3$. Let

$$P = \begin{pmatrix} 1 & 1 & 1 \\ 1 & e & e^2 \\ 1 & e^2 & e \end{pmatrix},$$

where $e = \frac{1}{2}(-1 + i\sqrt{3})$. Show that C is similar to a diagonal matrix D and compute D. (Observe that $e^3 = 1$, so that $e^2 + e + 1 = 0$.)

5. Let $\mathbf{T}$ be the linear transformation on $\mathcal{E}_3$ whose matrix relative to the $\{\epsilon_1, \epsilon_2, \epsilon_3\}$ basis is

$$A = \begin{pmatrix} 1 & 2 & -1 \\ 2 & 0 & 2 \\ 1 & -2 & 3 \end{pmatrix}.$$

(i) Show that the vectors $\gamma_1 = (1, 1, 0)$, $\gamma_2 = (1, 0, 1)$, and $\gamma_3 = (1, -1, 1)$ are linearly independent and hence form a basis.

(ii) If $\mathbf{R}$ is the linear mapping defined by $\gamma_i \mathbf{R} = \epsilon_i$, $i = 1, 2, 3$, show that $\mathbf{R}$ is represented relative to the γ-basis by the matrix

$$P = \begin{pmatrix} 1 & -1 & 1 \\ 0 & 1 & -1 \\ -1 & 2 & -1 \end{pmatrix}.$$

(iii) Calculate the matrix C which represents **T** relative to the γ-basis by two methods: first, express $\gamma_i \mathbf{T}$ in terms of the γ's for $i = 1, 2, 3$; then compute $P^{-1}AP$.

6. Let **T** be a linear transformation of $\mathcal{E}_2$ into $\mathcal{E}_3$, whose matrix relative to the bases $\{\epsilon_1, \epsilon_2\}$ and $\{\epsilon_1, \epsilon_2, \epsilon_3\}$ is

$$A = \begin{pmatrix} 1 & 0 & -3 \\ 2 & 1 & -1 \end{pmatrix}.$$

Let new bases be defined by

$$\begin{cases} \alpha_1 = \epsilon_1 - 2\epsilon_2, \\ \alpha_2 = \epsilon_1 + \epsilon_2, \end{cases}$$

and

$$\begin{cases} \beta_1 = \epsilon_1 + \epsilon_2, \\ \beta_2 = \epsilon_2 + \epsilon_3, \\ \beta_3 = \epsilon_1 + \epsilon_3. \end{cases}$$

Compute the matrix which represents **T** relative to the α- and β-bases.

7. (i) Show that any two idempotent matrices of the same dimension and rank are similar.

(ii) Describe a form for idempotent matrices which is canonical with respect to similarity.

8. If A and B are similar, determine whether or not each of the following pairs are similar:

(i) A^k and B^k,
(ii) A' and B',
(iii) A^{-1} and B^{-1}, assuming A is nonsingular.

9. Prove Theorem 6.20 in detail.

CHAPTER 7

A Canonical Form for Similarity

For the remainder of this book we shall restrict our investigation in two ways, sometimes by necessity and sometimes for convenience.

We shall consider only square matrices, unless otherwise noted; thus linear transformations will be regarded as mapping a space into itself.

We shall assume that the scalar field is either the real or complex numbers. By this time you should have little difficulty in discerning which theorems can be extended beyond the limits imposed by these restrictions.

§7.1. *Characteristic Vectors and Values*

The general problem which we undertake in this chapter was stated at the end of § 6.5. A linear transformation $\mathbf{T}$ on $\mathbb{U}_n$ may be regarded as a rearrangement of the points of the space, without reference to particular coordinate systems. Indeed, those properties which distinguish $\mathbf{T}$ intrinsically must hold in any coordinate system and hence must be invariant under a change of coordinates. Since equal transformations are represented by similar matrices, our investigation will make heavy use of similarity, with a major objective being the derivation of a canonical form for similarity. Another problem which we shall solve in this chapter is to determine under what conditions a given matrix is similar to a diagonal matrix. Since calculations with diagonal matrices are quite easy, the relation of this problem to the simple representation of a linear transformation is apparent.

When we regard $\mathbf{T}$ as a rearrangement of the vectors of $\mathbb{U}$, it is natural to look for vectors which are mapped by **T** in some simple way. The null space, for example, is the set of vectors mapped into θ. Also, we might look for a *fixed point*—a vector which is mapped into itself. More generally, we search for any vector which is mapped by **T** into a *scalar multiple* of itself:

$$\xi\mathbf{T} = \lambda\xi \quad \text{for some scalar } \lambda.$$

(The use of the Greek letter λ for a scalar is an exception to the notation adopted for this book. It is used for characteristic values to conform with generally accepted notation.) Clearly, for any **T**, θ is such a vector (indeed, a fixed point), so we are interested only in nonzero vectors which have this property.

For example, consider the linear transformation **T** defined on $\mathcal{E}_3$ by the matrix

$$A = \begin{pmatrix} 1 & 2 & -1 \\ 2 & 0 & 2 \\ 1 & -2 & 3 \end{pmatrix}.$$

The point (a, b, c) is mapped by **T** into $(a + 2b + c, 2a - 2c, -a + 2b + 3c)$. In particular, for any value of a, $(a, 0, a)\mathbf{T} = 2(a, 0, a)$ and $(a, -a, a)\mathbf{T} = 0(a, -a, a)$. Hence the vectors γ_2 and γ_3 of the new basis described in Exercise 5, § 6.5, are mapped by **T** into scalar multiples of themselves: $\gamma_2\mathbf{T} = 2\gamma_2$ and $\gamma_3\mathbf{T} = 0\gamma_3$. The vector γ_1 is mapped by **T** in a manner which is only slightly more complicated: $\gamma_1\mathbf{T} = 2\gamma_1 + \gamma_2$. This geometric simplicity makes the γ-basis a natural (although oblique) coordinate system for representing **T**

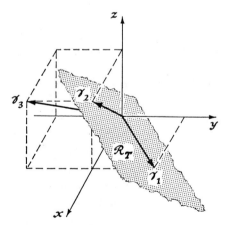

Figure 7.1

(Figure 7.1), and we have seen that this geometric simplicity is reflected in the algebraic representation of **T** relative to the γ-basis:

$$C = \begin{pmatrix} 2 & 1 & 0 \\ 0 & 2 & 0 \\ 0 & 0 & 0 \end{pmatrix}.$$

The work which ensues will show that no simpler representation of **T** is possible.

Definition 7.1. A nonzero vector ξ such that

$$\xi\mathbf{T} = \lambda\xi \quad \text{for some scalar } \lambda$$

is called a *characteristic vector* of **T**. The scalar λ is called the *characteristic value* of **T** which is associated with the characteristic vector ξ. The set of all characteristic values of **T** is called the *spectrum* of **T**.

In the literature of matrices there is a wide variety of synonyms for characteristic vectors (eigenvectors, proper vectors, proper states) and for characteristic values (eigenvalues, proper values, characteristic numbers, characteristic roots, latent roots).

Suppose that **T** is represented by $A = (a_{ij})$ and ξ is represented by the row vector $X = (x_1 \ldots x_n)$, relative to a fixed basis. If ξ is a characteristic vector associated with the characteristic value λ, then

$$\xi\mathbf{T} = \lambda\xi,$$
$$XA = \lambda X,$$
$$X(A - \lambda I) = Z.$$

This is the matrix form of a system of n linear homogeneous equations, and by Theorem 5.1 a nonzero solution X exists if and only if $A - \lambda I$ is singular. This occurs if and only if

$$\det(A - \lambda I) = 0.$$

From our knowledge of determinants we see that

$$\det(A - \lambda I) = \begin{vmatrix} a_{11} - \lambda & a_{12} & \cdots & a_{1n} \\ a_{21} & a_{22} - \lambda & \cdots & a_{2n} \\ \cdot & \cdot & & \cdot \\ \cdot & \cdot & & \cdot \\ \cdot & \cdot & & \cdot \\ a_{n1} & a_{n2} & \cdots & a_{nn} - \lambda \end{vmatrix} = 0$$

is a polynomial equation of degree n in λ, say

$$(-1)^n\lambda^n + b_1\lambda^{n-1} + \cdots + b_{n-1}\lambda + b_n = 0,$$

where the b's are sums of products of the a_{ij}. If the scalar field is the field of real or complex numbers, we know by the fundamental theorem of algebra and its corollaries that there are exactly n complex numbers λ (not necessarily distinct from one another) which satisfy this equation. In order that we may be sure that the characteristic values λ are in the scalar field of $\mathcal{V}$, we shall make the simplifying assumption during the remainder of this chapter that $\mathfrak{F}$ is the field of complex numbers.

Definition 7.2. The polynomial $\det(A - \lambda I)$ is called the *characteristic polynomial* of the matrix A. The equation $\det(A - \lambda I) = 0$ is called the *characteristic equation* of A.

Definition 7.3. The *characteristic values of a matrix* A are the roots of the characteristic equation of A.

Our discussion has established the following result.

Theorem 7.1. The characteristic values of a matrix A are the characteristic values of the linear transformation represented by A in any coordinate system.

Theorem 7.2. If A and B are similar, then A and B have the same characteristic polynomial and hence the same characteristic values.

P R O O F : If $A = PBP^{-1}$, then

$$A - \lambda I = PBP^{-1} - \lambda I = P(B - \lambda I)P^{-1},$$
$$\det(A - \lambda I) = (\det P)\det(B - \lambda I)(\det P^{-1}) = \det(B - \lambda I).$$

Theorem 7.3. The characteristic values of a triangular matrix are the diagonal elements. Thus the characteristic values of a diagonal matrix are the diagonal elements.

P R O O F : Exercise.

So far we have found out how to determine the characteristic values $\lambda_1, \ldots, \lambda_n$ of A. To determine characteristic vectors associated with the value λ_i, we solve for X the matrix equation

$$X(A - \lambda_i I) = Z.$$

Suppose that X_i is the matrix representation of a characteristic vector associated with λ_i. Then for any scalar c, cX_i is also a characteristic vector associated with λ_i. Similarly, if Y_i is a characteristic vector associated with λ_i, then $(X_i + Y_i)$ is also a characteristic vector associated with λ_i.

Theorem 7.4. Let λ be a characteristic value of the linear mapping **T**. The set of all characteristic vectors of **T** associated with λ, together with the zero vector, form a subspace $\mathcal{C}_\lambda$ of $\mathcal{V}$, and $\xi \mathbf{T} \in \mathcal{C}_\lambda$ for every $\xi \in \mathcal{C}_\lambda$.

Exercises

1. Find the characteristic polynomial, the characteristic values, and the characteristic vectors of each of the following matrices:

(i)
$$\begin{pmatrix} 0 & 3 \\ 2 & -1 \end{pmatrix},$$

(ii)
$$\begin{pmatrix} 3 & 2 & 4 \\ 2 & 0 & 2 \\ 4 & 2 & 3 \end{pmatrix},$$

(iii)
$$\begin{pmatrix} 3 & 0 & 0 & 0 \\ 2 & 1 & 2 & 0 \\ 1 & 0 & 1 & 0 \\ 0 & 1 & 0 & 1 \end{pmatrix}.$$

2. Prove that if X is a row vector and D a diagonal matrix such that $XD^2 = Z$, then $XD = Z$.

3. Prove Theorem 7.3.

4. Verify in detail the proof of Theorem 7.4.

5. Referring to Theorem 7.4, suppose that we choose any basis for $\mathcal{C}_\lambda$ and extend it to a basis for $\mathcal{U}$. Describe the matrix which represents **T** relative to that basis.

6. Prove that if A is nonsingular then the characteristic values of A^{-1} are the reciprocals of the characteristic values of A. What can be said about the corresponding characteristic vectors?

7. Show that if X is a characteristic vector of A associated with the value λ, then for any natural number k, X is a characteristic vector of A^k associated with the characteristic value λ^k.

8. If $\lambda_1, \ldots, \lambda_n$ are the characteristic values of A, show that

$$\det A = \lambda_1 \lambda_2 \cdots \lambda_n$$

by relating each side to the constant term of the characteristic polynomial of A.

9. Prove that if $S = \{\xi_1, \ldots, \xi_k\}$ is a set of characteristic vectors of **T** associated respectively with distinct characteristic values $\lambda_1, \ldots, \lambda_k$, then S is linearly independent.

10. A Markov matrix was defined in Exercise 8, § 4.4. Prove that every characteristic value of a Markov matrix satisfies $|\lambda| \leq 1$.

11. Prove that $\lambda = 1$ is a characteristic value of every Markov matrix.

§7.2. *A Method of Diagonalization*

As a start on the problem of determining what matrices are similar to a diagonal matrix, the next theorem gives us a sufficient condition, which is later proved to be necessary also. In addition, we obtain a method of diagonalizing A; that is, we find P such that PAP^{-1} is diagonal.

Theorem 7.5. Let $X_i = (x_{i1}, \ldots, x_{in})$ be a characteristic vector of A associated with λ_i, $i = 1, 2, \ldots, n$. If the vectors X_i span $\mathcal{V}$, then the matrix $P = (x_{ij})$ is such that

$$PAP^{-1} = \begin{pmatrix} \lambda_1 & 0 & .. & 0 \\ 0 & \lambda_2 & .. & 0 \\ . & . & . & . \\ . & . & . & . \\ 0 & 0 & .. & \lambda_n \end{pmatrix} = \mathrm{diag}(\lambda_1, \ldots, \lambda_n) = D.$$

P R O O F : Notice that the row vectors of P are characteristic vectors X_i. If these n vectors span $\mathcal{V}$, they are linearly independent, so P is non-singular. We have

$$X_i A = \lambda_i X_i,$$

so

$$\sum_{k=1}^{n} x_{ik} a_{kj} = \lambda_i x_{ij}$$

for $j = 1, 2, \ldots, n$. Furthermore,

$$PA = (c_{ij}),$$

where $c_{ij} = \sum_{k-1}^{n} x_{ik} a_{kj} = \lambda_i x_{ij}$, and

$$DP = (b_{ij}),$$

where $b_{ij} = \lambda_i x_{ij}$. (You should verify these calculations.) Hence $PA = DP$.

Example

We shall find the characteristic values, characteristic vectors, and a diagonalizing matrix P for the matrix

$$A = \begin{pmatrix} 1 & 0 & -2 \\ 0 & 0 & 0 \\ -2 & 0 & 4 \end{pmatrix}.$$

The characteristic equation of A is

$$0 = \det(A - \lambda I) = \begin{vmatrix} 1 - \lambda & 0 & -2 \\ 0 & -\lambda & 0 \\ -2 & 0 & 4 - \lambda \end{vmatrix}$$

$$= (1 - \lambda)(-\lambda)(4 - \lambda) - (-2)(-\lambda)(-2)$$

$$= -\lambda^3 + 5\lambda^2.$$

Hence the characteristic values of A are $\lambda_1 = 0$, $\lambda_2 = 0$, $\lambda_3 = 5$. Let $X = (x_1, x_2, x_3)$. Then

$$XA = (x_1 - 2x_3, 0, -2x_1 + 4x_3)$$

and

$$\lambda X = (\lambda x_1, \lambda x_2, \lambda x_3).$$

Necessary and sufficient conditions that X be a characteristic vector associated with λ are therefore

$$x_1 - 2x_3 = \lambda x_1,$$

$$0 = \lambda x_2,$$

$$-2x_1 + 4x_3 = \lambda x_3.$$

For $\lambda = 0$ these reduce to

$$x_1 = 2x_3.$$

Hence any vector of the form $(2c, b, c)$ is characteristic. Two such vectors which are linearly independent are

$$X_1 = (2, 0, 1),$$

$$X_2 = (0, 1, 0).$$

Notice in this case that it is possible to select two linearly independent characteristic vectors both of which are associated with the same characteristic value. For $\lambda_3 = 5$ the conditions reduce to

$$-2x_1 = x_3,$$

$$x_2 = 0.$$

Hence any vector of the form $(a, 0, -2a)$ is characteristic. As a simple vector of this form we choose

$$X_3 = (1, 0, -2)$$

as a characteristic vector associated with $\lambda_3 = 5$. Then

$$P = \begin{pmatrix} 2 & 0 & 1 \\ 0 & 1 & 0 \\ 1 & 0 & -2 \end{pmatrix}$$

and $\det P = -5$, which checks the linear independence of X_1, X_2, and X_3. You should check the calculations which show that

$$P^{-1} = -\tfrac{1}{5}\begin{pmatrix} -2 & 0 & -1 \\ 0 & -5 & 0 \\ -1 & 0 & 2 \end{pmatrix}$$

and

$$PAP^{-1} = \begin{pmatrix} 0 & 0 & 0 \\ 0 & 0 & 0 \\ 0 & 0 & 5 \end{pmatrix}.$$

The geometric interpretation of these calculations is that in $\mathcal{E}_3$ each point η on the line determined by the origin and $\xi_3 = (1, 0, -2)$ is mapped by $\mathbf{T}$ into 5η, while each point ζ on the plane determined by the origin, $\xi_1 = (2, 0, 1)$, and $\xi_2 = (0, 1, 0)$ is mapped by $\mathbf{T}$ into $0 \cdot \zeta = \theta$. The three characteristic vectors ξ_1, ξ_2, and ξ_3 are linearly independent and may be chosen as a basis

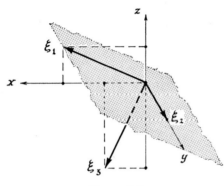

Figure 7.2

for $\mathcal{U}_3$. Relative to that basis, $\mathbf{T}$ is represented by the diagonal matrix $D = \mathrm{diag}(0, 0, 5)$.

When we attempt to diagonalize a given matrix A by the preceding method there are three possible situations:

If the characteristic values are all distinct, then there exist n linearly independent characteristic vectors; thus A can be diagonalized. (Proved later.)

If the characteristic values are not distinct, as in the preceding example, it might still be possible to find n linearly independent characteristic vectors so that A can be diagonalized.

If the characteristic values are not distinct, it can happen that no set of n linearly independent characteristic vectors exists. Then A cannot be diagonalized.

These three cases are illustrated in Exercise 1, below.

Exercises

1. For each of the following matrices determine the characteristic values and corresponding characteristic vectors; if the matrix is similar to a diagonal matrix, find P and show that PAP^{-1} is diagonal:

(i) $\begin{pmatrix} 2 & -2 & 3 \\ 1 & 1 & 1 \\ 1 & 3 & -1 \end{pmatrix}$
(iv) $\begin{pmatrix} 1 & 1 & -1 \\ 0 & 0 & 1 \\ 0 & -2 & -3 \end{pmatrix}$

(ii) $\begin{pmatrix} 7 & 4 & -1 \\ 4 & 7 & -1 \\ -4 & -4 & 4 \end{pmatrix}$
(v) $\begin{pmatrix} 1 & 0 & 0 \\ 3 & -2 & 6 \\ 0 & 0 & 1 \end{pmatrix}$

(iii) $\begin{pmatrix} 2 & -2 & 3 \\ 10 & -4 & 5 \\ 5 & -4 & 6 \end{pmatrix}$

2. Which matrices of Exercise 1, § 7.1, are similar to a diagonal matrix? Without computing P, write the diagonal form of each such matrix.

3. Prove that a transformation is nonsingular if and only if none of its characteristic values are zero.

4. Prove that a transformation is nilpotent if and only if all of its characteristic values are zero. Show by a particular example that part of the preceding statement is false if one is restricted to work within the field of real numbers.

5. (i) Without expanding a 4×4 determinant show that $a - b$, $a - c$, and $a - d$ are characteristic values of the matrix

$$A = \begin{pmatrix} a & b & c & d \\ b & a & c & d \\ b & c & a & d \\ b & c & d & a \end{pmatrix}.$$

(ii) What is the fourth characteristic value?

(iii) Find general conditions on the numbers a, b, c, d which are sufficient that A be similar to a diagonal matrix.

6. Prove that AB and BA have the same characteristic values by establishing the following assertions.

(i) If $D = PAQ$ is the canonical matrix equivalent to A (Theorem 6.14) then DC and CD have the same characteristic equation for all C.

(ii) $PABP^{-1}$ and $QBAQ^{-1}$ have the same characteristic equation if P and Q are as given in (i).

(iii) AB and BA have the same characteristic equation.

7. Prove that if either A or B is nonsingular, then AB and BA are similar.

8. Give an example of two matrices which have the same characteristic equation but are not similar.

9. Prove Theorem 7.5 by means of a geometric argument.

§7.3. *Minimal Polynomial of a Matrix*

In Theorem 4.2 and subsequent remarks it was proved that the set of all $n \times n$ matrices over a field forms a linear algebra of dimension n^2. Hence in this algebra the $n^2 + 1$ elements

$$I = A^0, A, A^2, \ldots, A^{n^2}$$

are linearly dependent for any $n \times n$ matrix A. By Theorem 2.8, a set is dependent only if some "vector" of the set is a linear combination of the ones which precede it. Let m be the integer such that $(I, A, \ldots, A^{m-1})$ is independent but $(I, A, \ldots, A^m)$ is dependent. For suitable scalars we have

$$a_0 A^m + a_1 A^{m-1} + \cdots + a_{m-1} A + a_m I = Z,$$

where $a_0 \neq 0$. Hence for $b_k = a_k a_0^{-1}$ we have

$$A^m + b_1 A^{m-1} + \cdots + b_{m-1} A + b_m I = Z.$$

This is a polynomial equation in the matrix A. The corresponding scalar polynomial is

$$M(x) = x^m + b_1 x^{m-1} + \cdots + b_m.$$

A polynomial, such as M, which has 1 as the coefficient of its largest power is called *monic*.

Definition 7.4. The *minimal polynomial* of the matrix A is the monic scalar polynomial

$$M(x) = x^m + a_1 x^{m-1} + \cdots + a_m$$

of least degree such that

$$A^m + a_1 A^{m-1} + \cdots + a_m I = Z.$$

We have seen that each matrix has a minimal polynomial, and as an exercise you may prove that the minimal polynomial of A is unique. A word of caution is justified at this point. The form of Definition 7.4 tempts us to define the minimal polynomial of A as "the monic polynomial of least degree for which A is a zero." However, we must distinguish between *matrix* polynomials and *scalar* polynomials. Since the properties of matrices and scalars are quite different, there is no *a priori* justification for substituting the matrix A for the scalar x. But every scalar polynomial determines a matrix polynomial which is formed by replacing the scalar x by the matrix X and each scalar coefficient a_i by the scalar matrix $a_i I$. In this sense it is correct to say that the minimal polynomial of A is the monic polynomial M of least degree and with scalar matrices as coefficients such that $M(A) = Z$.

The difficulties that arise in handling polynomials having matrices as coefficients are due principally to the existence of zero divisors and the lack of commutativity. For example, the matrix polynomial equation

$$(X - A)(X - B) = Z$$

does not imply that $X = A$ or $X = B$, because a product of nonzero matrices may be zero. Also, the matrix polynomial

$$X^2 - AX - BX + AB$$

cannot be factored as

$$(X - A)(X - B)$$

unless it is known that X and B commute. On the other hand, we know that any scalar matrix $B = bI$ commutes with any matrix, so that any factorization of a scalar polynomial

$$x^m + a_1 x^{m-1} + \cdots + a_m = (x - r_1) \cdots (x - r_m)$$

determines a like factorization of the corresponding matrix polynomial

$$X^m + a_1 X^{m-1} + \cdots + a_m I = (X - r_1 I) \cdots (X - r_m I).$$

A remarkable result concerning matrix polynomials is the Hamilton-Cayley theorem which may be stated loosely as "Every square matrix satisfies its characteristic equation." To see that this is so, consider a square matrix A and assume for the present that its characteristic vectors span $\mathcal{U}$. Let the characteristic polynomial of A be

$$(-1)^n \lambda^n + b_1 \lambda^{n-1} + \cdots + b_n.$$

Let B be the matrix defined by

$$B = (-1)^n A^n + b_1 A^{n-1} + \cdots + b_n I.$$

If X is a characteristic vector of A associated with the characteristic value λ, then by direct calculation using Exercise 7, § 7.1, we have

$$XB = [(-1)^n \lambda^n + b_1 \lambda^{n-1} + \cdots + b_n]X = 0 \cdot X = Z.$$

The transformation **S** associated with B maps every characteristic vector of A into zero. By assumption, the characteristic vectors of A span $\mathcal{U}$, so **S** is the zero transformation, and B must be the zero matrix. In the next section we shall prove the same result for any square matrix.

The Hamilton-Cayley theorem shows that the degree of the minimal polynomial of A does not exceed n. It can be proved that the minimal polynomial of A divides any polynomial p such that $p(A) = Z$; hence the minimal polynomial divides the characteristic polynomial.

Exercises

1. Show that the minimal polynomial of A is unique.

2. Prove that a matrix and its transpose have the same characteristic polynomial.

3. Prove the Hamilton-Cayley theorem for 2×2 matrices by direct calculations with matrices.

4. Prove that if A is similar to B and if $p(X)$ is any matrix polynomial with scalar coefficients, then $p(A)$ is similar to $p(B)$.

5. Prove that if A is similar to the scalar matrix cI, then $A = cI$.

6. (i) Determine all real 2×2 matrices A which satisfy $A^2 = -I$.

(ii) Show that no real 3×3 matrix A satisfies $A^2 = -I$.

7. (i) Let C be a square matrix with 1 in every position on the super-diagonal $(c_{i,i+1} = 1)$, $c_{n1}, \ldots, c_{nn}$ in the last row, and zeros elsewhere. Show that the characteristic polynomial of C is

$$(-1)^n [\lambda^n - c_{nn}\lambda^{n-1} - c_{n,n-1}\lambda^{n-2} - \cdots - c_{n2}\lambda - c_{n1}].$$

(ii) Deduce that every polynomial whose leading coefficient is ± 1, according to whether its degree is even or odd, is the characteristic polynomial of some matrix.

8. Use the Hamilton-Cayley theorem to solve Exercise 8, § 5.4.

§7.4. *Invariant Subspaces*

We have previously observed that the problem of finding a simple standard form for each similarity class of $n \times n$ matrices is equivalent to selecting a coordinate system which takes full advantage of the intrinsic geometric properties of the linear transformation which is represented by each matrix of that class. One very useful geometric property, which we first met as a special case in Exercise 8, § 3.2, is the existence of a subspace $\mathfrak{M}$, which is mapped into itself by $\mathbf{T}$. Clearly the range and null spaces of $\mathbf{T}$ are such spaces, as is the space $\mathfrak{C}_\lambda$ of Theorem 7.4.

> **Definition 7.5.** Let $\mathbf{T}$ be a linear transformation on $\mathfrak{V}$. A subspace $\mathfrak{M}$ of $\mathfrak{V}$ is said to be *invariant under* $\mathbf{T}$ (or $\mathbf{T}$-invariant) if and only if $\xi\mathbf{T} \in \mathfrak{M}$ for every $\xi \in \mathfrak{M}$.

A $\mathbf{T}$-invariant subspace therefore has the property that each vector of the subspace is mapped by $\mathbf{T}$ into a vector in the same subspace. A useful notation is to let $\mathfrak{M}\mathbf{T}$ denote the set of all images of the vectors of $\mathfrak{M}$. Then a space $\mathfrak{M}$ is invariant under $\mathbf{T}$ if and only if $\mathfrak{M}\mathbf{T} \subseteq \mathfrak{M}$. If $\mathfrak{M}$ is a $\mathbf{T}$-invariant subspace of $\mathfrak{V}$, it is possible to study the behavior of $\mathfrak{M}$ under $\mathbf{T}$, ignoring the effect of $\mathbf{T}$ on the rest of $\mathfrak{V}$, since vectors of $\mathfrak{M}$ are mapped into vectors of $\mathfrak{M}$. The transformation $\mathbf{T}$ on $\mathfrak{V}$ thus defines a transformation $\mathbf{T}_\mathfrak{M}$ on $\mathfrak{M}$, called $\mathbf{T}$ *restricted to* $\mathfrak{M}$.

The matrix interpretation of this notion is illuminating. Let $\{\alpha_1, \ldots, \alpha_k\}$ be a basis for the invariant space $\mathfrak{M}$, and let $\{\alpha_1, \ldots, \alpha_n\}$ be a basis for $\mathcal{U}$. Then $\alpha_i T = \sum_{j=1}^{k} a_{ij}\alpha_j$ for $i = 1, \ldots, k$, and the matrix of T in this new basis is of the block form

$$\begin{pmatrix} A_1 & Z \\ A_3 & A_2 \end{pmatrix},$$

where A_1 is a $k \times k$ matrix.

In the event that $\mathcal{U} = \mathfrak{M} \oplus \mathfrak{N}$ where $\mathfrak{M}$ and $\mathfrak{N}$ are both invariant under T, a basis for $\mathfrak{M}$ together with a basis for $\mathfrak{N}$ form a basis for $\mathcal{U}$, and relative to that basis T is represented by a matrix of the form

$$\begin{pmatrix} A_1 & Z \\ Z & A_2 \end{pmatrix},$$

where A_1 is a square array of dimension equal to the dimension of $\mathfrak{M}$ and A_2 is a square array of dimension equal to the dimension of $\mathfrak{N}$.

Actually there is an abundance of T-invariant subspaces of a special type, called *cyclic* subspaces, which also arose in Exercise 8, § 3.2. Let T be a linear transformation on a finite-dimensional space $\mathcal{U}$, and let ξ be any nonzero vector of $\mathcal{U}$. We consider the vectors $\xi, \xi T, \xi T^2, \ldots$. By Theorem 2.8 for some value of k, $\{\xi, \xi T, \ldots, \xi T^{k-1}\}$ is linearly independent but $\xi T^k \in [\xi, \xi T, \ldots, \xi T^{k-1}]$. Hence

$$\xi T^k = \sum_{i=1}^{k} c_i \xi T^{i-1}$$

for suitable c_i. But this implies that the space $[\xi, \xi T, \ldots, \xi T^{k-1}]$ is T-invariant, since

$$\left(\sum_{i=1}^{k} a_i \xi T^{i-1} \right) T = \sum_{i=1}^{k-1} a_i \xi T^i + a_k \xi T^k.$$

Definition 7.6. Let T be any linear transformation on $\mathcal{U}$, ξ any nonzero vector of $\mathcal{U}$, and k the largest positive integer for which $\{\xi, \xi T, \ldots, \xi T^{k-1}\}$ is linearly independent. The space $[\xi, \xi T, \ldots, \xi T^{k-1}]$ is called the T-*cyclic subspace generated by* ξ, and the basis $\{\xi, \xi T, \ldots, \xi T^{k-1}\}$ for that subspace is denoted $\{(\xi)_T\}$ and called the T-*cyclic basis generated by* ξ. More generally, any linearly independent set of the form $\{(\xi_1)_T, (\xi_2)_T, \ldots, (\xi_r)_T\}$ is called a T-*cyclic basis* for the space which it spans.

Again the matrix interpretation is useful. Let T be a linear transformation on $\mathcal{U}_n$, and let $\mathcal{S}$ denote the cyclic subspace, of dimension k, generated by a vector ξ. The transformation $T_{\mathcal{S}}$ is represented relative to the basis $\{\xi, \xi T, \ldots, \xi T^{k-1}\}$ by the $k \times k$ matrix

$$(7.1) \qquad C_1 = \begin{pmatrix} 0 & 1 & 0 & \cdots & 0 \\ 0 & 0 & 1 & \cdots & 0 \\ & \cdot & & & \\ & \cdot & & & \\ 0 & 0 & 0 & \cdots & 1 \\ c_1 & c_2 & c_3 & \cdots & c_k \end{pmatrix},$$

which has $c_1, \ldots, c_k$ in the last row, 1 in each superdiagonal position, and 0 elsewhere. A matrix of this form was studied in Exercise 7, § 7.3, where you were asked to show that the characteristic polynomial of C_1 is

$$P_1(x) = (-1)^k(x^k - c_k x^{k-1} - \cdots - c_1).$$

C_1 is called the *companion matrix* of the polynomial P_1.

It can be proved that $\mathcal{V}_n$ is a direct sum of cyclic subspaces, and hence that $\mathbf{T}$ can be represented by a matrix of diagonal block form

$$C = \begin{pmatrix} C_1 & Z & \cdots & Z \\ Z & C_2 & \cdots & Z \\ \cdot & \cdot & & \cdot \\ \cdot & \cdot & & \cdot \\ Z & Z & \cdots & C_t \end{pmatrix},$$

where each C_i is the companion matrix of a particular polynomial which divides the minimal polynomial of $\mathbf{T}$. Also the product of these polynomials is the characteristic polynomial of $\mathbf{T}$. This form is canonical for the similarity class of matrices which represent $\mathbf{T}$, and is called the *rational* canonical form (or sometimes the Jordan canonical form, a term that we reserve for the form derived in § 7.7). For further information you may consult the references given at the end of this book.

We are now ready to prove the Hamilton-Cayley theorem.

Theorem 7.6. (Hamilton-Cayley.) If A is a matrix with characteristic equation

$$(-1)^n \lambda^n + b_1 \lambda^{n-1} + \cdots + b_n = 0,$$

then

$$(-1)^n A^n + b_1 A^{n-1} + \cdots + b_n I = Z.$$

P R O O F : Given an $n \times n$ matrix A, choose any basis for $\mathcal{V}_n$ and let $\mathbf{T}$ be the linear transformation represented by A relative to that basis. Let P be the characteristic polynomial of A,

$$P(\lambda) = \det(A - \lambda I) = (-1)^n(\lambda^n + b_1 \lambda^{n-1} + \cdots + b_n),$$

and consider the transformation $P(\mathbf{T})$ defined by

$$P(\mathbf{T}) = (-1)^n(\mathbf{T}^n + b_1 \mathbf{T}^{n-1} + \cdots + b_n \mathbf{I}).$$

We shall show that $\xi P(\mathbf{T}) = \theta$ for every $\xi \in \mathcal{V}_n$. Since $P(\mathbf{T})$ is repre‐ sented by the matrix $P(A)$, we can then conclude that $P(A) = Z$.

Let ξ be any nonzero vector of $\mathcal{V}_n$, and let S be the cyclic subspace generated by ξ, say of dimension k. Then relative to the basis $\{\xi, \xi\mathbf{T}, \ldots, \xi\mathbf{T}^{k-1}\}$ for S, the transformation $\mathbf{T}_S$ is represented by the matrix C_1 given by (7.1) above. The characteristic polynomial Q_1 of C_1 is given by

$$Q_1(\lambda) = \det(C_1 - \lambda I) = (-1)^k(\lambda^k - c_k\lambda^{k-1} - \cdots - c_1),$$

where the coefficients c_i are obtained from the relation

$$\xi\mathbf{T}^k = c_1\xi + c_2\xi\mathbf{T} + \cdots + c_k\xi\mathbf{T}^{k-1}.$$

Since $\mathbf{T}$ and $\mathbf{T}_S$ coincide on S, we combine the last two equations to obtain

$$
\begin{aligned}
\theta &= \xi\mathbf{T}_S^k - (c_k\xi\mathbf{T}_S^{k-1} + \cdots + c_2\xi\mathbf{T}_S + c_1\xi) \\
&= \xi[\mathbf{T}_S^k - (c_k\mathbf{T}_S^{k-1} + \cdots + c_1I] \\
&= (-1)^k\xi Q_1(\mathbf{T}_S).
\end{aligned}
$$

Now extend this basis for S to a basis for $\mathcal{V}_n$. Then $\mathbf{T}$ is represented by a matrix C, which is similar to A and of the form

$$C = \begin{pmatrix} C_1 & Z \\ C_3 & C_4 \end{pmatrix}.$$

Then

$$
\begin{aligned}
P(\lambda) &= \det(A - \lambda I) = \det(C - \lambda I) \\
&= \det(C_1 - \lambda I)\det(C_4 - \lambda I) \\
&= Q_1(\lambda)Q_4(\lambda),
\end{aligned}
$$

where Q_4 is the characteristic polynomial of C_4. Hence $P(\mathbf{T}_S) = Q_1(\mathbf{T}_S)Q_4(\mathbf{T}_S)$. But $\xi \in S$, so

$$\xi P(\mathbf{T}) = \xi P(\mathbf{T}_S) = \xi Q_1(\mathbf{T}_S)Q_4(\mathbf{T}_S) = \theta Q_4(\mathbf{T}_S) = \theta,$$

as we wished to prove.

A stronger form of invariance occurs in connection with familiar mappings called *projections* which are also intimately related to direct sums. A projection $\mathbf{E}$ is defined simply as any idempotent linear transformation:

$$\mathbf{E}^2 = \mathbf{E}.$$

In Exercise 5, § 3.6, it was shown that any idempotent linear mapping is the identity transformation on its range space $\mathcal{R}_\mathbf{E}$. Hence not only is $\mathcal{R}_\mathbf{E}$ invariant under $\mathbf{E}$ as a subspace, but each point of $\mathcal{R}_\mathbf{E}$ is invariant: $\xi\mathbf{E} = \xi$ for every $\xi \in \mathcal{R}_\mathbf{E}$. Furthermore, $\mathcal{R}_\mathbf{E} \cap \mathcal{N}_\mathbf{E} = [\theta]$, so $\mathcal{V} = \mathcal{R}_\mathbf{E} \oplus \mathcal{N}_\mathbf{E}$. Hence any projection $\mathbf{E}$ on $\mathcal{V}$ decomposes $\mathcal{V}$ into the direct sum of two subspaces; $\mathbf{E}$ is the identity mapping on one of these subspaces and the zero mapping on the other. Conversely, if $\mathcal{V} = \mathcal{M}_1 \oplus \mathcal{M}_2$, each $\xi \in \mathcal{V}$ has a unique expression

$\xi = \mu_1 + \mu_2$, where $\mu_1 \in \mathfrak{M}_1$ and $\mu_2 \in \mathfrak{M}_2$. The mapping $\mathbf{T}$ defined by $\xi\mathbf{T} = \mu_1$ is linear and idempotent, and hence a projection, called the projection of $\mathcal{V}$ *on* $\mathfrak{M}_1$ *along* $\mathfrak{M}_2$. Clearly $\mathfrak{M}_1 = \mathfrak{R}_\mathbf{T}$ and $\mathfrak{M}_2 = \mathfrak{N}_\mathbf{T}$.

Projections have many important properties, some of which are developed in Exercises 3 to 6 of this section. Although we shall not make systematic use of projections, we shall see in the next section that they are closely related to the diagonability problem for matrices. You are urged to study these exercises and to prove the results stated therein.

Exercises

1. Refer to the linear transformation $\mathbf{T}_3$ of Example (c), § 3.1.

(i) Find two invariant subspaces such that $\mathcal{E}_2$ is the direct sum of these subspaces.

(ii) Write the matrix A for $\mathbf{T}_3$ relative to the $\{\epsilon_1, \epsilon_2\}$ basis.

(iii) Write the matrix B for $\mathbf{T}_3$ relative to a basis $\{\beta_1, \beta_2\}$, where each β_i spans one of the invariant subspaces of (i).

(iv) Find a matrix P for which

$$B = PAP^{-1}.$$

2. Prove that if $\mathcal{S}$ and $\mathfrak{R}$ are $\mathbf{T}$-invariant subspaces, then so are $\mathcal{S} \cap \mathfrak{R}$ and $\mathcal{S} + \mathfrak{R}$.

3. Determine the possible characteristic values of a projection, and describe a simple matrix representation of a projection. (See Exercise 5, § 3.7.)

4. Let $\mathcal{V} = \mathfrak{M}_1 \oplus \mathfrak{M}_2$, and let $\mathbf{E}_1$ and $\mathbf{T}$ be linear mappings of $\mathcal{V}$. Prove the following theorems.

(i) $\mathbf{E}_1$ is the projection on $\mathfrak{M}_1$ along $\mathfrak{M}_2$ if and only if $\mathbf{I} - \mathbf{E}_1$ is the projection on $\mathfrak{M}_2$ along $\mathfrak{M}_1$.

(ii) $\mathfrak{M}_1$ is $\mathbf{T}$-invariant if and only if $\mathbf{E}_1\mathbf{T}\mathbf{E}_1 = \mathbf{E}_1\mathbf{T}$, where $\mathbf{E}_1$ is the projection on $\mathfrak{M}_1$ along $\mathfrak{M}_2$.

(iii) $\mathfrak{M}_1$ and $\mathfrak{M}_2$ are $\mathbf{T}$-invariant if and only if $\mathbf{E}_1\mathbf{T} = \mathbf{T}\mathbf{E}_1$, where $\mathbf{E}_1$ is the projection on $\mathfrak{M}_1$ along $\mathfrak{M}_2$.

5. Let $\{\mathbf{E}_1, \dots, \mathbf{E}_k\}$ be a set of projections. These projections are called *orthogonal* if and only if $\mathbf{E}_i\mathbf{E}_j = \mathbf{Z}$ whenever $i \neq j$, and are called *supplementary* if and only if $\mathbf{I} = \mathbf{E}_1 + \cdots + \mathbf{E}_k$. Prove the following theorems.

(i) If $\mathbf{E}_1, \dots, \mathbf{E}_k$ are orthogonal, then $\mathbf{E}_1, \dots, \mathbf{E}_k, \mathbf{I} - \sum_{i=1}^k \mathbf{E}_i$ are orthogonal and supplementary.

(ii) If $\mathbf{E}_1, \dots, \mathbf{E}_k$ are orthogonal and supplementary, then

$$\mathcal{V} = \mathfrak{R}_{\mathbf{E}_1} \oplus \mathfrak{R}_{\mathbf{E}_2} \oplus \cdots \oplus \mathfrak{R}_{\mathbf{E}_k}.$$

(iii) Let $\mathcal{V} = \mathcal{S}_1 \oplus \mathcal{S}_2 \oplus \cdots \oplus \mathcal{S}_k$, let $\xi = \xi_1 + \xi_2 + \cdots + \xi_k$ where

$\xi_i \in S_i$, and let $\mathbf{E}_i$ be defined for $i = 1, 2, \ldots, k$ by $\xi \mathbf{E}_i = \xi_i$. Then $\{\mathbf{E}_1, \ldots, \mathbf{E}_k\}$ is a set of orthogonal and supplementary projections.

(iv) Describe a simple matrix representation for each projection $\mathbf{E}_i$ of (iii).

6. Let $\mathbf{E}$ be the projection of $\mathcal{V}$ on $\mathfrak{M}_1$ along $\mathfrak{M}_2$; let $\mathbf{F}$ be the projection of $\mathcal{V}$ on $\mathfrak{N}_1$ along $\mathfrak{N}_2$. Prove that $\mathbf{E} + \mathbf{F}$ is a projection if and only if $\mathbf{E}$ and $\mathbf{F}$ are orthogonal, and in that case that $\mathbf{E} + \mathbf{F}$ is the projection on $\mathfrak{M}_1 + \mathfrak{N}_1$ along $\mathfrak{M}_2 \cap \mathfrak{N}_2$.

§7.5. *Diagonalization Theorems*

In this section we shall establish a variety of criteria for determining whether a given matrix A is similar to a diagonal matrix D. Since the diagonal elements of D are the characteristic values of D (hence of A), we need only know that such a D exists in order to write one, merely by placing the characteristic values of A along the diagonal.

Theorem 7.7. Each of the following conditions is necessary and sufficient that A be similar to a diagonal matrix.

(a) There exist n linearly independent characteristic vectors of A.

(b) For every row vector X and scalar λ, if $X(A - \lambda I)^2 = Z$, then $X(A - \lambda I) = Z$.

(c) If X_0 is a characteristic row vector corresponding to the characteristic value λ_0, then there is no row vector Y such that $Y(A - \lambda_0 I) = X_0$.

(d) There exists a scalar polynomial P with distinct zeros such that $P(A) = Z$.

(e) There exist an integer r, distinct scalars $a_1, \ldots, a_r$, and nonzero matrices $E_1, \ldots, E_r$ such that

$$\sum_{j=1}^{r} a_j E_j = A,$$

$$\sum_{j=1}^{r} E_j = I.$$

$$E_i E_j = Z \qquad \text{if } i \neq j.$$

P R O O F : Theorem 7.5 has established that (a) implies that A can be diagonalized. We shall show that diagonalization implies (b), (b) implies (c), (c) implies (d), (d) implies (e), and (e) implies (a), thus completing the cycle.

Diagonalization implies (b): Let $D = PAP^{-1}$ be diagonal, let $Y = XP^{-1}$ for a given row vector X, and suppose $X(A - \lambda I)^2 = Z$ for some scalar λ. Then

$$Z = YP(A - \lambda I)^2 = YP(P^{-1}DP - \lambda I)^2 = Y(D - \lambda I)^2 P.$$

Since P is nonsingular, $Y(D - \lambda I)^2 = Z$, and hence $Y(D - \lambda I) = Z$ since $D - \lambda I$ is diagonal (Exercise 2, § 7.1). Thus $X(A - \lambda I)P^{-1} = Z$, so $X(A - \lambda I) = Z$.

(b) implies (c): Let λ_0 be a characteristic value and X_0 a corresponding characteristic row vector. Then $X_0 A = \lambda_0 X_0$. If a vector Y exists such that $Y(A - \lambda_0 I) = X_0$, then we have

$$Y(A - \lambda_0 I)^2 = X_0(A - \lambda_0 I) = Z,$$

so by (b) we have

$$Y(A - \lambda_0 I) = Z = X_0.$$

This contradicts the hypothesis that X_0 is a characteristic row vector, so no vector Y exists with the stated property.

(c) implies (d): We prove that the minimal polynomial M of A has distinct zeros if (c) is satisfied. Assume that M has λ_0 as a repeated zero. Then

$$M(x) = f(x)(x - \lambda_0)^2.$$

Since M is minimal, $f(A)(A - \lambda_0 I)$ is a nonzero matrix, and for some row vector Y_0,

$$Y_0[f(A)(A - \lambda_0 I)] \neq Z.$$

Let us call this nonzero row vector X_0. Then

$$X_0(A - \lambda_0 I) = Y_0 f(A)(A - \lambda_0 I)^2 = Y_0 M(A) = Z$$

since $M(A) = Z$. Hence X_0 is characteristic, corresponding to λ_0. But then the equation

$$Y(A - \lambda_0 I) = X_0$$

has the solution $Y_0 f(A)$, which contradicts (c).

(d) implies (e): Let P be a scalar polynomial of degree r such that its zeros $a_1, \ldots, a_r$ are distinct and such that $P(A) = Z$. Without loss of generality we can assume that no polynomial of degree less than r has these properties. We define r other polynomials p_i by the relations

$$P(x) = (x - a_i)p_i(x), \qquad i = 1, \ldots, r.$$

Then $p_i(a_j) = 0$ if and only if $i \neq j$. Let the polynomial g be defined by

$$g(x) = 1 - \sum_{i=1}^{r} [p_i(a_i)]^{-1} p_i(x),$$

and observe that g is a polynomial of degree less than r such that $g(a_k) = 0$ for $k = 1, \ldots, r$. Hence $g(x) = 0$ for every x, and each coefficient of g is zero. Hence $g(B) = Z$ for every matrix B. Now consider the r matrices

$$E_i = [p_i(a_i)]^{-1}p_i(A), \qquad i = 1, \ldots, r.$$

By our choice of r, $E_i \neq Z$. We have $\sum_{i=1}^r E_i = I$. Also,

$$P(A) = (A - a_iI)p_i(A) = Z,$$

so

$$a_ip_i(A) = Ap_i(A).$$

Thus

$$\sum_{i=1}^r a_iE_i = \sum_{i=1}^r [p_i(a_i)]^{-1}Ap_i(A) = A \sum_{i=1}^r E_i = A.$$

Finally, if $i \neq j$, we have

$$E_iE_j = [p_i(a_i)p_j(a_j)]^{-1}p_i(A)p_j(A)$$
$$= cP(A)h(A),$$

where c is a scalar and $h(A)$ is the product of the $r - 2$ matrices $A - a_kI$, where $k \neq i$ and $k \neq j$. Therefore $E_iE_j = Z$ if $i \neq j$.

(e) implies (a): Assuming (e), we shall show that for an arbitrary vector X, XE_i is either characteristic or zero:

$$(XE_i)A = XE_i\left(\sum_{j=1}^r a_jE_j\right) = X \sum_{j=1}^r a_iE_iE_j$$
$$= a_iXE_i^2 = a_i(XE_i).$$

The last equality follows from the fact that the matrices E_i are idempotent. (See Exercise 4.) In addition, we have

$$X = XI = X \sum_{i=1}^r E_i = \sum_{i=1}^r (XE_i),$$

so that any vector is a linear combination of characteristic vectors, which means that there are n linearly independent characteristic vectors. The proof of Theorem 7.7 is now complete.

Of these five criteria for diagonability the first is perhaps the most useful for the problems we are considering. Given an $n \times n$ matrix A, we need only compute the characteristic vectors and see if there are n of these which are linearly independent. This usually requires a considerable amount of computation. However, if the n characteristic values of A are distinct, the diagonalization problem is easily solved. In that event, A is similar to a diagonal matrix because the characteristic values are the distinct zeros of the characteristic polynomial f, and $f(A) = Z$ by the Hamilton-Cayley theorem. Alternatively we could argue that by Exercise 9, § 7.1, n distinct characteristic values determine a set of n linearly independent vectors, which guarantees diagonability. In case the characteristic values are not all distinct, n linearly independent vectors might still exist. This will occur whenever k linearly independent characteristic vectors correspond to each characteristic value of multiplicity k.

Theorem 7.8. A sufficient (but not necessary) condition that A be similar to a diagonal matrix is that the characteristic values of A are distinct.

Statement (e) of Theorem 7.7 also deserves special comment. Interpreted in terms of linear transformations, it says that a linear mapping $\mathbf{T}$ can be represented by a diagonal matrix if and only if $\mathbf{T}$ is a linear combination of a set of orthogonal and supplementary projections (Exercise 5, § 7.4). The coefficients a_i of that linear combination are the distinct characteristic values of $\mathbf{T}$, as we observed in the last section of the proof of Theorem 7.7. Furthermore, $\mathbf{E}_i$ is a projection on the space $\mathcal{C}_{a_i}$ spanned by the characteristic vectors associated with a_i. The decomposition

$$\mathbf{T} = \sum_{i=1}^{r} a_i \mathbf{E}_i$$

is sometimes called the *spectral form* of $\mathbf{T}$, and the diagonability problem for matrices is equivalent to the problem of characterizing those linear mappings that possess a spectral form. We shall return to this problem in § 8.6.

Exercises

1. Determine whether each of the following matrices is similar to a diagonal matrix. (Exercise 7, § 7.3, may be of assistance.)

(i) $\begin{pmatrix} 2 & 0 & 0 \\ 0 & 1 & 2 \\ 0 & 0 & 2 \end{pmatrix}$,
(iii) $\begin{pmatrix} 0 & 1 & 0 \\ 0 & 0 & 1 \\ 0 & -9 & 6 \end{pmatrix}$,

(ii) $\begin{pmatrix} 0 & 1 & 0 \\ 0 & 0 & 1 \\ -1 & -3 & -3 \end{pmatrix}$,
(iv) $\begin{pmatrix} 0 & 1 & 0 & 0 \\ 0 & 0 & 1 & 0 \\ 0 & 0 & 0 & 1 \\ 0 & -4 & 4 & 1 \end{pmatrix}$.

2. Show that the following $n \times n$ matrices are similar:

$$A = \begin{pmatrix} 1 & 1 \dots 1 \\ 1 & 1 \dots 1 \\ \cdot & \cdot \quad \cdot \\ \cdot & \cdot \quad \cdot \\ 1 & 1 \dots 1 \end{pmatrix}, \quad B = \begin{pmatrix} n & 0 \dots 0 \\ 0 & 0 \dots 0 \\ \cdot & \cdot \quad \cdot \\ \cdot & \cdot \quad \cdot \\ 0 & 0 \dots 0 \end{pmatrix}.$$

3. Show that the following $n \times n$ matrices are similar:

$$A = \begin{pmatrix} 0 & 1 & 0 \dots 0 \\ 0 & 0 & 1 \dots 0 \\ \cdot & \cdot & \cdot & \cdot \\ \cdot & \cdot & \cdot & \cdot \\ \cdot & \cdot & \cdot & \cdot \\ 0 & 0 & 0 \dots 1 \\ 1 & 0 & 0 \dots 0 \end{pmatrix}, \qquad B = \begin{pmatrix} e_1 & 0 & 0 \dots 0 \\ 0 & e_2 & 0 \dots 0 \\ \cdot & \cdot & \cdot & \cdot \\ \cdot & \cdot & \cdot & \cdot \\ \cdot & \cdot & \cdot & \cdot \\ 0 & 0 & 0 \dots e_n \end{pmatrix},$$

where $e_1, e_2, \dots, e_n$ are the n distinct nth roots of unity,

$$e_k = \cos \frac{2\pi k}{n} + i \sin \frac{2\pi k}{n}.$$

4. Let $E_1, \dots, E_r$ be a set of matrices which have the second and third properties of Theorem 7.7 (e). Prove that each E_i is idempotent.

5. Show that if $A = \sum_{i=1}^{r} a_i E_i$, where the E_i have the properties listed in Theorem 7.7 (e), then each a_i is a characteristic value of A. Find a corresponding characteristic vector.

6. Give a necessary and sufficient condition for the diagonability of the block matrix

$$\begin{pmatrix} A & Z \\ Z & D \end{pmatrix}$$

in terms of the diagonability of the square blocks A and D.

§7.6. *Nilpotent Transformations*

Let us summarize the results concerning diagonalization obtained thus far. Any square matrix is *equivalent* to a diagonal matrix, and a matrix is *similar* to a diagonal matrix if and only if the characteristic vectors span the full space. Since similar matrices represent the same transformation, we are particularly interested in the second result, and we recall that the diagonal entries must be the characteristic values. The next question is this: Suppose A cannot be diagonalized by a change of coordinates; how close can we come to diagonalizing A? Or, is there some simple matrix form such that every matrix is similar to a matrix in this canonical form and such that the form is *almost* diagonal? We shall show that A is similar to a matrix J which is the sum of two matrices, $J = D + N$, where D has zeros everywhere except on the main diagonal and N has zeros everywhere except on the superdiagonal. Thus N is nilpotent. Furthermore, the diagonal elements of D are the characteristic values of A, and the superdiagonal elements of N are either 0 or 1. An example of a matrix in this form is

$$J = \begin{pmatrix} \lambda_1 & 1 & 0 & 0 & 0 \\ 0 & \lambda_1 & 0 & 0 & 0 \\ 0 & 0 & \lambda_1 & 0 & 0 \\ 0 & 0 & 0 & \lambda_2 & 1 \\ 0 & 0 & 0 & 0 & \lambda_2 \end{pmatrix}.$$

To be more precise, let **T** be a linear mapping on $\mathcal{V}_n$ having r distinct characteristic values; $\lambda_1, \ldots, \lambda_r$. We shall show that there exists a basis for $\mathcal{V}_n$, relative to which **T** is represented by a diagonal block matrix of r blocks,

$$J = \begin{pmatrix} A_1 & & & & \\ & A_2 & & & \\ & & \cdot & & \\ & & & \cdot & \\ & & & & A_r \end{pmatrix}.$$

The size of the block A_i is s_i, the multiplicity of λ_i as a characteristic value of **T**; hence $s_1 + s_2 + \cdots + s_r = n$. Furthermore, for each i the block A_i is itself a diagonal block matrix of $k(i)$ blocks,

$$A_i = \begin{pmatrix} B_{i1} & & & & \\ & B_{i2} & & & \\ & & \cdot & & \\ & & & \cdot & \\ & & & & B_{ik(i)} \end{pmatrix}.$$

The blocks can be arranged in nonincreasing order of size; if p_{ij} denotes the size of the block B_{ij}, then for $i = 1, 2, \ldots, r$,

$$p_{i1} \geq p_{i2} \geq \cdots \geq p_{ik(i)},$$

$$p_{i1} + p_{i2} + \cdots + p_{ik(i)} = s_i.$$

For each $i = 1, 2, \ldots, r$, each diagonal element of A_i (and hence of each B_{ij}) is λ_i. Each superdiagonal element of J which lies within one of the sub-blocks B_{ij} is 1; each superdiagonal element of J which lies between adjacent blocks or sub-blocks is 0, as is every other element of J.

To show the existence of such a basis, it is clear that we shall make frequent use of the concepts of direct sum and invariant spaces. Also since $A_i - \lambda_i I$ is a nilpotent matrix, we can anticipate that a detailed study of nilpotent transformations will be required. We now undertake such a study.

From Exercise 8, § 3.2, we recall that if **T** is nilpotent of index p on $\mathcal{V}$, and if $\xi \mathbf{T}^{p-1} \neq \theta$, then $\{\xi, \xi \mathbf{T}, \ldots, \xi \mathbf{T}^{p-1}\}$ is linearly independent. In the terminology of Definition 7.6, $\{(\xi)_{\mathbf{T}}\}$ is a basis for the **T**-invariant, **T**-cyclic subspace generated by ξ. We now show that $\mathcal{U}$ is a direct sum of such spaces, proving that result in a form given by H. F. Trotter.

Theorem 7.9. If $\mathbf{T}$ is nilpotent of index p on $\mathcal{U}$, then there exists a $\mathbf{T}$-cyclic basis for $\mathcal{U}$. Moreover, any set of vectors $\{\xi_1, \ldots, \xi_r\}$ having the property that

$$\sum_{i=1}^{r} c_i \xi_i \mathbf{T}^{p-1} = \theta \quad \text{only if every } c_i = 0$$

can be extended to a set $\{\xi_1, \ldots, \xi_r, \zeta_1, \ldots, \zeta_s\}$ such that

$$\mathcal{U} = [(\xi_1)_{\mathbf{T}}] \oplus \cdots \oplus [(\xi_r)_{\mathbf{T}}] \oplus [(\zeta_1)_{\mathbf{T}}] \oplus \cdots \oplus [(\zeta_s)_{\mathbf{T}}].$$

P R O O F : We proceed by induction on p. If $p = 1$, $\mathbf{T}$ is the zero mapping and any linearly independent set $\{\xi_1, \ldots, \xi_r\}$ can be extended to a basis $\{\xi_1, \ldots, \xi_r, \eta_1, \ldots, \eta_s\}$ for $\mathcal{U}$ for which all assertions of the theorem are valid. For $p > 1$, we first observe that $\mathbf{T}$ is nilpotent of index $p - 1$ on the $\mathbf{T}$-invariant space $\mathfrak{N}_{\mathbf{T}^{p-1}}$. Let $\{\alpha_1, \ldots, \alpha_t\}$ be any basis for $\mathfrak{N}_{\mathbf{T}^{p-1}}$, and let $\{\alpha_1, \ldots, \alpha_t, \beta_1, \ldots, \beta_{n-t}\}$ be any extension to a basis for $\mathcal{U}$. Then the β_i must satisfy the special property stated in the theorem, because if

$$\sum_{i=1}^{n-t} b_i \beta_i \mathbf{T}^{p-1} = \theta,$$

then

$$\sum_{i=1}^{n-t} b_i \beta_i \in \mathfrak{N}_{\mathbf{T}^{p-1}};$$

since the α's and β's are linearly independent, each $b_i = 0$. In particular, any β_i used in the extension must be such that $\beta_i \mathbf{T}^{p-1} \neq \theta$, and such vectors exist in $\mathcal{U}$ since $\mathbf{T}$ is nilpotent of index p on $\mathcal{U}$.

Let $\xi_1, \xi_2, \ldots, \xi_r$ be a maximal set of vectors of $\mathcal{U}$ satisfying the special property

$$\sum_{i=1}^{r} c_i \xi_i \mathbf{T}^{p-1} = \theta \quad \text{only if every } c_i = 0.$$

It is easily verified that $\{\alpha_1, \ldots, \alpha_t, \xi_1, \ldots, \xi_r\}$ is linearly independent. Furthermore, $\mathcal{U} = [\alpha_1, \ldots, \alpha_t, \xi_1, \ldots, \xi_r]$, for otherwise we could extend that set to a basis $\{\alpha_1, \ldots, \alpha_t, \xi_1, \ldots, \xi_r, \xi_{r+1}, \ldots, \xi_s\}$ for $\mathcal{U}$. But then $\{\xi_1, \ldots, \xi_s\}$ would satisfy the special property, contradicting the maximality of $\{\xi_1, \ldots, \xi_r\}$.

Now let $\eta_i = \xi_i \mathbf{T}$. Then $\eta_i \in \mathfrak{N}_{\mathbf{T}^{p-1}}$ and

$$\sum_{i=1}^{r} c_i \eta_i \mathbf{T}^{p-2} = \theta \quad \text{only if every } c_i = 0.$$

By the induction hypothesis, $\mathfrak{N}_{\mathbf{T}^{p-1}}$ has a **T**-cyclic basis, and moreover the set $\{\eta_1, \ldots, \eta_r\}$ can be extended to a set $\{\eta_1, \ldots, \eta_r, \zeta_1, \ldots, \zeta_s\}$ such that $\{(\eta_1)_\mathbf{T}, \ldots, (\eta_r)_\mathbf{T}, (\zeta_1)_\mathbf{T}, \ldots, (\zeta_s)_\mathbf{T}\}$ is a **T**-cyclic basis for $\mathfrak{N}_{\mathbf{T}^{p-1}}$. Using the vectors of this basis in place of the α's above, we obtain a basis for $\mathcal{V}$. Also since $\{(\eta_i)_\mathbf{T}\} \cup \{\xi_i\} = \{(\xi_i)_\mathbf{T}\}$, then $\{(\xi_1)_\mathbf{T}, \ldots, (\xi_r)_\mathbf{T}, (\zeta_1)_\mathbf{T}, \ldots, (\zeta_s)_\mathbf{T}\}$ is a **T**-cyclic basis for $\mathcal{V}$, as the theorem asserts.

Thus any nilpotent transformation **T** on $\mathcal{V}_n$ can be used to decompose $\mathcal{V}_n$ into a direct sum of a certain number of **T**-invariant **T**-cyclic subspaces, say $[(\xi_i)_\mathbf{T}]$, $i = 1, 2, \ldots, k$. If $\xi_i \mathbf{T}^{p_i} = \theta$ but $\xi_i \mathbf{T}^{p_i - 1} \neq 0$, then $[(\xi_i)_\mathbf{T}]$ is of dimension p_i, since $\{\xi_i, \xi_i \mathbf{T}, \ldots, \xi_i \mathbf{T}^{p_i - 1}\}$ is linearly independent. By suitably rearranging the indices, we can arrange these **T**-cyclic subspaces according to their dimensions, in nonincreasing order. Then since at least one such subspace is of order p, we have

$$p = p_1 \geq p_2 \geq \cdots \geq p_k,$$
$$n = p_1 + p_2 + \cdots + p_k.$$

Our next objective is to show that the positive integers $k, p_1, \ldots, p_k$ are *uniquely* determined by **T**, even though the vectors ξ_i are not. To do so, write the basis vectors in an array of the form

$$\xi_1 \mathbf{T}^{p_1 - 1}, \xi_1 \mathbf{T}^{p_1 - 2}, \ldots \ldots \ldots \ldots \ldots, \xi_1$$
$$\xi_2 \mathbf{T}^{p_2 - 1}, \xi_2 \mathbf{T}^{p_2 - 2}, \ldots \ldots \ldots \ldots, \xi_2$$
$$\vdots \qquad \vdots$$
$$\xi_k \mathbf{T}^{p_k - 1}, \ldots \ldots \ldots, \xi_k$$

The rows of the array are of nonincreasing length: $p_1 \geq p_2 \geq \cdots \geq p_k$. Likewise the columns are of nonincreasing length. The first column is of length k, and the second column is of smaller length only if $p_k = 1$. Indeed, the length of the second column is simply the number of vectors ξ_i for which $p_i \geq 2$ (that is, the number of rows of length 2 or more). Similarly the length of column j is the number of ξ_i for which $p_i \geq j$.

Since $\xi_i \mathbf{T}^{p_i} = \theta$ for each i, the first column of the array is a basis for $\mathfrak{N}_\mathbf{T}$. Hence $k = \nu(\mathbf{T})$, a number which is uniquely determined by **T**. In general, the vectors of the first j columns form a basis for $\mathfrak{N}_{\mathbf{T}^j}$. Hence the length of column j is simply $\nu(\mathbf{T}^j) - \nu(\mathbf{T}^{j-1})$, which is uniquely determined by **T**. Thus **T** uniquely determines the number k of rows in the array, the length $p = p_1$ of the first row, and the length of each column. Hence the complete arrangement, including the lengths $p_1, p_2, \ldots, p_k$ of the rows, is uniquely determined by **T**.

Theorem 7.10. If **T** is nilpotent of index p on $\mathcal{V}_n$, then there exist uniquely determined positive integers $k, p_1, \ldots, p_k$ such that

$$p = p_1 \geq p_2 \geq \cdots \geq p_k$$
$$n = p_1 + p_2 + \cdots + p_k.$$

Also there exist vectors $\xi_1, \ldots, \xi_k$ such that $[(\xi_i)_\mathbf{T}]$ is a **T**-cyclic, **T**-invariant subspace of dimension p_i and

$$\mathcal{V}_n = [(\xi_1)_\mathbf{T}] \oplus \cdots \oplus [(\xi_k)_\mathbf{T}].$$

Relative to the corresponding cyclic basis for $\mathcal{V}_n$, **T** is represented by a diagonal block matrix

$$B = \begin{pmatrix} B_1 & & & \\ & B_2 & & \\ & & \cdot & \\ & & & \cdot \\ & & & & B_k \end{pmatrix},$$

where B_i is a $p_i \times p_i$ square matrix with 1 in each superdiagonal position. All other entries of each B_i and of B are zero.

Theorem 7.11. Any nilpotent matrix is similar to a matrix with a certain arrangement of 1 and 0 on the superdiagonal and 0 elsewhere. More precisely, the superdiagonal elements consist of several sequences of consecutive 1's separated by a single 0, the sequences of 1's being of nonincreasing, nonnegative length.

P R O O F : If A is nilpotent on $\mathcal{V}_n$, choose any basis for $\mathcal{V}_n$ and let **T** be the linear transformation represented by A. Then change bases to a **T**-cyclic basis of the form described in Theorem 7.10, obtaining the numbers $k, p_1, \ldots, p_k$ determined by **T**. The matrix B which represents **T** relative to the new basis is similar to A. Also B is of diagonal block form with k square blocks, $B_1, \ldots, B_k$. The dimension of B_i is p_i, and B_i has $p_i - 1$ superdiagonal elements, each of them 1. Hence the superdiagonal of B is an arrangement of 1 and 0 as follows:

$$\underbrace{(11\cdots1)}_{p_1 - 1}0\underbrace{(11\cdots1)}_{p_2 - 1}0\cdots\underbrace{(11\cdots1)}_{p_{k-1} - 1}0\underbrace{(11\cdots1)}_{p_k - 1}.$$

The sequences of 1 are of nonincreasing length, since $p_1 \geq p_2 \geq \cdots \geq p_k$; in particular, if any $p_j = 1$, the superdiagonal of B will end with a string of consecutive 0's:

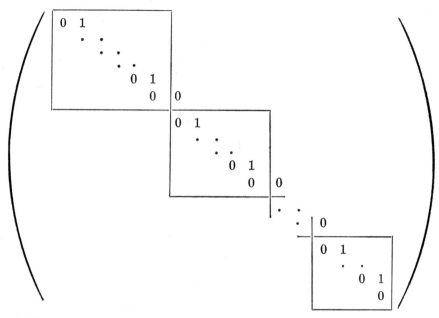

Theorem 7.12. Let **T** and **S** be nilpotent linear transformations on $\mathcal{V}_n$. In the notation of Theorem 7.10 let **T** determine the integers k, $p_1 \geq p_2 \geq \cdots \geq p_k$; let **S** determine the integers j, $q_1 \geq q_2 \geq \cdots \geq q_j$. Then $k = j$ and $p_i = q_i$ for $i = 1, \ldots, k$ if and only if there exists a nonsingular transformation **R** on $\mathcal{V}_n$ such that

$$\mathbf{S} = \mathbf{RTR}^{-1}.$$

P R O O F : Suppose $k = j$ and $p_i = q_i$ for $i = 1, \ldots, k$. As in Theorem 7.6 choose as a basis for $\mathcal{V}_n$ the vectors

$$\xi_1, \ \xi_1\mathbf{T}, \ldots, \ \xi_1\mathbf{T}^{p_1-1}$$
$$\xi_2, \ \xi_2\mathbf{T}, \ldots, \ \xi_2\mathbf{T}^{p_2-1}$$
$$\vdots \qquad \vdots \qquad \qquad \vdots$$
$$\xi_k, \ \xi_k\mathbf{T}, \ldots, \ \xi_k\mathbf{T}^{p_k-1}.$$

Relative to this basis, **T** is represented by a matrix N whose superdiagonal has 1 in the first $p_1 - 1$ positions, followed by 0, then 1 in the next $p_2 - 1$ positions, followed by 0, and so on. All other entries of N are zero. In the same way, choose a basis according to the properties of **S**. The matrix representing **S** in this basis will also be N, so by Theorem 6.20, $\mathbf{S} = \mathbf{RTR}^{-1}$ for some nonsingular linear transformation **R**.

Conversely, suppose $\mathbf{S} = \mathbf{RTR}^{-1}$. Choose as a basis for $\mathcal{V}_n$ the vectors,

$$\eta_1, \ \eta_1\mathbf{S}, \ \ldots, \ \eta_1\mathbf{S}^{q_1-1}$$
$$\eta_2, \ \eta_2\mathbf{S}, \ \ldots, \ \eta_2\mathbf{S}^{q_2-1}$$
$$\cdot \qquad \cdot \qquad \qquad \cdot$$
$$\cdot \qquad \cdot \qquad \qquad \cdot$$
$$\cdot \qquad \cdot \qquad \qquad \cdot$$
$$\eta_j, \ \eta_j\mathbf{S}, \ \ldots, \ \eta_j\mathbf{S}^{q_j-1},$$

as guaranteed by Theorem 7.10. Since $\mathbf{R}$ is nonsingular, we obtain a new basis by mapping each of these basis vectors by $\mathbf{R}$. But if $t > 0$,

$$\eta_i\mathbf{S}^t\mathbf{R} = \eta_i\mathbf{S}^{t-1}(\mathbf{S}\mathbf{R}) = \eta_i\mathbf{S}^{t-1}(\mathbf{R}\mathbf{T}) = (\eta_i\mathbf{S}^{t-1}\mathbf{R})\mathbf{T}.$$

Hence if we let $\xi_i = \eta_i\mathbf{R}$, the new basis can be written

$$\xi_1, \ \xi_1\mathbf{T}, \ \ldots, \ \xi_1\mathbf{T}^{q_1-1}$$
$$\xi_2, \ \xi_2\mathbf{T}, \ \ldots, \ \xi_2\mathbf{T}^{q_2-1}$$
$$\cdot \qquad \cdot \qquad \qquad \cdot$$
$$\cdot \qquad \cdot \qquad \qquad \cdot$$
$$\cdot \qquad \cdot \qquad \qquad \cdot$$
$$\xi_j, \ \xi_j\mathbf{T}, \ \ldots, \ \xi_j\mathbf{T}^{q_j-1}.$$

But

$$\xi_i\mathbf{T}^{q_i-1}\mathbf{T} = \eta_i\mathbf{R}\mathbf{T}\mathbf{T}^{q_i-1} = \eta_i\mathbf{S}\mathbf{R}\mathbf{T}^{q_i-1} = \eta_i\mathbf{S}^2\mathbf{R}\mathbf{T}^{q_i-2}$$
$$= \cdots = \eta_i\mathbf{S}^{q_i}\mathbf{R} = \theta\mathbf{R} = \theta.$$

Hence the ξ-basis is of the form of Theorem 7.10, and therefore $\mathbf{T}$ determines the same integers as does $\mathbf{S}$.

As a consequence of Theorem 7.12 we can show that for nilpotent $n \times n$ matrices the standard superdiagonal form described in Theorem 7.11 is canonical with respect to similarity. If A is nilpotent, relative to a chosen basis A represents a nilpotent linear transformation $\mathbf{T}$. Relative to a different basis A represents a linear transformation $\mathbf{S}$, where $\mathbf{S} = \mathbf{R}\mathbf{T}\mathbf{R}^{-1}$. Relative to a $\mathbf{T}$-cyclic basis, $\mathbf{T}$ is represented by a nilpotent matrix N_1 in standard superdiagonal form. Relative to an $\mathbf{S}$-cyclic basis, $\mathbf{S}$ is represented by N_2, also in standard form. By Theorem 7.12 $\mathbf{S}$ and $\mathbf{T}$ determine the same set of integers $(k, p_1, \ldots, p_k)$, so $N_1 = N_2$. Hence any nilpotent matrix is similar to one and only one matrix in standard superdiagonal form.

Exercises

1. Prove that any matrix which is similar to a nilpotent matrix of index p is itself nilpotent of index p.

2. Let

$$A = \begin{pmatrix} 0 & 2 & 1 \\ 0 & 0 & 3 \\ 0 & 0 & 0 \end{pmatrix}$$

be the matrix of a transformation $\mathbf{T}$ on $\mathcal{E}_3$.

(i) Find the rank of A, the null space of A, and the index of nilpotency of A.

(ii) Following the method of Theorem 7.10 and starting with $\xi_1 = (1, -1, 0)$, find a basis for $\mathcal{E}_3$ such that with respect to this basis $\mathbf{T}$ is represented by a matrix in the canonical form of Theorem 7.11.

(iii) Calculate this new matrix from the new basis, and find the integers $k, p_1, \ldots, p_k$.

3. Let N be the $n \times n$ matrix which has 1 in each superdiagonal position and zeros elsewhere.

(i) Prove that A and N commute if and only if A is of the form

$$\begin{pmatrix} a_1 & a_2 & a_3 & \cdots & a_n \\ 0 & a_1 & a_2 & \cdots & a_{n-1} \\ 0 & 0 & a_1 & \cdots & a_{n-2} \\ \cdot & \cdot & \cdot & & \cdot \\ \cdot & \cdot & \cdot & & \cdot \\ 0 & 0 & 0 & \cdots & a_1 \end{pmatrix}.$$

(ii) If A is of the form above and if $a_2 \neq 0$, show that the space spanned by the characteristic vectors of A is one-dimensional.

(iii) Let $k \geq 2$. If $a_2 = a_3 = \cdots = a_k = 0$ and $a_{k+1} \neq 0$, show that the space spanned by the characteristic vectors of A is k-dimensional.

4. Find necessary and sufficient conditions that the matrix C of Exercise 7, § 7.3, be nilpotent.

5. Prove that if $\mathbf{T}$ is nilpotent of index p on $\mathcal{V}_n$, then $\mathcal{R}_{\mathbf{T}^{p-k}} \subseteq \mathcal{N}_{\mathbf{T}^k}$ for $k = 1, 2, \ldots, p - 1$, with equality holding either for *all* values of k or for *none*.

6. Let $f(n)$ denote the number of distinct $n \times n$ nilpotent matrices in canonical superdiagonal form.

(i) Show that $f(i) = i$ for $i = 1, 2, 3; f(4) = 5; f(5) = 7$.

(ii) Try to develop a general formula for $f(n)$.

§7.7. *Jordan Canonical Form*

We have referred at various times to the difference between the properties of field elements and the properties of matrices of field elements. One more contrast is worth examining, namely, the existence of inverses. The inverse of a field element b exists if and only if $b \neq 0$, so "inverse" and "nonzero" are closely related notions. For a matrix B, the existence of B^{-1} certainly implies $B \neq Z$, but the reverse implication is not valid since nonzero matrices may be singular. Again, the concept of nilpotency with positive index never arises in a field, but it has come into our study of matrices in an essential way.

A nonzero nilpotent matrix, we feel, is an example of something which barely escapes being zero, while a nonsingular matrix is quite the opposite. It is of interest therefore to show that every matrix is a combination of a nonsingular matrix and a nilpotent matrix.

Theorem 7.13. Let $\mathbf{T}$ be any linear transformation on $\mathcal{V}$. There exist subspaces $\mathcal{R}$ and $\mathcal{S}$ such that

(a) $\mathcal{R}$ and $\mathcal{S}$ are $\mathbf{T}$-invariant,
(b) $\mathcal{V} = \mathcal{R} \oplus \mathcal{S}$,
(c) $\mathbf{T}$, restricted to $\mathcal{R}$, is nonsingular, and $\mathbf{T}$, restricted to $\mathcal{S}$, is nilpotent.

P R O O F : We consider successive powers of $\mathbf{T}$. From Theorem 3.5 we recall that the range and null spaces of powers of $\mathbf{T}$ form chains such that

$$\mathcal{V} \supset \mathcal{R}_{\mathbf{T}} \supset \mathcal{R}_{\mathbf{T}^2} \supset \cdots \supset \mathcal{R}_{\mathbf{T}^k} = \mathcal{R}_{\mathbf{T}^{k+1}} = \cdots$$

$$[\theta] \subset \mathcal{N}_{\mathbf{T}} \subset \mathcal{N}_{\mathbf{T}^2} \subset \cdots \subset \mathcal{N}_{\mathbf{T}^k} = \mathcal{N}_{\mathbf{T}^{k+1}} = \cdots$$

for some integer $k \geq 0$. Let $\mathcal{R} = \mathcal{R}_{\mathbf{T}^k}$ and $\mathcal{S} = \mathcal{N}_{\mathbf{T}^k}$, and suppose $\xi \in \mathcal{R} \cap \mathcal{S}$. Then $\xi = \eta \mathbf{T}^k$ for some $\eta \in \mathcal{V}$, and $\xi \mathbf{T}^k = \theta$. Hence $\theta = \xi \mathbf{T}^k = (\eta \mathbf{T}^k)\mathbf{T}^k$. Hence $\eta \in \mathcal{N}_{\mathbf{T}^{2k}} = \mathcal{N}_{\mathbf{T}^k}$, so $\theta = \eta \mathbf{T}^k = \xi$. Now $\mathcal{R}$ and $\mathcal{S}$ have only θ in common, and the sum of their dimensions is n. Hence

$$\mathcal{V} = \mathcal{R} \oplus \mathcal{S}.$$

Also, $\mathcal{R}_{\mathbf{T}^k}\mathbf{T} = \mathcal{R}_{\mathbf{T}^{k+1}} = \mathcal{R}_{\mathbf{T}^k}$, and similarly for $\mathcal{S}$, so $\mathcal{R}$ and $\mathcal{S}$ are $\mathbf{T}$-invariant. Now $\mathbf{T}$ maps $\mathcal{R}$ onto $\mathcal{R}$, so $\mathbf{T}_{\mathcal{R}}$ is nonsingular. The vectors of $\mathcal{S}$ are mapped into θ by $\mathbf{T}^k$, so $\mathbf{T}_{\mathcal{S}}$ is nilpotent.

The next theorem, which is stated in terms of linear transformations, gives us the Jordan canonical form for a matrix, as stated at the beginning of § 7.6.

Theorem 7.14. Let $\mathbf{T}$ be a linear transformation with the distinct characteristic values $\lambda_1, \ldots, \lambda_r$, and let s_i be the multiplicity of λ_i for $i = 1, \ldots, r$. Then $\mathcal{V}$ is the direct sum of r subspaces,

$$\mathcal{V} = \mathcal{S}_1 \oplus \mathcal{S}_2 \oplus \cdots \oplus \mathcal{S}_r,$$

such that for $i = 1, \ldots, r$

(a) $\mathcal{S}_i$ is $\mathbf{T}$-invariant,
(b) $\mathcal{S}_i$ is of dimension s_i,
(c) when restricted to the space $\mathcal{S}_i$, $\mathbf{T}$ has the form $\mathbf{T}_{\mathcal{S}_i} = \lambda_i \mathbf{I} + \mathbf{N}_i$, where $\mathbf{N}_i$ is nilpotent.

P R O O F : Given $\mathbf{T}$, we consider the linear transformation $\mathbf{T}_1$ defined by

$$\mathbf{T}_1 = \mathbf{T} - \lambda_1 \mathbf{I}$$

and apply Theorem 7.13 to obtain $\mathbf{T}_1$-invariant subspaces $\mathcal{S}_1$ and $\mathcal{R}_1$ such that

$$\mathcal{V} = \mathcal{S}_1 \oplus \mathcal{R}_1,$$

where $\mathbf{T}_1$ is nilpotent on $\mathcal{S}_1$ and nonsingular on $\mathcal{R}_1$. Clearly, $\mathcal{S}_1$ and $\mathcal{R}_1$ are $\mathbf{T}$-invariant, since $\mathbf{T} = \mathbf{T}_1 + \lambda_1\mathbf{I}$; also $\mathbf{T}_{\mathcal{S}_1} = (\mathbf{T}_1 + \lambda_1\mathbf{I})_{\mathcal{S}_1}$ is of the form (c), since $\mathbf{T}_1$ is nilpotent on $\mathcal{S}_1$. We next prove $s_1 = \dim \mathcal{S}_1$. Since $\mathcal{S}_1$ and $\mathcal{R}_1$ form a direct sum, we may choose any basis for $\mathcal{S}_1$ and any basis for $\mathcal{R}_1$, combining them to give a basis for $\mathcal{V}$. With respect to any such basis, $\mathbf{T}$ is represented by a matrix of the block form

$$A = \begin{pmatrix} A_{\mathcal{S}_1} & Z \\ Z & A_{\mathcal{R}_1} \end{pmatrix},$$

where $A_{\mathcal{S}_1}$ and $A_{\mathcal{R}_1}$ represent $\mathbf{T}$ restricted to the $\mathbf{T}$-invariant spaces $\mathcal{S}_1$ and $\mathcal{R}_1$, respectively. Hence $A_{\mathcal{R}_1} - \lambda_1 I_{\mathcal{R}_1}$ represents $\mathbf{T}_1$ on $\mathcal{R}_1$. Now for any λ,

$$\det(A - \lambda I) = \det(A_{\mathcal{S}_1} - \lambda I_{\mathcal{S}_1}) \cdot \det(A_{\mathcal{R}_1} - \lambda I_{\mathcal{R}_1}).$$

Since $\mathbf{T}_1$ is nonsingular on $\mathcal{R}_1$, $\det(A_{\mathcal{R}_1} - \lambda_1 I_{\mathcal{R}_1}) \neq 0$, and the dimension of $\mathcal{S}_1$ is at least as great as the multiplicity of the characteristic value λ_1;

$$\dim \mathcal{S}_1 \geq s_1.$$

On the other hand, $\mathbf{T}_1$ is nilpotent on $\mathcal{S}_1$ and we apply Theorem 7.10 to choose a basis for $\mathcal{S}_1$ such that $\mathbf{T}_1$ restricted to $\mathcal{S}_1$ is represented by a matrix with zeros and ones on the superdiagonal and zeros elsewhere. Since $\mathbf{T}_{\mathcal{S}_1} = (\mathbf{T}_1 + \lambda_1\mathbf{I})_{\mathcal{S}_1}$, the matrix $A_{\mathcal{S}_1}$ has λ_1 in every diagonal position, zeros and ones on the superdiagonal, and zeros elsewhere. Thus $A_{\mathcal{S}_1}$ has λ_1 as its only characteristic value, so

$$\dim \mathcal{S}_1 \leq s_1.$$

Part (b) of the theorem follows from the two inequalities which we have obtained.

Now all parts of the theorem are established for the case $i = 1$. We next consider the transformation $\mathbf{T}_{\mathcal{R}_1}$ and repeat the argument, using

$$\mathbf{T}_2 = \mathbf{T}_{\mathcal{R}_1} - \lambda_2\mathbf{I}_{\mathcal{R}_1}.$$

By finite dimensionality the theorem follows after r steps.

The matrix interpretation of this theorem gives the Jordan canonical form for a matrix. Let A be a matrix with distinct characteristic values λ_i, each of multiplicity s_i for $i = 1, \ldots, r$. Then A is similar to a matrix in the block form

$$\begin{pmatrix} A_1 & & & & \\ & A_2 & & & \\ & & \cdot & & \\ & & & \cdot & \\ & & & & \cdot \\ & & & & A_r \end{pmatrix},$$

where A_i is $s_i \times s_i$ with λ_i in every diagonal position, zeros and ones on the superdiagonal in a certain arrangement, and zeros elsewhere.

Theorem 7.15. A matrix with characteristic values λ_i, $i = 1, \ldots, n$ is similar to a matrix with these characteristic values in the diagonal positions, zeros and ones along the superdiagonal, and zeros elsewhere.

The following observations add real information to the rather loose statement of Theorem 7.15. Any Jordan matrix that is similar to A has r major blocks A_i on the diagonal whenever A has r distinct characteristic values. A_i is a square block of dimension s_i, the multiplicity of λ_i as a characteristic value. Each diagonal element of A_i is λ_i, and any other nonzero entry of A_i must be 1 and must occur on the superdiagonal of A_i. Furthermore, λ_i can appear as a diagonal element of no block other than A_i. Hence if A and B are similar, and therefore have the same characteristic polynomial, the Jordan form of each must contain the same number of blocks, each of the same dimension. Except for possible permutations of the blocks along the diagonal, the two Jordan matrices can possibly differ only on the superdiagonal.

Now consider the distribution of 0's and 1's on the superdiagonal of the block A_i:

$$A_i = \begin{pmatrix} \lambda_i & * & 0 & \cdots & 0 & 0 \\ 0 & \lambda_i & * & \cdots & 0 & 0 \\ \cdot & \cdot & & & \cdot & \cdot \\ \cdot & \cdot & & & \cdot & \cdot \\ \cdot & \cdot & & & \cdot & \cdot \\ 0 & 0 & 0 & \cdots & \lambda_i & * \\ 0 & 0 & 0 & \cdots & 0 & \lambda_i \end{pmatrix}, \quad * = 0 \text{ or } 1.$$

Since $(A_i - \lambda_i I)^{s_i} = Z$, we can apply Theorem 7.10 to decompose $A_i - \lambda_i I$ into sub-blocks B_{ij} along the diagonal, $j = 1, 2, \ldots, k(i)$:

$$A_i - \lambda_i I = \begin{pmatrix} B_{i1} & & & \\ & B_{i2} & & \\ & & \cdot & \\ & & & \cdot \\ & & & & B_{ik(i)} \end{pmatrix}.$$

The dimensions of the sub-blocks are given by the uniquely determined numbers of Theorem 7.10,

$$p_{i1} \geq p_{i2} \geq \cdots \geq p_{ik(i)}.$$

This implies that the distribution of 0's and 1's on the superdiagonal of each A_i is uniquely determined; therefore, except for permutations of the major blocks A_i of A, the distribution of 0's and 1's on the superdiagonal of A is uniquely determined. Hence for a given matrix A and a given ordering of its distinct characteristic values, A is similar to one and only one matrix in Jordan form. This is the assertion that for the $n \times n$ matrices the Jordan form is canonical with respect to similarity.

This means that a linear transformation $\mathbf{T}$ determines r numbers, $s_1, \ldots, s_r$, where each s_i is the multiplicity of λ_i as a root of the characteristic equation. Each s_i determines other numbers p_{ij}, in decreasing order,

$$p_{i1} \geq p_{i2} \geq \cdots \geq p_{ik(i)},$$
$$s_i = p_{i1} + p_{i2} + \cdots + p_{ik(i)}, \qquad i = 1, \ldots, r.$$

The number p_{ij} is the dimension of the block B_{ij} within the block A_i. The superdiagonal elements of A are a string of $p_{11} - 1$ ones followed by a zero, then $p_{12} - 1$ ones, and another zero, and so on. Finally, the Jordan form is completely determined by the numbers,

$$\lambda_1, \ldots, \lambda_r$$
$$s_1, \ldots, s_r$$
$$p_{11}, \ldots, p_{1k(1)}$$
$$\cdot \qquad \cdot$$
$$\cdot \qquad \cdot$$
$$\cdot \qquad \cdot$$
$$p_{r1}, \ldots, p_{rk(r)}.$$

The numbers p_{ij} are often written in the form

$$\{(p_{11}, p_{12}, \ldots, p_{1k(1)})(p_{21}, p_{22}, \ldots, p_{2k(2)}) \cdots (p_{r1}, p_{r2}, \ldots, p_{rk(r)})\},$$

and this form is called the *Segre characteristic* of A.

As an example, suppose that $\mathbf{T}$ has three distinct characteristic values, $\lambda_1 = 2, \lambda_2 = -2, \lambda_3 = 0$ with Segre characteristic $\{(3, 2, 1)(3, 1)(1, 1)\}$. Then the Jordan matrix that represents $\mathbf{T}$ is

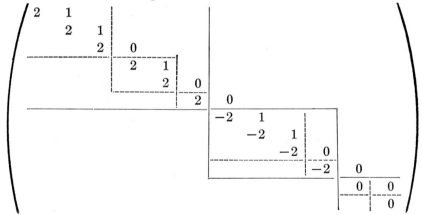

Given an $n \times n$ matrix A, we frequently wish to find a Jordan matrix J which is similar to A. It is possible to give a systematic procedure for determining P such that PAP^{-1} is in Jordan form. (See Exercise 9). But in many examples we can find J without computing P. First we determine the distinct characteristic values $\lambda_1, \ldots, \lambda_r$ and their multiplicities $s_1, \ldots, s_r$. Only for those i, for which $s_i > 1$, is there any ambiguity about the size of the subblocks within the major block A_i. Then we calculate the number c_i of linearly independent characteristic vectors that correspond to λ_i. If $c_i = s_i$ then A_i is diagonal: $A_i = \lambda_i I$. Even if $c_i < s_i$, if s_i is small, there are a limited number of possible forms for A_i, and by studying the indices of nilpotency of $A_i - \lambda_i I$, the exact form of A_i can be determined. Indeed if $s_i = 3$, then the form of A_i is immediately determined by c_i, since $s_i - c_i$ is the number of 1's on the superdiagonal of A_i. If $s_i = 4$, no ambiguity exists for $c_i = 3$ or $c_i = 1$; for $c_i = 2$, however, either of the superdiagonal patterns $1, 0, 1$ or $1, 1, 0$ is possible, depending on whether $A_i - \lambda_i I$ is nilpotent of index 2 or of index 3.

We state a few more facts, which are of importance but are not pursued in this book. Let the characteristic polynomial of A be

$$P(\lambda) = (\lambda - \lambda_1)^{s_i}(\lambda - \lambda_2)^{s_2} \cdots (\lambda - \lambda_r)^{s_r}.$$

The polynomials $D_{ij}(\lambda) = (\lambda - \lambda_i)^{p_{ij}}$ are called *elementary eivisors* of A, since each is a divisor of $P(\lambda)$. It can be shown that the minimal polynomial of A is

$$M(\lambda) = (\lambda - \lambda_1)^{p_{11}}(\lambda - \lambda_2)^{p_{21}} \cdots (\lambda - \lambda_r)^{p_{r1}},$$

the product of the distinct elementary divisors of highest power. From this it is clear that $P(\lambda)$ is a multiple of $M(\lambda)$ and that $P(A) = Z$ since $M(A) = Z$. We shall give an independent proof of this, the Hamilton-Cayley theorem, in the next section.

Finally, we remind ourselves that the theory of the Jordan form depended upon a factorization of $P(\lambda)$ into linear factors. This is always possible if the base field is the field of complex numbers, but other canonical forms might be needed if we are restricted to work, for example, entirely within the field of real numbers.

Exercises

1. Use the Jordan canonical form to solve the following problems.
   (i) Exercise 8, § 7.1.
   (ii) Exercise 3, § 7.2.
   (iii) Exercise 4, § 7.2.
   (iv) Prove Theorem 7.8.

2. Determine whether or not the following matrices are similar:

$$A = \begin{pmatrix} 1 & 4 \\ -1 & -3 \end{pmatrix}, \qquad B = \begin{pmatrix} -1 & 1 \\ 0 & -1 \end{pmatrix}.$$

3. Determine necessary and sufficient conditions on a, b, c, d so that the matrix

$$\begin{pmatrix} a & b \\ c & d \end{pmatrix}$$

will *not* be similar to a diagonal matrix.

4. Determine the Jordan form of the following matrices.

    (i) Exercise 1 (iii), § 7.2.

    (ii) Exercise 1 (ii), § 7.5.

(iii) $\begin{pmatrix} 0 & 1 & 0 \\ 0 & 0 & 1 \\ -1 & 1 & 1 \end{pmatrix}.$

5. State and prove a theorem which gives a matrix interpretation of Theorem 7.13.

6. Prove that the inverse of a nonsingular Jordan matrix has nonzero entries only on and above the diagonal but in general is not in Jordan form.

7. Given the 12×12 Jordan matrix J whose diagonal elements in order are 2, 2, 2, 2, 2, 2, 0, 0, 0, 0, 1, 1 and whose superdiagonal elements in order are 1, 1, 1, 0, 1, 0, 1, 1, 1, 0, 0. In the terminology of the discussion following Theorem 7.15, supply the following information.

    (i) Write J in block form, showing the sub-blocks of each major block.

    (ii) Write the characteristic values and the multiplicity of each.

    (iii) Write the numbers p_{ij}.

    (iv) Write the Segre characteristic of J.

    (v) Write the characteristic polynomial of J.

    (vi) Write the minimal polynomial of J.

    (vii) Write the elementary divisors of J.

    (viii) By examining the block form of J, show that $M(J) = Z$ for the polynomial M of (vi).

8. Write a matrix whose characteristic values are 2, 3, 4, 5 and whose Segre characteristic is $\{(2, 1, 1)(1, 1, 1)(3, 2)(1)\}$.

9. Read "The companion matrix and its properties" by Louis Brand, *American Mathematical Monthly*, vol. 71 (1964), pp. 629–634. This article describes a method of finding P such that $P^{-1}AP$ is in Jordan form.

10. Given the matrix

$$A = \begin{pmatrix} 0 & 1 & 0 & 0 \\ 0 & 0 & 1 & 0 \\ 0 & 0 & 0 & 1 \\ 4 & -4 & -3 & 4 \end{pmatrix},$$

determine a Jordan matrix which is similar to A by finding the characteristic values of A and, if necessary, some of the characteristic vectors. Then check your conclusion by showing that $P^{-1}AP$ is a Jordan matrix, where

$$P = \begin{pmatrix} 1 & 1 & 1 & 0 \\ -1 & 1 & 2 & 1 \\ 1 & 1 & 4 & 4 \\ -1 & 1 & 8 & 12 \end{pmatrix}.$$

§7.8. *An Application of the Hamilton-Cayley Theorem*

We are now able to give an easy proof of the Hamilton-Cayley theorem. Let A be a matrix with characteristic polynomial

$$P(\lambda) = (-1)^n(\lambda - \lambda_1)(\lambda - \lambda_2)\cdots(\lambda - \lambda_n),$$

and let J be a Jordan matrix which is similar to A.

$$J = \begin{pmatrix} \lambda_1 & * & & & \\ & \lambda_2 & * & & \\ & & \lambda_3 & \cdot & \\ & & & \cdot & \cdot \\ & & & & \cdot & * \\ & & & & & \lambda_n \end{pmatrix},$$

where $* = 0$ or 1. Let $J_i = J - \lambda_i I$, $i = 1, 2, \ldots, n$, so that

$$P(J) = (-1)^n J_1 J_2 \cdots J_n,$$

since the factoring for $P(\lambda)$ holds for the matrix polynomial $P(X)$. Now the ith row of J_i has $*$ in the $i + 1$ column and zeros elsewhere. Therefore the nth row of J_n is a zero row; the last two rows of $J_{n-1}J_n$ are zero; the last three rows of $J_{n-2}J_{n-1}J_n$ are zero rows, and so on. Therefore successive multiplication of the J_i gives

$$P(J) = Z.$$

By Exercises 4 and 5, § 7.3, $P(A)$ is similar to $P(J) = Z$, and hence $P(A) = Z$, which is the desired conclusion.

We now apply the Hamilton-Cayley theorem to obtain another method of calculating the inverse of a nonsingular matrix A. Let the characteristic polynomial of A be

$$(-1)^n(\lambda^n + c_1\lambda^{n-1} + \cdots + c_n).$$

Since A is nonsingular, $\lambda = 0$ is not a characteristic value, so $c_n \neq 0$. We have

$$A^n + c_1 A^{n-1} + \cdots + c_n I = Z,$$

$$(A^n + c_1 A^{n-1} + \cdots + c_{n-1}A) = -c_n I,$$

and therefore
$$A^{-1} = -c_n^{-1}(A^{n-1} + c_1 A^{n-2} + \cdots + c_{n-1}I).$$
Thus A^{-1} may be calculated as a combination of powers of A and the coefficients of the characteristic polynomial of A. For large values of n the c_i may be very hard to compute directly, but an alternate method is described below.

Definition 7.7. The *trace* of A, denoted tr A, is the sum of the n characteristic values of A;
$$\mathrm{tr}\,A = \sum_{i=1}^{n} \lambda_i.$$

In addition to the present application, the concept of trace is quite useful. We recall that similar matrices have equal characteristic values and therefore have equal traces. Thus the trace of a linear transformation $\mathbf{T}$ can be defined to be the trace of any matrix that represents $\mathbf{T}$. We now prove that tr A is the sum of the diagonal elements of A.

Theorem 7.16. $\mathrm{tr}\,A = \sum_{i=1}^{n} a_{ii},$

and hence if A and B are similar,
$$\sum_{i=1}^{n} a_{ii} = \sum_{i=1}^{n} b_{ii}.$$
PROOF: Consider the characteristic polynomial of A,
$$\det(A - \lambda I) = (-1)^n(\lambda^n + c_1\lambda^{n-1} + \cdots + c_n)$$
$$= (-1)^n(\lambda - \lambda_1)\cdots(\lambda - \lambda_n).$$
From the determinant form, the coefficient of λ^{n-1} is seen to be
$$(-1)^{n-1}\sum_{i=1}^{n} a_{ii} = (-1)^n c_1,$$
while from the factored form we get
$$(-1)^{n+1}\sum_{i=1}^{n} \lambda_i = (-1)^n c_1.$$
Hence
$$\mathrm{tr}\,A = \sum_{i=1}^{n} \lambda_i = \sum_{i=1}^{n} a_{ii}.$$
As a corollary we have the equation
$$c_1 = -\mathrm{tr}\,A.$$
The other c_i can be determined similarly to give the following set of equations:

$$c_1 = -\text{tr } A$$
$$c_2 = -2^{-1}[c_1 \text{ tr } A + \text{tr } A^2]$$
$$c_3 = -3^{-1}[c_2 \text{ tr } A + c_1 \text{ tr } A^2 + \text{tr } A^3]$$

.

.

.

$$c_n = -n^{-1}[c_{n-1} \text{ tr } A + c_{n-2} \text{ tr } A^2 + \cdots + c_1 \text{ tr } A^{n-1} + \text{tr } A^n].$$

These equations permit us to calculate A^{-1} by calculating $A, A^2, \ldots, A^{n-1}$ and the diagonal elements of A^n. From these matrices we can calculate the traces as sums of the diagonal elements, determine the c_i, and finally use the equation

$$A^{-1} = -c_n^{-1}(A^{n-1} + c_1 A^{n-2} + \cdots + c_{n-1}I).$$

This method for finding A^{-1} requires fewer than n^4 multiplications and is easily described in the language of high speed computers. Also we obtain the characteristic polynomial of A as a by-product of the computation of A^{-1}.

Exercises

1. Use the preceding method to calculate the inverse and the characteristic polynomial of the matrix of Exercise 1 (ii), § 6.3.

2. Prove that the trace of A^k is the sum of the kth powers of the characteristic values of A.

3. Verify that
$$c_2 = -\tfrac{1}{2}(c_1 \text{ tr } A + \text{tr } A^2).$$

4. Prove the following properties of the trace.

   (i) If A is nilpotent, $\text{tr } A = 0$.

   (ii) If A is idempotent, $\text{tr } A = \rho(A)$.

   (iii) $\text{tr}(A + B) = \text{tr } A + \text{tr } B$.

   (iv) $\text{tr}(kA) = k \text{ tr } A$.

   (v) $\text{tr } A' = \text{tr } A$.

   (vi) $\text{tr}(AB) = \text{tr}(BA)$.

5. Let A and B be 2×2 matrices for which $\det A = \det B$ and $\text{tr } A = \text{tr } B$.

   (i) Do A and B have the same characteristic values? Prove your answer.

   (ii) Are A and B similar? Prove your answer.

   (iii) Would your answers to (i) or (ii) be different if A and B were 3×3 matrices?

6. (i) Prove that if $\mathbf{T}$ is a projection, then for any matrix which represents $\mathbf{T}$, the sum of the diagonal elements is a nonnegative integer.

(ii) Prove that any projection can be represented by a diagonal matrix whose nonzero entries must be 1.

7. Show that the number of 12×12 matrices, all of which have $\lambda^5(\lambda - 1)^4(\lambda + 1)^3$ as characteristic polynomial but no two of which are similar, exceeds 100.

8. Let H_n be the $n \times n$ matrix obtained by reflecting I_n across a horizontal line through its center.

(i) Show that H_nA is the matrix obtained by reflecting A across a horizontal line through its center, while AH_n is the matrix obtained by reflecting A across a vertical line through its center.

(ii) Describe $H_nAH_n^{-1}$.

9. Prove that any matrix and its transpose are similar.

10. Let A be an $n \times n$ matrix such that $a_{ik}a_{jk} = a_{kk}a_{ij}$ for all i, j, and k. Determine the characteristic values of A.

CHAPTER 8

Metric Concepts

§8.1. *Conjugate Bilinear Functions*

Up to this point our study of vector spaces has been accomplished without any reference to the customary concepts of geometric measurement such as length, distance, angle, and perpendicularity. This is in sharp contrast to the usual development of the geometry of the plane or three-dimensional space, which from the start assumes a rectangular coordinate system and defines distance in terms of that system; for an abstract n-dimensional space in which we wish to consider a variety of coordinate systems, such an approach would be too confining. We shall now see how metric notions can be derived generally. In so doing we shall discover an interpretation of matrices which is distinct from the matrix representations of linear transformations and linear equations studied previously.

A moment's reflection makes it clear that length, distance, and angle are scalar quantities which are attached to each vector or each pair of vectors of a space. Thus, it is natural that we consider various functions from vector spaces to the scalar field.

We have already seen that linear functions from $\mathcal{V}$ to $\mathcal{F}$ form a vector space $\mathcal{V}'$, the dual space of $\mathcal{V}$. We now select two vector spaces $\mathcal{V}_m$ and $\mathcal{W}_n$ over the same field $\mathcal{F}$ and consider functions which map the cartesian product $\mathcal{V}_m \times \mathcal{W}_n$ into $\mathcal{F}$. Since the properties of $\mathcal{F}$ come into greater prominence here than in our earlier work, we shall develop two parallel theories according to whether $\mathcal{F}$ is the real or the complex field. (Readers who are not fully familiar with the arithmetic of complex numbers should study Exercise 1 before proceeding.)

The *conjugate* $\overline{A}$ of a complex matrix $A = (a_{ij})$ is defined by

$$\overline{A} = (\overline{a}_{ij});$$

then a real matrix is characterized by $\bar{A} = A$. Other conjugate properties of complex matrices, which may be proved as an exercise, are

$$\bar{\bar{A}} = A,$$
$$\overline{AB} = \bar{A}\bar{B},$$
$$\bar{A}' = \overline{A'},$$
$$\overline{A + B} = \bar{A} + \bar{B}.$$

Definition 8.1. Let $\mathcal{V}_m$ and $\mathcal{W}_n$ be vector spaces over $\mathcal{F}$ (real or complex). A *conjugate bilinear function f* is a function that assigns to each pair of vectors $(\xi, \eta) \in \mathcal{V}_m \times \mathcal{W}_n$ a scalar value $f(\xi, \eta)$ in such a way that the following properties hold:

(a) $\qquad\qquad f(a\xi_1 + b\xi_2, \eta) = af(\xi_1, \eta) + bf(\xi_2, \eta),$

(b) $\qquad\qquad f(\xi, a\eta_1 + b\eta_2) = \bar{a}f(\xi, \eta_1) + \bar{b}f(\xi, \eta_2).$

Condition (a) states that f is a linear function of its first variable (which is a vector); condition (b) is a modified form of linearity in the second variable:

$$f(\xi, \eta_1 + \eta_2) = f(\xi, \eta_1) + f(\xi, \eta_2),$$
$$f(\xi, b\eta) = \bar{b}f(\xi, \eta).$$

If the scalar field is real, then $\bar{b} = b$, in which case f is called simply a *bilinear function*.

First we see how conjugate bilinear functions may be represented by matrices; the work we do here will bear a striking similarity to the corresponding matrix representation of linear transformations. Let $\{\alpha_1, \ldots, \alpha_m\}$ be a basis for $\mathcal{V}_m$ and $\{\beta_1, \ldots, \beta_n\}$ a basis for $\mathcal{W}_n$. Let $\xi = \sum_{i=1}^{m} x_i\alpha_i \in \mathcal{V}_m$, and $\eta = \sum_{j=1}^{n} y_j\beta_j \in \mathcal{W}_n$. Then

$$f(\xi, \eta) = f\left(\sum_{i=1}^{m} x_i\alpha_i, \eta\right) = \sum_{i=1}^{m} x_i f(\alpha_i, \eta)$$

$$= \sum_{i=1}^{m} x_i f\left(\alpha_i, \sum_{j=1}^{n} y_j\beta_j\right) = \sum_{i=1}^{m} x_i\left[\sum_{j=1}^{n} \bar{y}_j f(\alpha_i, \beta_j)\right]$$

$$= \sum_{i=1}^{m} \sum_{j=1}^{n} x_i\bar{y}_j f(\alpha_i, \beta_j).$$

The mn scalars $f(\alpha_i, \beta_j)$ therefore completely determine the value of the function f. Now consider the $m \times n$ matrix

$$A = (a_{ij}), \text{ where } a_{ij} = f(\alpha_i, \beta_j),$$

which is uniquely determined by f relative to the α- and β-bases. Then an easy calculation shows that

$$f(\xi, \eta) = XA\bar{Y}'.$$

Definition 8.2. An expression of the type

$$\sum_{i=1}^{m} \left(\sum_{j=1}^{n} a_{ij} x_i \bar{y}_j \right)$$

is called a *conjugate bilinear form* in the $m + n$ variables $x_1, \ldots, x_m$, $y_1, \ldots, y_n$.

Thus each conjugate bilinear function f on $\mathcal{U}_m \times \mathcal{W}_n$ determines, relative to chosen bases, a conjugate bilinear form whose coefficient matrix represents f relative to those bases. For a different choice of bases we can expect to obtain a form with different coefficients and therefore a different matrix representation of f. As in § 6.5, suppose that $\{\gamma_1, \ldots, \gamma_m\}$ is a basis for $\mathcal{U}_m$ and that $\{\delta_1, \ldots, \delta_n\}$ is a basis for $\mathcal{W}_n$. Let $\mathbf{R}$, $\mathbf{S}$ be the linear transformations $\gamma_i \mathbf{R} = \alpha_i$ and $\delta_j \mathbf{S} = \beta_j$; suppose that $\mathbf{R}$ is represented relative to the γ-basis by P and that $\mathbf{S}$ is represented relative to the δ-basis by Q. The matrix C which represents f relative to the γ- and δ-bases is defined by $c_{rs} = f(\gamma_r, \delta_s)$. Then

$$a_{ij} = f(\alpha_i, \beta_j) = f(\gamma_i \mathbf{R}, \delta_j \mathbf{S}) = f\left(\sum_{r=1}^{m} p_{ir} \gamma_r, \sum_{s=1}^{n} q_{js} \delta_s \right)$$

$$= \sum_{r=1}^{m} p_{ir} \left[f\left(\gamma_r, \sum_{s=1}^{n} q_{js} \delta_s \right) \right] = \sum_{r=1}^{m} p_{ir} \left[\sum_{s=1}^{n} \bar{q}_{js} f(\gamma_r, \delta_s) \right]$$

$$= \sum_{s=1}^{n} \left[\sum_{r=1}^{m} p_{ir} c_{rs} \right] \bar{q}_{js}.$$

A direct computation shows that the last expression is the (i, j) element of the matrix $PC\bar{Q}'$. Thus $A = PC\bar{Q}'$.

Theorem 8.1. A conjugate bilinear function f from $\mathcal{U}_m \times \mathcal{W}_n$ to $\mathcal{F}$ is represented uniquely relative to a pair α, β of bases by the $m \times n$ matrix

$$A = (a_{ij}), \quad \text{where} \quad a_{ij} = f(\alpha_i, \beta_j);$$

if ξ, η are represented by X, Y, then

$$f(\xi, \eta) = XA\bar{Y}'.$$

Furthermore, $m \times n$ matrices A and C represent the same conjugate bilinear function relative to different pairs of bases if and only if A and C are equivalent.

P R O O F : The representation of f by A was established by the previous discussion. Uniqueness follows easily since two functions are different if their functional values differ at any point. The discussion also shows that the same f is represented relative to two pairs of bases by equivalent matrices. Conversely, if A and C are equivalent matrices, let $A = PCR$

for nonsingular P, R. Let $Q = \overline{R}'$, and retrace the calculations already made to show that if C represents f relative to the γ-, δ-bases, then A represents f relative to the bases $\gamma\mathbf{R}$, $\delta\mathbf{S}$ obtained from the nonsingular linear transformations represented by P and Q.

Since a conjugate bilinear function is represented in different coordinate systems by equivalent matrices, and since equivalent matrices have the same rank, we define the *rank* of a conjugate bilinear function (or a conjugate bilinear form) to be the rank of any representative matrix.

Theorem 8.2. Let f be a conjugate bilinear function of rank r from $\mathcal{V}_m \times \mathcal{W}_n$ into $\mathfrak{F}$, where $r \leq m, n$. There exist bases for $\mathcal{V}_m$ and $\mathcal{W}_n$ such that if $\xi \in \mathcal{V}_m$ and $\eta \in \mathcal{W}_n$, then

$$f(\xi, \eta) = x_1\overline{y}_1 + x_2\overline{y}_2 + \cdots + x_r\overline{y}_r.$$

PROOF: Let f be represented by an $m \times n$ matrix A of rank r relative to some pair of bases for $\mathcal{V}_m$ and $\mathcal{W}_n$. Any matrix equivalent to A has the same rank and represents the same conjugate bilinear function f. By Theorem 6.14, A is equivalent to the canonical matrix C which has the block I_r in the upper left corner and zeros elsewhere. Then from the proof of Theorem 8.1,

$$f(\xi, \eta) = XC\overline{Y}' = x_1\overline{y}_1 + x_2\overline{y}_2 + \cdots + x_r\overline{y}_r.$$

In many important applications we are interested in conjugate bilinear functions from $\mathcal{V} \times \mathcal{V}$ to $\mathfrak{F}$. In this case a sharpened form of Theorem 8.1 can be obtained by using two bases rather than two pairs of bases. Thus in the proof of Theorem 8.1 if we specify that γ and α be the same basis, and that δ and β be the same basis, then $\mathbf{T} = \mathbf{S}$ and $P = Q$. We obtain the following result.

Theorem 8.3. A conjugate bilinear function f from $\mathcal{V}_n \times \mathcal{V}_n$ to $\mathfrak{F}$ is represented relative to two bases for $\mathcal{V}_n$ by two $n \times n$ matrices A, C if and only if there exists a nonsingular matrix P such that

$$A = PC\overline{P}'.$$

The relation $A = PC\overline{P}'$ obtained in Theorem 8.3 defines two special types of matrix equivalence, according to whether $\mathfrak{F}$ is complex or not.

Definition 8.3. Two complex $n \times n$ matrices A, C are said to be *conjunctive* over $\mathcal{C}$ if and only if

$$A = PC\overline{P}'$$

for some nonsingular complex matrix P. For any field $\mathfrak{F}$ two $n \times n$ matrices A, C with elements in $\mathfrak{F}$ are said to be *congruent* over $\mathfrak{F}$ if and only if

$$A = PCP'$$

for some nonsingular matrix P with elements in $\mathfrak{F}$.

It is easy to verify that conjunctivity and congruence are further examples of equivalence relations on matrices, distinct from the equivalence relations we have considered previously: row equivalence, equivalence, and similarity.

In terms of row and column operations, the description of congruence of matrices is easily stated. Since P describes a sequence of elementary row operations, P' describes the same sequence of elementary column operations. Hence A and B are congruent if and only if A can be obtained by transforming B by a sequence of changes, each change being an elementary operation on rows followed by the same operation on the corresponding columns.

For conjunctivity a slight modification of this result is needed. P still represents a sequence of elementary row operations. For the three types of row operations, specified in § 6.2, we have $\overline{P'_{ij}} = P'_{ij} = P_{ij}$ and $\overline{A'_{ij}} = A'_{ij} = A_{ji}$, but $\overline{M'_i(c)} = M'_i(\bar{c}) = M_i(\bar{c})$. Hence A and B are conjunctive if and only if A can be obtained by transforming B by a sequence of changes, each change being an elementary operation on rows followed by the corresponding *conjugate* operation on columns.

It is convenient to use the symbol A^* to denote the conjugate transpose $\overline{A}'$ of A. In § 8.6 we shall see that if A represents a linear transformation $\mathbf{T}$ on $\mathcal{V}$, then A^* also represents a transformation $\mathbf{T}^*$ on $\mathcal{V}$. The transformation $\mathbf{T}^*$ is called the *adjoint* of $\mathbf{T}$, but since the term "adjoint" has already been introduced for matrices in Definition 5.3 to mean a matrix of cofactors, we avoid calling the matrix A^* the adjoint of A.

Definition 8.4. An $n \times n$ complex matrix is said to be *Hermitian* if and only if $A^* = A$, where $A^* = \overline{A}'$. A is said to be *skew*-Hermitian if and only if $A^* = -A$.

In the literature the term Hermitian congruence is sometimes used in place of conjunctivity, and a Hermitian matrix is sometimes called self-adjoint. Just as an arbitrary square matrix was shown in § 4.2 to have a unique representation as the sum of a symmetric matrix and a skew-symmetric matrix, any complex matrix has a unique representation as the sum of a Hermitian matrix and a skew-Hermitian matrix:

$$A = \tfrac{1}{2}[(A + A^*) + (A - A^*)].$$

Separate canonical forms relative to conjunctivity can be obtained for Hermitian and for skew-Hermitian matrices, and for reasons which will become apparent in § 8.5, we are more interested in the Hermitian case. (See also Exercises 8 and 9.)

Theorem 8.4. Every complex Hermitian matrix of rank r is conjunctive over $\mathcal{C}$ to a diagonal matrix with nonzero real numbers in the first r diagonal position and zero elsewhere.

PROOF: Let A be Hermitian and P nonsingular. Then $(PAP^*)^* = P^{**}A^*P^* = PAP^*$, so that a Hermitian matrix of the same rank is obtained from A by applying an elementary row operation followed by the corresponding conjugate column operation. Every diagonal element of a Hermitian matrix is real. We show that if $A \neq Z$, A is conjunctive to a matrix in which some diagonal element is nonzero. Suppose that all diagonal elements of A are zero, and let $a_{ij} \neq 0$. We may assume that the real part of a_{ij} is nonzero, for otherwise A is conjunctive to $M_i(i)AM_i(-i)$, in which the (i, j) entry is real and nonzero. Then $B = A_{ij}AA_{ij}^* = A_{ij}AA_{ij}'$ is Hermitian, obtained from A by adding row i to row j and then adding column i to column j. Hence $b_{jj} = a_{ij} + a_{ji} = a_{ij} + \bar{a}_{ij} \neq 0$. By permuting row j and row 1, then column j and column 1, we obtain a matrix C conjunctive to A and having $c_{11} = b_{jj}$. If $c_{i1} \neq 0$, the sequence $A_{1i}M_i(-c_{11}c_{i1}^{-1})$ of row operations and the corresponding conjugate column operations will then produce zeros in the $(i, 1)$ and $(1, i)$ positions for $i = 2, \ldots, n$. The resulting matrix is

$$P_1AP_s^* = \begin{pmatrix} c_{11} & 0\ldots0 \\ 0 & \\ \cdot & \\ \cdot & A_1 \\ \cdot & \\ 0 & \end{pmatrix}.$$

If $A_1 = Z$, we are through; otherwise the process may be repeated on A_1. Since conjunctive matrices have the same rank, after r steps we are through.

Theorem 8.5. Every symmetric matrix of rank r over $\mathcal{F}$ is congruent over $\mathcal{F}$ to a diagonal matrix with nonzero elements in the first r diagonal positions and zeros elsewhere, provided $1 + 1 \neq 0$ in $\mathcal{F}$.

PROOF: The proof of Theorem 8.4, modified by using transposes instead of conjugate transposes, is effective.

Theorem 8.6. Every complex Hermitian matrix of rank r is conjunctive over $\mathcal{C}$ to a diagonal matrix with 1 in the first p diagonal positions, -1 in the next $r - p$ diagonal positions, and zeros elsewhere.

PROOF: Let a Hermitian matrix A be conjunctive to a matrix D in the diagonal form of Theorem 8.4:

$$D = \begin{pmatrix} d_1 & & & & & \\ & \cdot & & & & \\ & & \cdot & & & \\ & & & d_r & & \\ & & & & 0 & \\ & & & & & \cdot \\ & & & & & & \cdot \\ & & & & & & & 0 \end{pmatrix}$$

Let p denote the number of positive elements of D. Then $P_{ij}DP_{ij}^*$ coincides with D except that d_i and d_j have been interchanged. Hence A is conjunctive to a diagonal matrix E in which the positive diagonal elements come first, say $e_1, \ldots, e_p$; the negative diagonal elements can be expressed as $-e_{p+1}, \ldots, -e_r$, and the remaining elements are zero. Thus $e_i^{-1/2}$ is a real number for $i = 1, \ldots, r$, and

$$PEP^*$$

is in the form stated in the theorem, where

$$P = M_r(e_r^{-1/2}) \cdots M_1(e_1^{-1/2}).$$

Theorem 8.7. Every real symmetric matrix of rank r is congruent over $\mathfrak{R}$ to a diagonal matrix with 1 in the first p diagonal positions, -1 in the next $r - p$ diagonal positions, and zeros elsewhere.

P R O O F : The proof of Theorem 8.6, modified for congruence instead of conjunctivity, is effective. Notice that the argument will not be valid in any field that fails to contain a positive square root of each of its positive elements.

It is an important fact that the form stated in Theorem 8.6 is canonical for Hermitian matrices under conjunctivity. Similarly, the form stated in Theorem 8.7 is canonical for real symmetric matrices under congruence. This means, of course, that each Hermitian matrix determines a unique value of r and of p, and similarly for each real symmetric matrix.

To prove uniqueness, let A be an $n \times n$ Hermitian matrix. Relative to an arbitrary basis $\{\alpha_1, \ldots, \alpha_n\}$ for $\mathcal{U}_n$, A determines a conjugate bilinear function f from $\mathcal{U}_n \times \mathcal{U}_n$ to $\mathcal{C}$: $f(\alpha_i, \alpha_j) = a_{ij}$. Since A is Hermitian, Theorem 8.6 guarantees that there exists a basis $\{\beta_1, \ldots, \beta_n\}$, relative to which f is represented by the matrix $B = PAP^*$ of the block form

$$B = \begin{pmatrix} I_p & & \\ & -I_{r-p} & \\ & & Z \end{pmatrix}$$

for some r and p. Suppose there exists another basis $\{\gamma_1, \ldots, \gamma_n\}$, relative to which f is represented by $C = QAQ^*$, where

$$C = \begin{pmatrix} I_q & \\ & -I_{s-q} \\ Z & \end{pmatrix}.$$

Since conjunctive matrices have the same rank,

$$r = \rho(B) = \rho(A) = \rho(C) = s.$$

Let $\xi = \sum_{i=1}^{n} x_i \beta_i = \sum_{i=1}^{n} u_i \gamma_i$ and $\eta = \sum_{i=1}^{n} y_i \beta_i = \sum_{i=1}^{n} v_i \gamma_i$. Then

$$f(\xi, \eta) = XBY^* = x_1 \bar{y}_1 + \cdots + x_p \bar{y}_p - x_{p+1} \bar{y}_{p+1} - \cdots - x_r \bar{y}_r,$$

$$= UCV^* = u_1 \bar{v}_1 + \cdots + u_q \bar{v}_q - u_{q+1} \bar{v}_{q+1} - \cdots - u_r \bar{v}_r.$$

Furthermore let $\mathfrak{M} = [\beta_{p+1}, \ldots, \beta_r]$ and $\mathfrak{N} = [\gamma_1, \ldots, \gamma_q, \gamma_{r+1}, \ldots, \gamma_n]$. Then $\dim \mathfrak{M} + \dim \mathfrak{N} = (r - p) + (n - r + q) = n + (q - p)$. Suppose that $q > p$; then $\mathfrak{M} \cap \mathfrak{N} \neq [\theta]$. For any nonzero $\xi \in \mathfrak{M} \cap \mathfrak{N}$ we have

$$f(\xi, \xi) = -x_{p+1} \bar{x}_{p+1} - \cdots - x_r \bar{x}_r < 0,$$

$$= u_1 \bar{u}_1 + \cdots + u_q \bar{u}_q \geq 0,$$

a contradiction. Hence $q \leq p$. By reversing the roles of p and q, the reverse inequality follows, so $p = q$.

Hence any $n \times n$ Hermitian matrix A uniquely determines two non-negative numbers p and r such that A is conjunctive to one and only one matrix B in the form given above. Instead of specifying r and p to identify the conjunctivity class to which A belongs, it is customary to specify r and s, where $s = 2p - r$; clearly s is uniquely determined by A.

Definition 8.5. The *signature* s of a Hermitian matrix A is defined by

$$s = p - (r - p) = 2p - r,$$

which is the number of diagonal 1's diminished by the number of diagonal -1's in the canonical form of A relative to conjunctivity over $\mathcal{C}$. Similarly, the *signature* of a real symmetric matrix A is $2p - r$, where p and r are determined from the canonical form of A relative to congruence over $\mathcal{R}$.

The second part of this definition anticipates that p and r are uniquely determined for each real symmetric matrix, which may be proved by a straightforward modification of the argument given for the Hermitian case, preceding Definition 8.5.

Theorem 8.8. Two $n \times n$ Hermitian matrices are conjunctive over $\mathcal{C}$ if and only if they have the same rank and the same signature.

PROOF: If A and B have the same rank and signature each is conjunctive over $\mathcal{C}$ to the same matrix in canonical form, and hence are conjunctive to each other. Conversely, if A and B are conjunctive, so are their respective canonical forms, which by the uniqueness argument must be equal. Hence they have the same rank and the same signature.

Theorem 8.9. Two $n \times n$ real symmetric matrices are congruent over $\mathfrak{R}$ if and only if they have the same rank and the same signature.

P R O O F : Exercise. First you must establish the uniqueness of the canonical form for congruence over $\mathfrak{R}$ of a real symmetric matrix.

Finally we observe that for complex symmetric matrices the diagonalization process described for the real case by Theorem 8.7 can be extended to obtain a particularly simple standard form for congruence over $\mathcal{C}$.

Theorem 8.10. Every complex symmetric matrix of rank r is congruent over $\mathcal{C}$ to the matrix

$$\begin{pmatrix} I_r & Z \\ Z & Z \end{pmatrix}.$$

P R O O F : Exercise.

Exercises

1. Operations for complex numbers are defined as follows, where a, b, c, and d are real:

Sum: $(a + ib) + (c + id) = (a + c) + i(b + d)$.
Product: $(a + ib)(c + id) = (ac - bd) + i(ad + bc)$.
Conjugate: $\overline{a + ib} = a - ib$.
Magnitude: $|a + ib| = \sqrt{a^2 + b^2}$.

Show that if x, y are complex numbers, then

  (i) $\overline{x + y} = \bar{x} + \bar{y}$,
  (ii) $\overline{xy} = \bar{x}\,\bar{y}$,
  (iii) $\bar{\bar{x}} = x$,
  (iv) $x\bar{x} = |x|^2$,
  (v) $x + \bar{x}$ is real,
  (vi) $|x|$ is real and nonnegative,
  (vii) $|xy| = |x| \cdot |y|$,
 (viii) $|x + y| \leq |x| + |y|$.

2. (i) Write a matrix representation of each of the bilinear forms on $\mathcal{V}_2$

$$x_1 y_1 - x_2 y_1 + 2x_2 y_2,$$

and

$$4u_1 v_1 + 4u_1 v_2 + 2u_2 v_1 + 4u_2 v_2.$$

(ii) Are these matrices congruent?

(iii) What does your answer to (ii) imply about the two forms?

3. Prove that congruence over $\mathfrak{F}$ is an equivalence relation on $n \times n$ matrices.

4. Prove that B is congruent to A if and only if B can be obtained from A by identical sequences of elementary row and column operations.

5. Let A be a skew matrix.

(i) Show that $a_{ii} = 0$ if $1 + 1 \neq 0$ in $\mathfrak{F}$.

(ii) Prove that if B is congruent to A, then B is skew.

6. Prove the following properties of the conjugate transpose operation on complex matrices.

(i) $(A^*)^* = A$.

(ii) $\rho(A^*) = \rho(A)$.

(iii) $(A + B)^* = A^* + B^*$.

(iv) $(AB)^* = B^*A^*$.

(v) If A is nonsingular, $(A^{-1})^* = (A^*)^{-1}$.

(vi) If A is complex, AA^* and A^*A are Hermitian.

(vii) If A is Hermitian, then a_{ii} is real for each i; if A is real and symmetric, A is Hermitian.

(viii) If A is skew-Hermitian, then a_{ii} is pure imaginary for each i; if A is real and skew, then A is skew-Hermitian.

(ix) Let B be conjunctive to A. If A is Hermitian, so is B; if A is skew-Hermitian, so is B.

7. Prove that any $n \times n$ complex matrix A has a unique representation $A = H + K$, where H is Hermitian and K is skew-Hermitian.

8. (i) Prove that H is Hermitian if and only if iH is skew-Hermitian, where $i^2 = -1$.

(ii) Combine (i) and Theorem 8.6 to deduce a canonical form for conjunctivity of skew-Hermitian matrices.

9. Let A be an $n \times n$ skew-symmetric matrix over a field $\mathfrak{F}$ in which $1 + 1 \neq 0$. Recalling the results of Exercise 5, use appropriate row and column operations to show that A is congruent to a matrix of the diagonal block form

$$\begin{pmatrix} A_1 & & & \\ & \ddots & & \\ & & A_t & \\ & & & Z \end{pmatrix}, \qquad \text{where} \quad A_i = \begin{pmatrix} 0 & -1 \\ 1 & 0 \end{pmatrix}$$

for $i = 1, \ldots, t$. Deduce that A has an even rank, and that this form is canonical relative to congruence over $\mathcal{F}$ for skew-symmetric matrices; that is, two $n \times n$ skew-symmetric matrices are congruent if and only if they have the same rank.

10. Perform row and column operations to reduce the following skew matrix to a congruent matrix in the canonical form stated in Exercise 9:

$$\begin{pmatrix} 0 & 3 & -2 & 1 & 0 \\ -3 & 0 & 1 & -4 & 1 \\ 2 & -1 & 0 & 0 & -2 \\ -1 & 4 & 0 & 0 & 1 \\ 0 & -1 & 2 & -1 & 0 \end{pmatrix}.$$

11. Given $A = \begin{pmatrix} -10 & 5 & 2 \\ 5 & 0 & 3 \\ 2 & 3 & 6 \end{pmatrix}$.

(i) Find a matrix congruent to A over the rational field and in the form of Theorem 8.5.

(ii) Find a matrix congruent to A over $\mathcal{R}$ and in the form of Theorem 8.7. Determine the rank and signature of A.

(iii) Find a matrix congruent to A over $\mathcal{C}$ and in the form of Theorem 8.10.

(iv) Illustrate that Theorem 8.5 does not describe a canonical form for congruence over $\mathcal{F}$.

12. Determine the canonical form relative to conjunctivity of the following Hermitian matrix and determine its rank and signature:

$$\begin{pmatrix} 1 & i & 1+i \\ -i & 0 & 1 \\ 1-i & 1 & 2 \end{pmatrix}, \qquad i^2 = -1.$$

13. Prove Theorem 8.10 and deduce that two symmetric complex matrices are congruent over $\mathcal{C}$ if and only if they have the same rank.

§8.2. *Inner Product*

Before continuing with a general investigation of the background of metric notions, let us return to a familiar example to see where we have been and where we are going. In the real plane $\mathcal{E}_2$, the dot product of vectors is a bilinear function. If $\xi = (x_1, x_2)$ and $\eta = (y_1, y_2)$, then

$$\xi \cdot \eta = f(\xi, \eta) = x_1 y_1 + x_2 y_2.$$

The length of the vector ξ is

$$\|\xi\| = \sqrt{x_1^2 + x_2^2} = [f(\xi, \xi)]^{1/2},$$

which has one important property that length should possess; namely, that the length of a vector is a positive real number, except for the zero vector which has zero length.

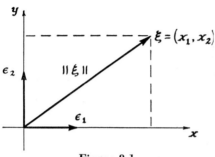

Figure 8.1

If we attempt to parallel this construction for the two-dimensional complex space, then the same dot product (with x_1, x_2, y_1, y_2 complex) is a bilinear form; since root extraction is defined for all complex numbers, it would be possible to define $\|\xi\|$ as we have for the real case. But then $\|\xi\|$ would be a complex number, hardly suitable for expressing length. It is for this reason that we use conjugates of complex numbers to define the conjugate bilinear function

$$g(\xi, \eta) = x_1\bar{y}_1 + x_2\bar{y}_2,$$

where $\xi = (x_1, x_2)$ and $\eta = (y_1, y_2)$, each component complex. It is important to observe that if the components are real, g reduces to the bilinear form defined above. Now if length is defined by

$$\|\xi\| = [g(\xi, \xi)]^{1/2} = \sqrt{|x_1|^2 + |x_2|^2},$$

the length of every nonzero vector is a positive real number, as desired.

From this we see that not all bilinear functions lead to a reasonable concept of length. The important distinction is the type of symmetry in the two vector variables possessed by the functions, for we observe by direct calculation that

$$f(\xi, \eta) = f(\eta, \xi),$$

while

$$g(\xi, \eta) = \overline{g(\eta, \xi)}.$$

Now we are ready to define the concept of an *inner product*, which is based upon these considerations.

Definition 8.6. Let $\mathcal{V}$ be a vector space over $\mathcal{R}$ (or $\mathcal{C}$). A real (or complex) *inner product* is a function p with domain $\mathcal{V} \times \mathcal{V}$ and range $\mathcal{R}$ (or $\mathcal{C}$) which satisfies

(a) $p(c_1\xi_1 + c_2\xi_2, \eta) = c_1p(\xi_1, \eta) + c_2p(\xi_2, \eta)$,

(b) $p(\xi, \eta) = \overline{p(\eta, \xi)}$,

(c) $p(\xi, \xi) > 0$ if $\xi \neq \theta$, and $p(\theta, \theta) = 0$.

This definition asserts that an inner product is a scalar-valued function which is *conjugate bilinear*, (a) and (b), and *positive definite*, (c). For a real inner product, (b) reduces to the assertion of symmetry in ξ and η. Thus a real inner product is a real valued function of two vector variables which is bilinear, symmetric, and positive definite. In the complex case property (b) is called *conjugate symmetry* or *Hermitian symmetry*. In either case, (b) implies that $p(\xi, \xi)$ is real.

Definition 8.7.

(a) A real vector space $\mathcal{U}$ for which a real inner product is defined is called a *Euclidean space*.

(b) A complex vector space $\mathcal{U}$ for which a complex inner product is defined is called a *unitary space*.

(c) Euclidean spaces and unitary spaces collectively are called *inner product spaces*.

Examples of Inner Product Spaces

(a) Euclidean n-space $\mathcal{R}_n$ with the dot product

$$p(\xi, \eta) = x_1 y_1 + x_2 y_2 + \cdots + x_n y_n.$$

(b) The infinite-dimensional space of all real valued functions continuous on the interval $0 \le t \le 1$ with the inner product

$$p(f, g) = \int_0^1 f(t) g(t) dt.$$

(c) Unitary n-space $\mathcal{C}_n$ with the inner product

$$p(\xi, \eta) = x_1 \bar{y}_1 + x_2 \bar{y}_2 + \cdots + x_n \bar{y}_n.$$

(d) The infinite-dimensional space of all complex valued functions continuous on the real interval $0 \le t \le 1$ with the inner product

$$p(f, g) = \int_0^1 f(t) \overline{g(t)} dt.$$

We conclude this section by deriving a general inequality which has many important applications in Euclidean and unitary spaces.

Theorem 8.11. (The Schwarz inequality.) In any inner product space $\mathcal{U}$

$$|p(\xi, \eta)|^2 \le p(\xi, \xi) p(\eta, \eta)$$

for all $\xi, \eta \in \mathcal{U}$.

P R O O F : For any α, $p(\alpha, \alpha)$ is real and nonnegative. Let $\alpha = a\xi + b\eta$, where $a = -p(\eta, \xi)$ and $b = p(\xi, \xi)$; then $\bar{b} = b \ge 0$, and $\bar{a} = -p(\xi, \eta)$. Therefore, we have

$$0 \le p(a\xi + b\eta, a\xi + b\eta) = ap(\xi, a\xi + b\eta) + bp(\eta, a\xi + b\eta)$$
$$= a\bar{a}p(\xi, \xi) + a\bar{b}p(\xi, \eta) + b\bar{a}p(\eta, \xi) + b\bar{b}p(\eta, \eta)$$

$$= a\bar{a}b - ab\bar{a} - b\bar{a}a + bbp(\eta, \eta) = b[-a\bar{a} + bp(\eta, \eta)]$$
$$= b[p(\xi, \xi)p(\eta, \eta) - p(\xi, \eta)\overline{p(\xi, \eta)}].$$

If $b = 0$, we have $\xi = \theta$, and the Schwarz inequality is trivially valid with both sides equal to zero. Otherwise, the last bracket above must be nonnegative, which is the assertion of the Schwarz inequality.

Exercises

1. Verify that examples (b) and (c) actually satisfy the definition of an inner product.

2. If p is any inner product verify that

(i) $p(c\xi, d\eta) = c\bar{d}p(\xi, \eta)$,

(ii) $p(\theta, \eta) = p(\xi, \theta) = 0$.

3. If p is any inner product and if η_1 and η_2 are vectors such that $p(\xi, \eta_1) = p(\xi, \eta_2)$ for all ξ, then $\eta_1 = \eta_2$.

• 4. Carry out in detail the following outline of an alternative proof of the Schwarz inequality.

(i) For all complex numbers x, y and all vectors ξ, η

$$0 \le p(x\xi + y\eta, x\xi + y\eta) = x\bar{x}p(\xi, \xi) + 2\,\mathrm{Re}[x\bar{y}p(\xi, \eta)] + y\bar{y}p(\eta, \eta).$$

(ii) Specify x to be real and choose $y = p(\xi, \eta)$ to obtain the real quadratic inequality, valid for all real x,

$$0 \le p(\xi, \xi)x^2 + 2|p(\xi, \eta)|^2 x + |p(\xi, \eta)|^2 p(\eta, \eta).$$

(iii) Apply a criterion for a real quadratic function to be nonnegative, obtaining the Schwarz inequality.

5. Prove that equality holds in the Schwarz inequality if and only if the set $\{\xi, \eta\}$ is linearly dependent.

6. Show that the following general theorems are direct consequences of the Schwarz inequality:

(i) If $x_1, \ldots, x_n$ and $y_1, \ldots, y_n$ are any real numbers, then

$$\left(\sum_{i=1}^{n} x_i y_i\right)^2 \le \left(\sum_{i=1}^{n} x_i^2\right)\left(\sum_{i=1}^{n} y_i^2\right).$$

(ii) (Cauchy inequality.) If $x_1, \ldots, x_n$ and $y_1, \ldots, y_n$ are any complex numbers, then

$$\left|\sum_{i=1}^{n} x_i \bar{y}_i\right|^2 \le \left(\sum_{i=1}^{n} |x_i|^2\right)\left(\sum_{i=1}^{n} |y_i|^2\right).$$

(iii) If f and g are real functions continuous on the interval $a \leq x \leq b$, then

$$\left(\int_a^b f(x)g(x)dx \right)^2 \leq \int_a^b f^2(x)dx \cdot \int_a^b g^2(x)dx.$$

§8.3. *Length, Distance, and Orthogonality*

Let $\mathcal{V}$ be an inner product space that is either Euclidean or unitary. The inner product function p is used to define length, distance, and perpendicularity; we begin with length.

Definition 8.8. The *length* $\|\xi\|$ of a vector ξ is defined by

$$\|\xi\| = [p(\xi, \xi)]^{1/2}.$$

Theorem 8.12. Length has the following properties:
(a) $\|c\xi\| = |c| \cdot \|\xi\|$.
(b) $\|\xi\| > 0$ if $\xi \neq \theta$, and $\|\theta\| = 0$.
(c) $\|\xi + \eta\| \leq \|\xi\| + \|\eta\|$.

P R O O F : Property (a) follows from Exercise 2 of the preceding section, and property (b) from part (c) of Definition 8.6. To prove property (c) we first note that the Schwarz inequality can be written

$$|p(\xi, \eta)| = |p(\eta, \xi)| \leq \|\xi\| \cdot \|\eta\|.$$

Since $p(\xi, \eta) = \overline{p(\eta, \xi)}$, $p(\xi,\eta) + p(\eta, \xi)$ is real, and

$$|p(\xi, \eta) + p(\eta, \xi)| \leq |p(\xi, \eta)| + |p(\eta, \xi)| \leq 2\|\xi\| \cdot \|\eta\|.$$

Thus

$$\begin{aligned}
\|\xi + \eta\|^2 &= p(\xi + \eta, \xi + \eta) \\
&= p(\xi, \xi) + p(\xi, \eta) + p(\eta, \xi) + p(\eta, \eta) \\
&\leq p(\xi, \xi) + |p(\xi, \eta) + p(\eta, \xi)| + p(\eta, \eta) \\
&\leq \|\xi\|^2 + 2\|\xi\| \cdot \|\eta\| + \|\eta\|^2
\end{aligned}$$

from which (c) follows immediately.

For the case of Euclidean n-space where p is the dot product, the length of $\xi = (x_1, \ldots, x_n)$ is simply the familiar form

$$\|\xi\| = \sqrt{x_1^2 + x_2^2 + \cdots + x_n^2}.$$

Property (c) is interpreted geometrically as the observation that the length of any side of a triangle does not exceed the sum of the lengths of the other two sides. Hence (c) is called the *triangle inequality*.

Since the points of n-space may be interpreted as n-tuples, or vectors, the distance between vectors can be regarded as the distance between those points, or, equivalently, the length of the arrow from one point to the other.

Definition 8.9. The *distance* $d(\xi, \eta)$ between two vectors ξ and η is defined by

$$d(\xi, \eta) = \|\xi - \eta\|.$$

Theorem 8.13. Distance has the following properties:
(a) $d(\xi, \eta) = d(\eta, \xi)$,
(b) $d(\xi, \eta) > 0$ if $\xi \neq \eta$, and $d(\xi, \xi) = 0$,
(c) $d(\xi, \eta) \leq d(\xi, \zeta) + d(\zeta, \eta)$.

PROOF : Exercise.

Thus the distance which results from any inner product has the familiar properties of distance as defined by coordinates in analytic geometry: it is symmetric, is positive for distinct points, and satisfies the triangle inequality. Any space, for which a distance function is defined, satisfying these three properties is called a *metric space*.

When we come to angle, we must distinguish between Euclidean space and unitary space. The Schwarz inequality can be written

$$\frac{|p(\xi, \eta)|}{\|\xi\| \cdot \|\eta\|} \leq 1.$$

If $p(\xi, \eta)$ is real, as in the Euclidean case, this means that

$$\frac{p(\xi, \eta)}{\|\xi\| \cdot \|\eta\|}$$

is a real number between -1 and $+1$. Hence it is the cosine of a uniquely determined angle Ψ in the range $0 \leq \Psi \leq \pi$. In the unitary case $p(\xi, \eta)$ is complex, and the corresponding interpretation is not valid. For our work, however, it is not important to have a measure of the angle between two vectors, but it is most convenient to have a definition of orthogonality (perpendicularity). In the real case the necessary definition for orthogonality is clear because the cosine of the angle between perpendicular nonzero vectors must be zero, and hence $p(\xi, \eta) = 0$. This is the definition we adopt for the complex case as well.

Definition 8.10. Two vectors ξ and η are *orthogonal* if and only if $p(\xi, \eta) = 0$.

Theorem 8.14. In any inner product space $\mathcal{V}$,
(a) ξ is orthogonal to every $\eta \in \mathcal{V}$ if and only if $\xi = \theta$,

(b) if ξ is orthogonal to every vector of a set S, then ξ is orthogonal to the subspace spanned by S,

(c) any set of mutually orthogonal nonzero vectors is linearly independent.

PROOF : Exercise.

This theorem hints that several geometric properties which are familiar in $\mathcal{E}_2$ and $\mathcal{E}_3$ also hold in any inner product space. For example, (c) suggests that a basis of mutually orthogonal vectors (a rectangular coordinate system) always can be found for $\mathcal{V}$; in the next theorem we construct such a basis by use of projections to split a vector ξ into orthogonal components, $\xi = \sigma + \eta$. This construction in its general form is known as the *Gram-Schmidt orthogonalization process*.

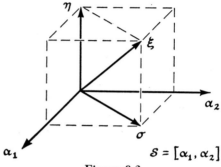

Figure 8.2

Theorem 8.15. In any finite-dimensional inner product space $\mathcal{V}$, there exists a basis consisting of mutually orthogonal vectors.

PROOF : If $\mathcal{V}$ is one-dimensional, any nonzero vector forms such a basis. We proceed by induction, assuming the theorem for any space of dimension k. Let $\mathcal{V}$ be of dimension $k + 1$, and let S be any subspace of dimension k. By the induction hypothesis there exists an orthogonal basis $\{\alpha_1, \ldots, \alpha_k\}$ for S. For $\xi \notin S$, let

$$\sigma = \sum_{i=1}^{k} \frac{p(\xi, \alpha_i)}{p(\alpha_i, \alpha_i)} \alpha_i = \sum_{i=1}^{k} c_i \alpha_i,$$

and let

$$\eta = \xi - \sigma.$$

Clearly, $\sigma \in S$, and we now show that η is orthogonal to each α_i:

$$p(\eta, \alpha_i) = p(\xi - \sigma, \alpha_i)$$

$$= p(\xi, \alpha_i) - p\left(\sum_{j=1}^{k} c_j \alpha_j, \alpha_i\right)$$

$$= p(\xi, \alpha_i) - \sum_{j=1}^{k} c_j p(\alpha_j, \alpha_i)$$

$$= p(\xi, \alpha_i) - c_i p(\alpha_i, \alpha_i)$$

$$= p(\xi, \alpha_i) - \frac{p(\xi, \alpha_i)}{p(\alpha_i, \alpha_i)} \cdot p(\alpha_i, \alpha_i) = 0.$$

Hence the vectors $\{\alpha_1, \ldots, \alpha_k, \eta\}$ are mutually orthogonal and by Theorem 8.14 (c) form a basis for $\mathcal{U}_{k+1}$.

The vector σ in the preceding proof is called the *orthogonal projection* of ξ on S; the coefficients c_i of σ relative to the α-basis for S can be written

$$c_i = \frac{p(\xi, \alpha_i)}{p(\alpha_i, \alpha_i)} = \frac{\|\xi\|}{\|\alpha_i\|} \cdot \frac{p(\xi, \alpha_i)}{\|\alpha_i\| \|\xi\|}.$$

In the Euclidean case if the basis vectors are so chosen that $\|\alpha_i\| = 1$, this reduces to

$$c_i = \|\xi\| \cos \Psi_i,$$

where Ψ_i is the angle between ξ and α_i. The numbers c_i are called *direction numbers* of ξ.

Theorem 8.16. If S is any subspace of an inner product space $\mathcal{U}_n$, there exists a unique subspace $S^\perp$ such that
(a) $\mathcal{U}_n = S \oplus S^\perp$,
(b) $p(\sigma, \sigma') = 0$ for every $\sigma \in S$ and $\sigma' \in S^\perp$.

P R O O F : Exercise. ($S^\perp$ is called the *orthogonal complement* of S.)

Now we combine the notions of length and orthogonality to define a normal orthogonal basis, which is simply a basis of the form $\{\epsilon_1, \ldots, \epsilon_n\}$ for $\mathcal{E}_n$, and show that these metric concepts assume a very familiar form relative to such a basis.

Definition 8.11. In any inner product space a vector of unit length is called *normal*. A set of mutually orthogonal vectors, each of which is normal, is called a *normal orthogonal* (or *orthonormal*) set.

If α is any nonzero vector in an inner product space, then $\|\alpha\|^{-1}\alpha$ is normal. Hence a normal orthogonal basis is obtained by normalizing in this manner each vector of an orthogonal basis. The importance of a normal orthogonal basis is revealed by the next theorem which implies that in Euclidean space any inner product p assumes the form of the dot product relative to a normal orthogonal basis.

Theorem 8.17. Let p be any inner product for the space $\mathcal{U}_n$, let $\{\alpha_1, \ldots, \alpha_n\}$ be a normal orthogonal basis for $\mathcal{U}_n$, let $\xi = \sum_{i=1}^{n} x_i \alpha_i$, and let $\eta = \sum_{i=1}^{n} y_i \alpha_i$. Then

$$p(\xi, \eta) = x_1 \bar{y}_1 + x_2 \bar{y}_2 + \cdots + x_n \bar{y}_n.$$

PROOF:

$$p(\xi, \eta) = p\left(\sum_{i=1}^{n} x_i\alpha_i, \sum_{j=1}^{n} y_j\alpha_j\right)$$

$$= \sum_{i=1}^{n} x_i p\left(\alpha_i, \sum_{i=1}^{n} y_j\alpha_j\right)$$

$$= \sum_{i=1}^{n} x_i \left(\sum_{j=1}^{n} \bar{y}_j p(\alpha_i, \alpha_j)\right)$$

$$= \sum_{i=1}^{n} x_i\bar{y}_i p(\alpha_i, \alpha_i)$$

$$= \sum_{i=1}^{n} x_i\bar{y}_i,$$

where the last equality holds since the α_i are normal, and the preceding equality holds since the α_i are orthogonal.

From this it is clear that in any n-dimensional Euclidean space, with the metric concepts defined by any inner product, if we choose a normal orthogonal basis, the following familiar formulas for length, distance, and angle are valid:

$$\|\xi\| = \sqrt{x_1^2 + x_2^2 + \cdots + x_n^2},$$

$$\|\xi - \eta\| = \sqrt{(x_1 - y_1)^2 + \cdots + (x_n - y_n)^2},$$

$$\cos \Psi(\xi, \eta) = \frac{x_1y_1 + \cdots + x_ny_n}{\sqrt{x_1^2 + \cdots + x_n^2}\sqrt{y_1^2 + \cdots + y_n^2}}.$$

This last formula is simply the law of cosines,

$$\|\xi - \eta\|^2 = \|\xi\|^2 + \|\eta\|^2 - 2\|\xi\| \cdot \|\eta\| \cos \Psi.$$

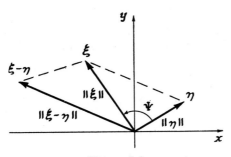

Figure 8.3

It is also worth noticing the relationship between matrix multiplication and a real inner product. If $A = (a_{ij})$, $B = (b_{ij})$, and $AB = (c_{ij})$, then

$$c_{ij} = \sum_{k=1}^{n} a_{ik}b_{kj}$$

$$= p(\alpha_i, \beta_j),$$

where p is the real dot product of the ith *row* vector α_i of A with the jth *column* vector β_j of B. This observation is valid for matrices over any field, but the dot product referred to has the form of the real dot product.

Exercises

1. Prove that the following theorems of geometry hold in any Euclidean space. Illustrate each in $\mathcal{E}_2$.

  (i) The Pythagorean theorem and its converse:
    ξ is orthogonal to η if and only if
    $$\|\xi\|^2 + \|\eta\|^2 = \|\xi + \eta\|^2.$$

  (ii) The law of cosines:
    $$\|\xi - \eta\|^2 = \|\xi\|^2 + \|\eta\|^2 - 2\|\xi\| \cdot \|\eta\| \cdot \cos \Psi.$$

  (iii) The diagonals of a rhombus are perpendicular:
    if $\|\xi\| = \|\eta\|$, then $p(\xi + \eta, \xi - \eta) = 0.$

2. (i) Prove that in any inner product space
    $$p(\xi + \eta, \xi + \eta) + p(\xi - \eta, \xi - \eta) = 2p(\xi, \xi) + 2p(\eta, \eta).$$

  (ii) What familiar geometric theorem does (i) assert?

3. State and prove in the language of arbitrary Euclidean space the theorem that the midpoints of the sides of any quadrilateral are the vertices of a parallelogram.

4. Let $\mathcal{V}$ be an inner product space with $\{\alpha_1, \ldots, \alpha_n\}$ as a normal orthogonal basis.

  (i) Prove Bessel's inequality:

    if $p(\xi, \alpha_i) = c_i$ for $i = 1, 2, \ldots, m \leq n$, then $\sum_{i=1}^{m} |c_i|^2 \leq \|\xi\|^2.$

  (ii) Prove Parseval's identity:

    $$p(\xi, \eta) = \sum_{i=1}^{n} p(\xi, \alpha_i)p(\alpha_i, \eta).$$

  (iii) Interpret each in $\mathcal{E}_3$ by a diagram.

5. Prove that in any Euclidean space $p(\alpha, \beta) = 0$ if and only if
  $$\|\alpha + c\beta\| \geq \|\alpha\|$$
for every real number c.

6. Prove Theorem 8.14.

7. Prove that if $\mathcal{S}$ is any subspace of an inner product space $\mathcal{V}$, then every $\xi \in \mathcal{V}$ has a unique decomposition
  $$\xi = \sigma + \eta,$$

where $\sigma \in S$ and η is orthogonal to S.

8. Prove Theorem 8.16.

9. Let S and $\mathfrak{I}$ be subspaces of an inner product space $\mathcal{V}$. Prove that

(i) $(S^\perp)^\perp = S$.

(ii) $(S + \mathfrak{I})^\perp = S^\perp \cap \mathfrak{I}^\perp$.

(iii) $(S \cap \mathfrak{I})^\perp = S^\perp + \mathfrak{I}^\perp$.

10. Beginning with the orthogonal vectors

$$\alpha_1 = (2, 1, -5, 0)$$

$$\alpha_2 = (3, -1, 1, 0)$$

in $\mathcal{E}_4$, use the Gram-Schmidt orthogonalization process on the normalized form of α_1 and α_2 to obtain a normal orthogonal basis for $\mathcal{E}_4$.

11. Prove that the mapping $\xi \longrightarrow \sigma$ as defined in the proof of Theorem 8.15 by the Gram-Schmidt orthogonalization process is a projection, as defined in § 7.4.

§8.4. *Isometries*

In many important physical problems the transformations which arise are ones which leave all distances fixed. Such a transformation is called a *rigid motion*, and any motion of a rigid body can be described by a transformation of this type. It is intuitively clear that the product of rigid motions is a rigid motion, that the identity transformation is a rigid motion, and that each rigid motion has an inverse that is a rigid motion. In other words, the set of all rigid motions of a space forms a group; for Euclidean space the group is called the *Euclidean group*, and for unitary space the group is called the *unitary group*.

A simple example of a rigid motion is a translation, wherein each point in space is moved the same fixed distance in the same direction:

$$\xi \mathbf{T} = \xi + \alpha \text{ for fixed } \alpha \text{ and all } \xi.$$

But for $\alpha \neq \theta$, $\theta \mathbf{T} = \theta + \alpha = \alpha$, so a nonzero translation is not linear. However, any rigid motion can be decomposed into the product of a linear transformation and a translation. It is the linear component of rigid motion which we now propose to study.

Definition 8.12. A linear transformation $\mathbf{T}$ on an inner product space is said to be an *isometry* if and only if

$$\|\xi \mathbf{T}\| = \|\xi\| \text{ for each } \xi \in \mathcal{V},$$

An isometry on a Euclidean space is called an *orthogonal* transformation; an isometry on a unitary space is called a *unitary* transformation.

Clearly, an isometry preserves distance; the following theorem shows that it also preserves the inner product and hence preserves orthogonality and all other metric notions that are defined in terms of the inner product.

Theorem 8.18. A linear transformation **T** on an inner product space $\mho$ is an isometry if and only if $p(\xi, \eta) = p(\xi\mathbf{T}, \eta\mathbf{T})$ for all $\xi, \eta \in \mho$.

P R O O F : We begin the proof in complex form:

$$p(\xi + \eta, \xi + \eta) = p(\xi, \xi) + p(\xi, \eta) + p(\eta, \xi) + p(\eta, \eta),$$

$$\|\xi + \eta\|^2 = \|\xi\|^2 + p(\xi, \eta) + \overline{p(\xi, \eta)} + \|\eta\|^2.$$

But $p(\xi, \eta) + \overline{p(\xi, \eta)}$ is twice the real part of $p(\xi, \eta)$, and it is expressed as an algebraic sum of squares of lengths which are preserved by **T**. If $p(\xi, \eta)$ is real, this means $p(\xi, \eta)$ is preserved by **T**. If $p(\xi, \eta)$ is complex, a similar calculation for $p(\xi + i\eta, \xi + i\eta)$ shows that the complex part of $p(\xi, \eta)$ is also preserved by **T**. Conversely, if p is preserved by **T**, length is also preserved, since $\|\xi\| = p(\xi, \xi)^{1/2}$.

Next we consider the effect of an isometry on a normal orthogonal basis $\{\alpha_1, \dots, \alpha_n\}$. Since **T** preserves inner product,

$$\|\alpha_i\mathbf{T}\| = 1, \qquad i = 1, \dots, n$$

and

$$p(\alpha_i\mathbf{T}, \alpha_j\mathbf{T}) = \delta_{ij}.$$

Thus an isometry maps a normal orthogonal basis into a normal orthogonal basis. The row vectors of the matrix A, which represents **T** relative to this basis, must therefore be of unit length and mutually orthogonal.

Definition 8.13. A real $n \times n$ matrix $A = (a_{ij})$ is said to be *orthogonal* if and only if

$$\sum_{k=1}^{n} a_{ik}a_{jk} = \delta_{ij}, \qquad i, j = 1, \dots, n.$$

A complex $n \times n$ matrix $A = (a_{ij})$ is said to be *unitary* if and only if

$$\sum_{k=1}^{n} a_{ik}\bar{a}_{jk} = \delta_{ij}, \qquad i, j = 1, \dots, n.$$

Theorem 8.19. A real $n \times n$ matrix A represents an orthogonal transformation **T** relative to a normal orthogonal basis if and only if A is orthogonal. A complex $n \times n$ matrix A represents a unitary transformation **T** relative to a normal orthogonal basis if and only if A is unitary.

P R O O F : Our previous remarks show that an orthogonal transformation is represented by an orthogonal matrix relative to a normal orthogonal basis. Conversely, the rows of a matrix represent the image of the basis vectors under the corresponding transformation. The proof is the same for the complex case.

Theorem 8.20. Any orthogonal or unitary matrix is nonsingular.

P R O O F : The row vectors are mutually orthogonal and hence linearly independent.

Theorem 8.21. A is an orthogonal matrix if and only if $A^{-1} = A'$. A is a unitary matrix if and only if $A^{-1} = A^*$.

P R O O F : Let A be orthogonal, and let $AA' = C = (c_{ij})$. Then $c_{ij} = \sum_{k=1}^{n} a_{ik}a'_{kj} = \sum_{k=1}^{n} a_{ik}a_{jk} = \delta_{ij}$. Hence $C = I$. Conversely, if $A' = A^{-1}$, $AA' = I$, so $\sum_{k=1}^{n} a_{ik}a_{jk} = \delta_{ij}$. The unitary case may be proved as an exercise.

Of all the methods described for calculating the inverse of a matrix, this is by far the simplest. Unfortunately, not every matrix is orthogonal or unitary.

Theorem 8.22. If A is orthogonal or unitary, $|\det A| = 1$.

P R O O F : Exercise.

Recall that two $n \times n$ matrices A and B are similar if and only if they represent the same linear transformation relative to two bases; if one basis can be carried into the other by an isometry, then

$$B = PAP^{-1}$$
$$= PAP' \quad \text{if } P \text{ is orthogonal,}$$
$$= PAP^* \quad \text{if } P \text{ is unitary.}$$

In particular, if one works *only* with normal orthogonal bases, similarity coincides with congruence in Euclidean spaces and with conjunctivity in unitary spaces. In numerous problems having physical significance, isometries are sufficient to carry out the desired changes of coordinates, as we shall see in the next section.

Exercises

1. (i) Find a matrix representation for the linear transformation which rotates each vector of the real plane through a fixed angle Ψ.
    (ii) Prove that this matrix A is orthogonal by verifying $AA' = I$.

2. Prove Theorem 8.22.

3. (i) Find a matrix representation B for the rigid motion of $\mathcal{E}_3$ which reflects each vector across the line

$$\begin{cases} x_3 = 0 \\ x_1 = x_2. \end{cases}$$

(ii) Prove that B is orthogonal since it satisfies Definition 8.13.

(iii) Find B^{-1} and describe the linear transformation it represents.

4. Reason as follows to show that any linear rigid motion of the real plane is either a rotation, or a rotation followed by a reflection across an axis.

(i) Write four quadratic conditions on the elements a, b, c, d of a real 2×2 matrix A that are necessary and sufficient that A be orthogonal.

(ii) Show that the only such matrices are

$$\begin{pmatrix} a & b \\ -b & a \end{pmatrix} \quad \text{and} \quad \begin{pmatrix} a & b \\ b & -a \end{pmatrix},$$

where $a^2 + b^2 = 1$.

(iii) Show that the former is a rotation through the angle $\cos^{-1} a$, while the latter is a rotation followed by a reflection across an axis.

5. Complete the proof of the unitary case of Theorem 8.18.

6. Prove the unitary case of Theorem 8.21.

7. Prove that each characteristic value of an isometry satisfies $|\lambda| = 1$, and that any two characteristic vectors which are associated with distinct characteristic values are orthogonal. What can you deduce about the Jordan form of any matrix that represents an isometry?

8. Does the following matrix represent a rigid motion in $\mathcal{E}_3$?

$$A = \frac{1}{6} \begin{pmatrix} 1 & -5 & \sqrt{10} \\ -5 & 1 & \sqrt{10} \\ \sqrt{10} & \sqrt{10} & 4 \end{pmatrix}.$$

9. Prove that if K is a real skew matrix and if $I + K$ is nonsingular, then

$$(I - K)(I + K)^{-1}$$

is orthogonal.

10. Let α_i denote the ith row of a real $n \times n$ matrix A; let $AA' = C = (c_{ij})$. Prove the following:

(i) $c_{ij} = p(\alpha_i, \alpha_j)$, p an inner product;

(ii) if the α_i are mutually orthogonal, $\det C = [\|\alpha_1\| \cdot \|\alpha_2\| \cdots \|\alpha_n\|]^2$;

(iii) if $|a_{ij}| \le k$ for $i, j = 1, 2, \ldots, n$ and some fixed number k, then $\|\alpha_i\| \le k \sqrt{n}$;

(iv) if $|a_{ij}| \le k$, and if the α_i are mutually orthogonal, then

$$|\det A| = \|\alpha_1\| \cdot \|\alpha_2\| \cdots \|\alpha_n\| \le k^n n^{n/2}.$$

§8.5. *Hermitian and Quadratic Functions*

Now we return to the study of conjugate bilinear functions, begun in § 8.1. We consider a vector space $\mathcal{V}$ over the complex numbers and a conjugate bilinear function f from $\mathcal{V} \times \mathcal{V}$ to $\mathcal{C}$,

$$f(\xi, \eta) \in \mathcal{C};$$

f is linear in the first component and conjugate linear in the second. We also consider the case in which $\mathcal{V}$ is a vector space over the real numbers and f is a bilinear function from $\mathcal{V} \times \mathcal{V}$ to $\mathcal{R}$. Since conjugate bilinearity then reduces to bilinearity, we shall first investigate the complex case, noting any differences which pertain to the real case.

By considering only the numbers $f(\xi, \xi)$ we obtain a function h, defined on $\mathcal{V}$ by

$$h(\xi) = f(\xi, \xi).$$

Since f is conjugate symmetric, $h(\xi)$ is *real* for every vector ξ of the complex space $\mathcal{V}$. Indeed it is precisely this property that makes conjugate bilinearity, rather than linearity, a natural condition to impose for complex spaces.

Relative to a basis $\{\alpha_1, \ldots, \alpha_n\}$ for $\mathcal{V}$ this function takes the form

$$h(\xi) = \sum_{i=1}^{n} \sum_{j=1}^{n} f(\alpha_i, \alpha_j) x_i \bar{x}_j = XAX^*,$$

where $\xi = \sum_{i=1}^{n} x_i \alpha_i$, and $a_{ij} = f(\alpha_i, \alpha_j)$, as in § 8.1. Thus h is represented by the Hermitian matrix A, which is uniquely determined by the choice of basis. From Theorem 8.8 we conclude that A and B both represent h relative to two bases if and only if A and B are conjunctive.

A real valued function h, obtained in this manner from a conjugate bilinear function on a complex vector space, is called a *Hermitian function*. Any expression of the form

$$XAX^* = \sum_{i=1}^{n} \sum_{j=1}^{n} a_{ij} x_i \bar{x}_j,$$

where A is Hermitian, is called a *Hermitian form*.

If we begin with a real vector space $\mathcal{V}$ and a bilinear function f from $\mathcal{V} \times \mathcal{V}$ to $\mathcal{R}$, then we define a function q from $\mathcal{V}$ to $\mathcal{R}$:

$$q(\xi) = f(\xi, \xi).$$

Relative to a choice of basis $\{\alpha_1, \ldots, \alpha_n\}$ this function takes the form

$$q(\xi) = \sum_{i=1}^{n} \sum_{j=1}^{n} f(\alpha_i, \alpha_j) x_i x_j = XAX',$$

where $A = (f(\alpha_i, \alpha_j))$ is real and symmetric. Thus q is represented by a real symmetric matrix, which is uniquely determined by the choice of basis. From Theorem 8.9, two such matrices represent q if and only if they are congruent.

A function q, obtained in this manner from a bilinear function on a real vector space, is called a *quadratic function*. Any expression of the form

$$XAX' = \sum_{i=1}^{n} \sum_{j=1}^{n} a_{ij}x_i x_j,$$

where A is real and symmetric, is called a *quadratic form*.

This discussion can be summarized by the following theorems.

Theorem 8.23. Let $\mathcal{V}_n$ be a complex vector space, and let h be a Hermitian function on $\mathcal{V}_n$. Relative to a basis $\{\alpha_1, \ldots, \alpha_n\}$ for $\mathcal{V}_n$, h is represented by a uniquely determined Hermitian matrix A, where if $\xi = \sum_{i=1}^{n} x_i \alpha_i$, then $h(\xi) = XAX^*$. Relative to a basis $\{\beta_1, \ldots, \beta_n\}$, h is represented by the Hermitian matrix B if and only if A and B are conjunctive over $\mathcal{C}$.

Theorem 8.24. Let $\mathcal{V}_n$ be a real vector space, and let q be a quadratic function on $\mathcal{V}_n$. Relative to a basis $\{\alpha_1, \ldots, \alpha_n\}$ for $\mathcal{V}_n$, q is represented by a uniquely determined real symmetric matrix A, where if $\xi = \sum_{i=1}^{n} x_i \alpha_i$, then $q(\xi) = XAX'$. Relative to a basis $\{\beta_1, \ldots, \beta_n\}$, q is represented by the real symmetric matrix B if and only if A and B are congruent over $\mathcal{R}$.

Each quadratic (or Hermitian) function on a real (or complex) vector space $\mathcal{V}$ determines a real symmetric (or Hermitian) matrix relative to a given basis, which in turn determines a quadratic (or Hermitian) form. We now consider the problem in reverse: starting with a quadratic (or Hermitian) form, can we find a quadratic (or Hermitian) function whose values are given by that form? To begin with, a quadratic form can be represented by various matrices. For example,

$$3x_1^2 + 4x_1x_2 - x_2^2$$

can be written as

$$(x_1\ x_2) \begin{pmatrix} 3 & 0 \\ 4 & -1 \end{pmatrix} \begin{pmatrix} x_1 \\ x_2 \end{pmatrix},$$

$$(x_1\ x_2) \begin{pmatrix} 3 & 4 \\ 0 & -1 \end{pmatrix} \begin{pmatrix} x_1 \\ x_2 \end{pmatrix},$$

$$(x_1\ x_2) \begin{pmatrix} 3 & 2 \\ 2 & -1 \end{pmatrix} \begin{pmatrix} x_1 \\ x_2 \end{pmatrix},$$

and so on. The variations occur from different decompositions of the coefficient of $x_i x_j$ into the two numbers a_{ij} and a_{ji}. An easy resolution of the ambiguity appears if we decompose A as the sum of its symmetric and skew-symmetric parts:

$$A = S + K.$$

Then

$$XAX' = X(S + K)X' = XSX' + XKX';$$

but a simple calculation verifies that

$$XKX' = 0.$$

Hence only the symmetric component of A contributes to the value of $q(\xi)$, and we lose nothing by insisting that the real form

$$\sum_{i=1}^{n} \sum_{j=1}^{n} a_{ij} x_i x_j$$

be represented by the *real symmetric* matrix $B = (b_{ij})$, where $b_{ii} = a_{ii}$ for $i = 1, \ldots, n$ and $b_{ij} = b_{ji} = \frac{1}{2}(a_{ij} + a_{ji})$.

Correspondingly, if for given complex numbers a_{ij} the form

$$\sum_{i=1}^{n} \sum_{j=1}^{n} a_{ij} x_i \bar{x}_j$$

is real for all complex vectors $(x_1, \ldots, x_n)$, then the form can be represented by the *Hermitian* matrix $B = (b_{ij})$, where $b_{ii} = a_{ii}$ for $i = 1, \ldots, n$ and $b_{ij} = \bar{b}_{ji} = \frac{1}{2}(a_{ij} + \bar{a}_{ji})$. (See Exercise 3.)

Henceforth we shall assume that the forms we consider have been appropriately symmetrized:

$$XAX^*, \quad \text{where} \quad a_{ij} = \bar{a}_{ji}.$$

This condition reduces in the real case to

$$XAX', \quad \text{where} \quad a_{ij} = a_{ji}.$$

Then for a given basis $\{\alpha_1, \ldots, \alpha_n\}$ for a complex vector space, the function $h(\xi) = XAX^*$, where $\xi = \sum_{i=1}^{n} x_i \alpha_i$, is a Hermitian function whose values are specified by the given form. Similarly, in the real case, $q(\xi) = XAX'$ is a quadratic function.

Theorems 8.8 and 8.23 show that two Hermitian matrices represent the same Hermitian function if and only if they have the same rank and signature. Similarly, two real symmetric matrices represent the same quadratic form if and only if they have the same rank and signature.

Definition 8.14.
   (a) The *rank* of a Hermitian function or of a Hermitian form is the rank of any Hermitian matrix which represents that function or form.
   (b) The *rank* of a quadratic function or of a quadratic form is the rank of any real symmetric matrix which represents that function or form.

(c) The *signature* of a Hermitian function or form is the signature of any Hermitian matrix which represents that function or form.

(d) The *signature* of a quadratic function or form is the signature of any real symmetric matrix which represents that function or form.

(e) A Hermitian (quadratic) function is said to be *positive definite* if and only if

$$h(\xi) > 0 \text{ for all } \xi \neq 0,$$
$$(q(\xi) > 0 \text{ for all } \xi \neq 0).$$

Theorem 8.25. A Hermitian function h on a comp'ex vector space $\mathcal{V}_n$ is positive definite if and only if it has rank n and signature n.

PROOF: According to Theorems 8.6 and 8.8, h is represented relative to a suitable basis $\{\alpha_1, \ldots, \alpha_n\}$ by the canonical form under conjunctivity,

$$h(\xi) = x_1 \bar{x}_1 + \cdots + x_p \bar{x}_p - x_{p+1} \bar{x}_{p+1} - \cdots - x_r \bar{x}_r,$$

where $s = 2p - r = p - (r - p)$. If $r = n = s$, then $p = n$ and $h(\xi) > 0$ for all $\xi \neq \theta$. If $r < n$, then $h(\alpha_n) = 0$, and h is not positive definite. If $s < n = r$, then $h(\alpha_n) = -1$, and again h is not positive definite.

Theorem 8.26. A quadratic function q on a real vector space is positive definite if and only if it has rank n and signature n.

PROOF: Exercise.

Theorem 8.27. A Hermitian matrix A represents a positive definite Hermitian function if and only if

$$A = PP^*$$

for some nonsingular complex matrix P.

PROOF: A positive definite quadratic function is represented in canonical form relative to conjunctivity by the identity matrix. Hence A represents that form if and only if

$$A = PIP^*$$

for some nonsingular complex matrix P.

Theorem 8.28. A real symmetric matrix A represents a positive definite quadratic function if and only if

$$A = PP'$$

for some nonsingular real matrix P.

PROOF: Exercise.

Examples of Real Symmetric Quadratic Forms

(a) The expression for the fundamental metric (element of arc length) in three-dimensional space is

$$ds^2 = \begin{cases} dx^2 + dy^2 + dz^2 & \text{in rectangular coordinates,} \\ dr^2 + r^2 d\theta^2 + dz^2 & \text{in cylindrical coordinates,} \\ d\rho^2 + \rho^\circ \sin^2 \psi d\theta^2 + \rho^\circ d\psi^2 & \text{in spherical coordinates.} \end{cases}$$

In the study of differential geometry the expression for the fundamental metric of a surface is of basic importance.

(b) In classical mechanics the kinetic energy of a particle of mass m and having n degrees of freedom is given by

$$KE = \frac{m}{2} \sum_{i=1}^{n} \left(\frac{dx_i}{dt} \right)^2,$$

where the x_i are the position coordinates of the particle. In more general systems the kinetic energy is represented by more complicated quadratic forms.

(c) The equation of a central quadric surface is

$$ax^2 + bxy + cy^2 + dxz + eyz + fz^2 = k,$$

the left hand member being a quadratic form. The numbers b, d, and e are zero only if the axes of the quadric surface coincide with the coordinate axes; in case these are not zero we are interested in finding an orthogonal change of coordinates which will simplify the form to a sum of squares.

Given a Hermitian or quadratic function, it is natural to search for a coordinate system relative to which the form that represents that function is as simple as possible. The usual situation is that we are given a Hermitian or quadratic form, as in Example (c), and we wish to change coordinates in such a way that the form is reduced to a sum of squares. With physical and geometric applications in mind, we are particularly interested in using only rigid motions (isometries) to change coordinates. Our investigation of Hermitian and quadratic forms reduces to a study of Hermitian and real symmetric matrices; we shall see that the characteristic values and vectors of such matrices possess remarkable properties.

Theorem 8.29. Let A be a matrix which is either Hermitian or real and symmetric. Every characteristic value of A is real.

PROOF : By either hypothesis, $A = A^*$. If X is a characteristic vector associated with the characteristic value λ, then

$$XA = \lambda X$$

$$XAX^* = \lambda XX^*.$$

Clearly XX^* is real and positive; also $c = XAX^*$ is real, since A is either Hermitian or real and symmetric. Hence λ is the quotient of two real numbers.

Theorem 8.29 implies that the characteristic polynomial, and therefore the minimal polynomial of A can be factored as a product of real linear factors.

Theorem 8.30. Let A be a matrix which is either Hermitian or real and symmetric. If X_1 and X_2 are characteristic vectors associated with distinct characteristic values λ_1 and λ_2, then $X_1 X_2^* = 0$.

P R O O F : Let $X_i A = \lambda_i X_i,$ $i = 1, 2.$
Then

$$(X_1 A) X_2^* = \lambda_1 X_1 X_2^*,$$

$$X_1 (A X_2^*) = X_1 (X_2 A^*)^* = X_1 (\lambda_2 X_2)^* = \lambda_2 X_1 X_2^*.$$

Hence $(\lambda_1 - \lambda_2) X_1 X_2^* = 0$. Since $\lambda_1 \neq \lambda_2$, we conclude that $X_1 X_2^* = 0$.

Geometrically, this proves that in a Euclidean space the characteristic vectors of a real symmetric matrix are orthogonal whenever they are associated with distinct characteristic values, since $X_1 X_2' = p(\xi_1, \xi_2)$ relative to a normal orthogonal basis. Similarly, in a unitary space two characteristic vectors of a Hermitian matrix are orthogonal whenever they are associated with distinct characteristic values.

The next result is the matrix form of the Principal Axes theorem which asserts that any quadratic form may be reduced to the sum of squares by an appropriate orthogonal transformation. In particular, the axes of any quadric surface are orthogonal, and a rigid motion of the axes of any rectangular coordinate system aligns the new coordinate axes with those of the quadric. The corresponding result for Hermitian forms is valid also.

Theorem 8.31. (Principal Axes theorem.) Any real symmetric matrix A is simultaneously similar to and congruent to a diagonal matrix D; that is, there exists an orthogonal matrix P, such that

$$D = PAP^{-1}$$

is diagonal, with the characteristic values of A along the diagonal.

P R O O F : Let $\{\alpha_1, \ldots, \alpha_n\}$ be a normal orthogonal basis for the Euclidean space $\mathcal{U}$, and let $\mathbf{T}$ be the linear transformation represented by A in that basis. If ξ is any characteristic vector of $\mathbf{T}$, then $\|\xi\|^{-1}\xi$ is of unit length, characteristic, and associated with the same characteristic value as is ξ. Let $\beta_1 = \|\xi\|^{-1}\xi$, where ξ is characteristic, associated with λ_1. Extend to a normal orthogonal basis $\{\beta_1, \ldots, \beta_n\}$ for $\mathcal{U}$. Relative to the new basis, **T** is represented by the matrix

$$B = RAR^{-1} = RAR',$$

where R represents an orthogonal change of basis and is therefore orthogonal. Thus B is real and symmetric, of the form

$$B = \begin{pmatrix} \lambda_1 & Z \\ Z & B_1 \end{pmatrix},$$

where B_1 is a real symmetric square matrix of dimension $n - 1$. We repeat the argument, selecting γ_2 as a normal characteristic vector in the space $[\beta_2, \ldots, \beta_n]$, letting $\gamma_1 = \beta_1$. Since β_1 is orthogonal to $[\beta_2, \ldots, \beta_n]$, γ_1 and γ_2 form a normal orthogonal set that can be extended to a normal orthogonal basis $\{\gamma_1, \gamma_2, \ldots, \gamma_n\}$ for $\mathcal{U}$. Then **T** is represented by C, where

$$C = SBS^{-1} = SBS', \ S \text{ orthogonal},$$

$$C = \left(\begin{array}{cc|c} \lambda_1 & 0 & \\ 0 & \lambda_2 & Z \\ \hline & Z & C_1 \end{array} \right).$$

Since R and S are orthogonal, so is SR, and

$$C = S(RAR')S' = (SR)A(SR)'.$$

Hence A is simultaneously similar and congruent to C; the theorem follows after n steps.

Theorem 8.32. (Principal Axes theorem). Any Hermitian matrix A is simultaneously similar to and conjunctive to a real diagonal matrix D having the characteristic values of A as the diagonal elements:

$$D = PAP^* = PAP^{-1}$$

for some unitary matrix P.

P R O O F : Exercise.

Observe that Theorems 8.31 and 8.32 are strengthened versions of Theorems 8.5 and 8.4, respectively. The reduction of a Hermitian (or real symmetric) matrix to diagonal form can be accomplished by means of unitary (or orthogonal) transformations. Indeed, it is clear that in selecting a basis in the proof of Theorem 8.32 (or 8.31) we could begin with a characteristic vector corresponding to a *positive* characteristic value (if such exists), and continue as long as such values remain; then we could select characteristic

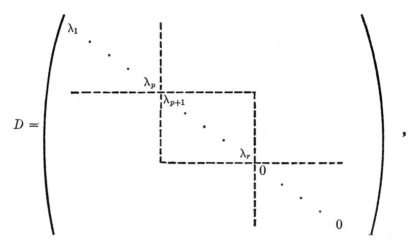

$$D = \begin{pmatrix} \lambda_1 & & & & & & & \\ & \ddots & & & & & & \\ & & \lambda_p & & & & & \\ & & & \lambda_{p+1} & & & & \\ & & & & \ddots & & & \\ & & & & & \lambda_r & & \\ & & & & & & 0 & \\ & & & & & & & \ddots \\ & & & & & & & & 0 \end{pmatrix} ,$$

vectors associated with negative characteristic values, as long as they remain, obtaining

where $\lambda_1, \ldots, \lambda_p$ are positive and $\lambda_{p+1}, \ldots, \lambda_r$ are negative. Clearly r is the rank and $2p - r$ is the signature of A and of the Hermitian (or quadratic) form that A represents. D is similar *and* conjunctive (or congruent) to A. But this is as far as unitary (or orthogonal) transformations can be used in reducing A to canonical form relative to conjunctivity (or congruence) as described by Theorem 8.6 (or Theorem 8.7). Indeed, D is the Jordan form of A, the canonical form of A relative to similarity. The further changes needed to produce 1 and -1 in the nonzero diagonal positions correspond to a change of scale along each of the principal axes already obtained.

Furthermore, we have obtained an alternative description of the rank and signature of a Hermitian (or real symmetric) matrix. As we already know, the rank of any matrix is the number of nonzero characteristic values, each counted according to its multiplicity as a zero of the characteristic polynomial. The signature of a Hermitian (or real symmetric) matrix is the number of positive characteristic values minus the number of negative characteristic values, again each counted according to its algebraic multiplicity.

The actual process of reducing a quadratic form to a sum and difference of squares can be accomplished by the classical process of successively completing squares. However, the Principal Axes theorem provides an alternative method, which we describe for quadratic forms although it is valid for Hermitian forms as well. Given a quadratic form we write the real symmetric matrix A which that form defines. The characteristic values of A are real and allow us to write immediately a diagonal matrix that represents the form after an orthogonal change of coordinates. If we wish also to describe this change of coordinates explicitly, we obtain a complete set of mutually orthogonal characteristic vectors $\xi_1, \xi_2, \ldots, \xi_n$, normalized so that each is of unit length, expressed in terms of the original coordinates. The matrix P, whose row vectors are $\xi_1, \ldots, \xi_n$, is then orthogonal, and $PAP' = D$. The change of coordinates can be obtained explicitly from P. Of course the calculation of characteristic values involves finding the solutions of a polynomial of degree n; this is often difficult. An alternate method of reducing A to diagonal form is to use row and column operations as in Theorem 8.4; however, the change of coordinates represented by such operations is not orthogonal in general.

As a final result, which is of importance in applications such as the solution of vibration problems in dynamics, we show that, given any two Hermitian (or quadratic) forms, one of which is positive definite, there exists a single change of coordinates that diagonalizes both forms. This result is easily explained in terms of two central quadric surfaces in three-dimensional Euclidean space. Each such surface determines a quadratic form, and positive definite forms correspond to ellipsoids. Given a central ellipsoid and a second quadric surface, we can rotate axes to align the new coordinate axes with the axes of the ellipse. This transformation is distance-preserving. Then we change scale along the axes of the ellipsoid, deforming it into a sphere for which any direction is a principal axis. Then we again rotate axes to align the coordinate axes with the principal axes of the second quadric surface. Since the two surfaces have a common center, the new equation for each will be of the form

$$a_1 x_1^2 + a_2 x_2^2 + a_3 x_3^2 = a_4,$$

where a_1, a_2 and a_3 are ± 1.

Theorem 8.33. Let A and B be $n \times n$ Hermitian matrices. If A is positive definite, there exists a nonsingular complex matrix P such that

$$PAP^* = I,$$
$$PBP^* = D, \qquad \text{where } D \text{ is diagonal.}$$

P R O O F : Since A is positive definite, there exists a nonsingular matrix Q such that

$$QAQ^* = I.$$

Then for any unitary matrix R,

$$RQAQ^*R^* = RIR^* = RR^{-1} = I.$$

Since B is Hermitian, QBQ^* is also Hermitian; so by Theorem 8.32 there exists a unitary matrix R such that

$$RQBQ^*R^* = D,$$

where D is diagonal. Let $P = RQ$. Then $PAP^* = I$, and $PBP^* = D$.

Exercises

1. Given the real quadratic form $ax_1^2 + 2bx_1x_2 + cx_2^2$.

(i) Prove that the form is positive definite if and only if $a > 0$ and $b^2 - ac < 0$.

(ii) Show that the central conic $ax^2 + 2bxy + cy^2 = 1$ is an ellipse or hyperbola, depending upon whether the quadratic form on the left has $r = 2$ and $s = 2$, or $r = 2$ and $s = 0$.

2. Represent each of the following quadratic forms by a real symmetric matrix, and determine the rank and signature of each.

(i) $x_1^2 - 2x_1x_3 + 2x_2^2 + 4x_2x_3 + 6x_3^2$.

(ii) $16x_1x_2 - x_3^2$.

(iii) $3x_1^2 + 4x_1x_2 + 8x_1x_3 + 4x_2x_3 + 3x_3^2$.

3. Let A be a complex $n \times n$ matrix with the property that for every complex row vector X, XAX^* is real. Let $A = H + K$ be the decomposition of A as the sum of a Hermitian matrix H and a skew-Hermitian matrix K. Prove that $XAX^* = XHX^*$.

4. Prove Theorems 8.26 and 8.28.

5. Prove Theorem 8.32.

6. The Taylor expansion of a function f of two variables at (a, b) is expressed in terms of the partial derivatives of f by

$$f(a + h, b + k) = f(a, b) + hf_x(a, b) + kf_y(a, b)$$
$$+ \tfrac{1}{2}[h^2 f_{xx}(a, b) + 2hk f_{xy}(a, b) + k^2 f_{yy}(a, b)] + \cdots,$$

provided that $f_{xy} = \dfrac{\partial}{\partial y}\left(\dfrac{\partial f}{\partial x}\right) = \dfrac{\partial}{\partial x}\left(\dfrac{\partial f}{\partial y}\right) = f_{yx}$. If $f_x(a, b) = 0 = f_y(a, b)$, then (a, b) is a critical point for maximum or minimum. The term in brackets is a quadratic form in h and k; if the form has rank 2, it determines whether f has a maximum or minimum or neither at (a, b). Assuming $r = 2$, show that

(i) $f(a, b)$ is a relative maximum if $s = -2$,

(ii) $f(a, b)$ is a relative minimum if $s = 2$,

(iii) $f(a, b)$ is neither maximum nor minimum otherwise.

7. As we know, any quadratic form in three variables can be reduced by an orthogonal change of coordinates to the form

$$\lambda_1 x_1^2 + \lambda_2 x_2^2 + \lambda_3 x_3^2,$$

where the λ_i are real. Hence any centrally symmetric quadric surface has an equation of the form

$$\lambda_1 x_1^2 + \lambda_2 x_2^2 + \lambda_3 x_3^2 = 1$$

in a suitable rectangular coordinate system. Use the rank and signature of the quadratic form to classify all possible types of centrally symmetric quadric surfaces, and identify each type by means of a sketch.

8. Use the following chain of reasoning to prove Hadamard's inequality: If A is a real $n \times n$ matrix such that $|a_{ij}| \leq k$ for all i, j, then

$$|\det A| \leq k^n n^{n/2}.$$

(A special case of this result was derived in Exercise 10, § 8.4.)

(i) Let $B_0 = AA'$; then B_0 is real and symmetric.

(ii) If A is nonsingular, B_0 is positive definite.

(iii) If B is any $n \times n$ real, symmetric, positive definite matrix, if $x_1, \ldots, x_n$ are any nonzero numbers, and if $c_{ij} = b_{ij}x_ix_j$, then C is symmetric and positive definite.

(iv) If C is any $n \times n$ real, symmetric, positive definite matrix, then

$$\det C \leq \left[\frac{\operatorname{tr} C}{n}\right]^n.$$

(v) Let C be defined as in (iii), using $B = B_0$ and $x_i = b_{ii}^{-1/2}$. Show that $\operatorname{tr} C = n$, and $\det B = \det C \cdot \Pi_{i=1}^n b_{ii}$.

(vi) Complete the proof of Hadamard's inequality.

9. Use Hadamard's inequality to show that if A is a real $n \times n$ matrix such that $|a_{ij}| \leq k$ for all i, j, and if the characteristic polynomial of A is

$$(-1)^n[\lambda^n + c_1\lambda^{n-1} + \cdots + c_n],$$

then

$$|c_j| \leq \binom{n}{j} j^{j/2}k^j, \text{ for } j = 1, 2, \ldots, n.$$

§8.6. *Normal Matrices and Transformations*

In the last section we saw that each Hermitian matrix and each real symmetric matrix is diagonable, and furthermore that the diagonalization can be performed by an isometry, a change of coordinates that corresponds to a rigid motion of the coordinate axes. When we first discussed diagonalization generally, no inner product had been defined on the underlying vector space, so we were not concerned with the type of transformation used to diagonalize a matrix, except that it had to be nonsingular. In this section we shall reconsider the diagonalization problem, regarding a given matrix as representing a linear transformation on an inner product space and restricting our attention to isometric transformations.

We recall that an isometry **T** is called unitary or orthogonal, according to whether the underlying vector space is complex or real; relative to a normal orthogonal basis, **T** is represented by a matrix P, which is unitary or orthogonal, respectively. A unitary matrix is characterized by the equation $P^* = P^{-1}$, an orthogonal matrix by $P' = P^{-1}$. Since the former condition reduces to the latter when A is real, we shall use the term *isometric* to describe a matrix that is either unitary or orthogonal; that is, any matrix P for which $P^* = P^{-1}$. We shall say that A is *isometrically diagonable* if and only if PAP^{-1} is diagonal for some isometric matrix P.

If A is isometrically diagonable, then for some isometric matrix P and some diagonal matrix D, we have

$$D = PAP^{-1} = PAP^*$$
$$D^* = \bar{D} = PA^*P^* = PA^*P^{-1}$$
$$DD^* = (PAP^{-1})(PA^*P^*) = PAA^*P^*$$
$$D^*D = (PA^*P^{-1})(PAP^*) = PA^*AP^*$$

Since diagonal matrices commute and P is nonsingular, we conclude that

$$AA^* = A^*A.$$

Hence, a necessary condition that A be isometrically diagonable is that A and A^* commute. Our next objective is to prove that this condition is also sufficient.

Definition 8.15. A matrix A of complex numbers is said to be *normal* if and only if

$$AA^* = A^*A.$$

Since any real number is also a complex number, this definition also applies to a real matrix, in which case $AA' = A'A$.

Theorem 8.34. Let A be any $n \times n$ matrix and P any $n \times n$ isometric matrix. Then A is normal if and only if PAP^* is normal.

P R O O F : Exercise.

The fact that normality is preserved under isometric changes of bases suggests a way to proceed. We first show that any matrix may be reduced to lower triangular form by means of an isometry. Then we show that any lower triangular matrix which is normal must be diagonal.

Theorem 8.35. If A is any $n \times n$ matrix, there exists a unitary matrix U such that UAU^* is lower triangular.

P R O O F : Choose any normal orthogonal basis for complex $\mathcal{V}_n$, and let **T** be the linear transformation represented by A relative to that basis. Let λ_1 be a characteristic value of **T**, and γ_1 a corresponding characteristic vector of unit length. Extend to a normal orthogonal basis $\{\gamma_1, \beta_2, \ldots, \beta_n\}$ for $\mathcal{U}_n$. Then **T** is represented relative to the new basis by a matrix $B = P_1 A P_1^*$, where P_1 is unitary and where B has the block form

$$B = \begin{pmatrix} \lambda_1 & Z \\ B_3 & B_4 \end{pmatrix}.$$

If $n = 1$ or 2, B is lower triangular, and the theorem is proved. For $n > 2$, we proceed by induction, assuming that the theorem is valid for all $(n - 1) \times (n - 1)$ matrices. Thus there exists a unitary matrix Q such that QB_4Q^* is lower triangular. Let P_2 be defined by the block form

$$P_2 = \begin{pmatrix} 1 & Z \\ Z & Q \end{pmatrix}.$$

Since Q is unitary, the row vectors of P_2 are orthogonal and of unit length. Hence P_2 is unitary, and by direct calculation

$$P_2 B P_2^* = \begin{pmatrix} \lambda_1 & Z \\ QB_3 & QB_4Q^* \end{pmatrix},$$

which is lower triangular. Let $U = P_2 P_1$. Then U is unitary, and UAU^* is lower triangular.

The reason for using unitary transformations and complex $\mathcal{U}_n$ in Theorem 8.35 was necessity rather than convenience: a real matrix need not have any real characteristic values. If a real matrix A is orthogonally similar over the real numbers to a lower triangular matrix B, the diagonal elements of B are real, and these are the characteristic values of B and of A. Conversely, if all the characteristic values of A are real, then the proof of Theorem 8.35 can be adapted to show that PAP' is lower triangular for some real orthogonal matrix P.

Theorem 8.36. An $n \times n$ matrix A is normal if and only if there exists a unitary matrix U such that UAU^* is diagonal.

P R O O F : The argument that precedes Definition 8.15 proves the "if" part. Suppose A is normal. Then by Theorems 8.34 and 8.35, for some unitary matrix U, UAU^* is lower triangular and normal:

$$B = UAU^* = \begin{pmatrix} b_{11} & 0 & \cdots & 0 \\ b_{21} & b_{22} & \cdots & 0 \\ \cdot & \cdot & \cdot & \cdot \\ \cdot & \cdot & \cdot & \cdot \\ \cdot & \cdot & \cdot & \cdot \\ b_{n1} & b_{n2} & \cdots & b_{nn} \end{pmatrix}.$$

Equating the expressions for the (i, j) elements of BB^* and B^*B, we have

$$\sum_{k=1}^{n} b_{ik}\bar{b}_{jk} = \sum_{k=1}^{n} \bar{b}_{ki}b_{kj}.$$

But $b_{rs} = 0$ whenever $r < s$. For $i = j = 1$, we have

$$b_{11}\bar{b}_{11} = b_{11}\bar{b}_{11} + b_{21}\bar{b}_{21} + \cdots + b_{n1}\bar{b}_{n1}.$$

Hence $b_{r1} = 0$ whenever $r > 1$. Then for $i = j = 2$, we have

$$b_{22}\bar{b}_{22} = b_{22}\bar{b}_{22} + b_{32}\bar{b}_{32} + \cdots + b_{n2}\bar{b}_{n2}.$$

Hence $b_{r2} = 0$ whenever $r > 2$. Continuing in this way, we have $b_{rs} = 0$ whenever $r > s$. Hence B is diagonal.

As a final consideration let us investigate what A^* means when interpreted as a linear transformation on an inner product space. That is, given a linear transformation $\mathbf{T}$ on a finite-dimensional inner product space $\mathcal{V}$, $\mathbf{T}$ is represented relative to a normal orthogonal basis by a matrix A, for which A^* is easily calculated. Relative to the same basis, A^* represents a linear transformation on $\mathcal{V}$, say $\mathbf{T}^*$. How are $\mathbf{T}$ and $\mathbf{T}^*$ related?

Let $\xi = \sum_{i=1}^{n} x_i\alpha_i$ and $\eta = \sum_{k=1}^{n} y_k\alpha_k$. We also have

$$\alpha_i\mathbf{T} = \sum_{j=1}^{n} a_{ij}\alpha_j, \qquad \alpha_k\mathbf{T}^* = \sum_{i=1}^{n} \bar{a}_{ik}\alpha_i.$$

Then

$$p(\xi\mathbf{T}, \eta) = p\left(\sum_{j=1}^{n}\left(\sum_{i=1}^{n} x_i a_{ij}\right)\alpha_j, \sum_{k=1}^{n} y_k\alpha_k\right),$$

$$= \sum_{j=1}^{n}\left(\sum_{i=1}^{n} x_i a_{ij}\right) p\left(\alpha_j, \sum_{k=1}^{n} y_k\alpha_k\right),$$

$$= \sum_{j=1}^{n}\left(\sum_{i=1}^{n} x_i a_{ij}\right)\bar{y}_j,$$

$$= \sum_{i=1}^{n} x_i\left(\sum_{j=1}^{n} a_{ij}\bar{y}_j\right),$$

$$= \sum_{i=1}^{n}\sum_{j=1}^{n} a_{ij}\bar{y}_j p\left(\sum_{k=1}^{n} x_k\alpha_k, \alpha_i\right),$$

$$= \sum_{i=1}^{n} p\left(\sum_{k=1}^{n} x_k\alpha_k, \sum_{j=1}^{n} y_j\bar{a}_{ij}\alpha_i\right),$$

$$= p\left(\sum_{k=1}^{n} x_k\alpha_k, \sum_{j=1}^{n} y_j\left(\sum_{i=1}^{n} \bar{a}_{ij}\alpha_i\right)\right),$$

$$= p\left(\xi, \sum_{j=1}^{n} y_j\alpha_j\mathbf{T}^*\right),$$

$$= p(\xi, \eta\mathbf{T}^*).$$

Hence for all $\xi, \eta \in \mathcal{V}$, $\mathbf{T}^*$ satisfies the property

$$p(\xi, \eta\mathbf{T}^*) = p(\xi\mathbf{T}, \eta).$$

But from Exercise 3, § 8.2 we recall that if β_1 and β_2 are vectors such that $p(\xi, \beta_1) = p(\xi, \beta_2)$ for all $\xi \in \mathcal{V}$, then $\beta_1 = \beta_2$. This means that a vector is uniquely determined by specifying the value of its inner product with each vector of the space. Thus $\mathbf{T}^*$ is uniquely defined on $\mathcal{V}$ by $\mathbf{T}$ and the given inner product.

Definition 8.16. The *adjoint* of a linear transformation $\mathbf{T}$ on an inner product space $\mathcal{V}$ is the mapping $\mathbf{T}^*$ of $\mathcal{V}$ into $\mathcal{V}$ which is defined by the equation

$$p(\xi, \eta\mathbf{T}^*) = p(\xi\mathbf{T}, \eta) \text{ for all } \xi, \eta \in \mathcal{V}.$$

As an exercise you may verify that $\mathbf{T}^*$ is linear; that is, for all ξ, η_1, $\eta_2 \in \mathcal{V}$ and all scalars a, b,

$$p(\xi, (a\eta_1 + b\eta_2)\mathbf{T}^*) = p(\xi, a(\eta_1\mathbf{T}^*) + b(\eta_2\mathbf{T}^*)).$$

Theorem 8.37. Relative to a given normal orthogonal basis, if $\mathbf{T}$ is represented by a matrix A and $\mathbf{T}^*$ by a matrix B, then $B = A^*$.

P R O O F : Exercise.

Following the terminology introduced for matrices, a *normal* transformation is one that commutes with its adjoint, $\mathbf{TT}^* = \mathbf{T}^*\mathbf{T}$. This class of transformations is of particular interest because Theorem 8.36 guarantees that a normal transformation decomposes the underlying space into a direct sum of the characteristic subspaces of $\mathbf{T}$ that furthermore are mutually orthogonal. This implies that if $\mathbf{T}$ is normal and if ξ_1 and ξ_2 are characteristic vectors associated with distinct characteristic values, then $p(\xi_1, \xi_2) = 0$. An important subclass of normal transformations are *self-adjoint* transformations, $\mathbf{T} = \mathbf{T}^*$. Since the characteristic values of $\mathbf{T}^*$ are the complex conjugates of the characteristic values of $\mathbf{T}$, the characteristic values of a self-adjoint transformation are real. Self-adjoint transformations are called *Hermitian* in the complex case, *symmetric* in the real case.

If we consider the real case, another question comes to mind. If $\mathbf{T}$ is represented by A, then $\mathbf{T}^*$, a transformation on $\mathcal{V}$, is represented by A'. But in Theorem 4.1 we saw that A' represents a mapping $\mathbf{T}'$ of the dual space $\mathcal{V}'$, relative to the dual basis. How are $\mathbf{T}^*$ and $\mathbf{T}'$ related? Even for complex inner product spaces it makes sense to ask whether there is a natural relation between the adjoint $\mathbf{T}^*$ and the transpose $\mathbf{T}'$ of $\mathbf{T}$, so we shall investigate the question in that form.

Let $\mathcal{V}$ be a finite-dimensional inner product space over the complex numbers, $\mathcal{V}'$ the dual space of all linear mappings from $\mathcal{V}$ to $\mathcal{C}$. With each $\mathbf{f} \in \mathcal{V}'$ we associate the vector $\phi_\mathbf{f} \in \mathcal{V}$, defined by

$$p(\xi, \phi_\mathbf{f}) = \xi\mathbf{f} \quad \text{for every } \xi \in \mathcal{V}.$$

As we observed previously, $\phi_\mathbf{f}$ is uniquely determined because the value of its inner product with each vector has been specified. This mapping ϕ from $\mathcal{V}'$ to $\mathcal{V}$ is one-to-one, for if $\phi_\mathbf{f} = \phi_\mathbf{g}$ then $\xi\mathbf{f} = \xi\mathbf{g}$ for all $\xi \in \mathcal{V}$, and $\mathbf{f} = \mathbf{g}$. Conversely, to each $\eta \in \mathcal{V}$ we can associate the function Ψ_η from $\mathcal{V}$ into $\mathcal{C}$, defined by

$$\xi\Psi_\eta = p(\xi, \eta),$$

which is linear because p is linear in its first component. Then $\Psi_\eta \in \mathcal{V}'$, so ψ is a mapping from $\mathcal{V}$ to $\mathcal{V}'$; furthermore

$$p(\xi, \phi_{\psi_\eta}) = \xi\Psi_\eta = p(\xi, \eta).$$

Hence $\phi_{\psi_\eta} = \eta$, and ϕ is onto $\mathcal{V}$. Clearly $\Psi = \phi^{-1}$.

It is a matter of direct computation to verify that

$$\phi_{\mathbf{f}+\mathbf{g}} = \phi_\mathbf{f} + \phi_\mathbf{g},$$

$$\phi_{a\mathbf{f}} = \bar{a}\phi_\mathbf{f},$$

since p is conjugate linear in the second component. Hence if $\mathcal{V}$ is a real vector space, ϕ is a vector space isomorphism from $\mathcal{V}'$ onto $\mathcal{V}$, but if $\mathcal{V}$ is complex, ϕ is one-to-one onto $\mathcal{V}$ but not an isomorphism.

Now we are ready to compare $\mathbf{T}'$ as a transformation of $\mathcal{V}'$ with $\mathbf{T}^*$ as a transformation of $\mathcal{V}$. These mappings were defined by the respective equations

$$\xi(f\mathbf{T}') = (\xi\mathbf{T})\mathbf{f} \text{ for all } \xi \in \mathcal{V}, \ \mathbf{f} \in \mathcal{V}',$$

$$p(\xi, \eta\mathbf{T}^*) = p(\xi\mathbf{T}, \eta) \text{ for all } \xi, \eta \in \mathcal{V}.$$

What we will show is that these two mappings preserve the one-to-one correspondence ϕ, which exists between the spaces $\mathcal{V}$ and $\mathcal{V}'$: $\phi_\mathbf{f}\mathbf{T}^* = \phi_{\mathbf{f}\mathbf{T}'}$ for all $\mathbf{f} \in \mathcal{V}'$. To see this we let $\xi \in \mathcal{V}$ and $\mathbf{f} \in \mathcal{V}'$; from the defining equations for ϕ, $\mathbf{T}'$, and $\mathbf{T}^*$ we have

$$\xi(f\mathbf{T}') = p(\xi, \phi_{\mathbf{f}\mathbf{T}'}),$$

$$= (\xi\mathbf{T})\mathbf{f},$$

$$= p(\xi\mathbf{T}, \phi_\mathbf{f}),$$

$$= p(\xi, \phi_\mathbf{f}\mathbf{T}^*).$$

Again using the fact that a vector is uniquely determined by values of its inner product with every vector of the space, we conclude that $\phi_\mathbf{f}\mathbf{T}^* = \phi_{\mathbf{f}\mathbf{T}'}$. Hence for a finite-dimensional real inner product space the isomorphism ϕ between $\mathcal{V}$ and its dual space $\mathcal{V}'$ permits us to regard $\mathbf{T}'$ either as a linear transformation on $\mathcal{V}'$ or as a linear transformation on $\mathcal{V}$, with the assurance that each pair of corresponding vectors in the two spaces is mapped by $\mathbf{T}'$ into a pair of corresponding vectors.

As a further result in this connection, Exercise 8 demonstrates that the mapping ϕ can be used to obtain an inner product p^* for $\mathcal{V}'$ in terms of a given inner product p for $\mathcal{V}$ by defining

$$p^*(\mathbf{f}, \mathbf{g}) = p(\phi_{\mathbf{g}}, \phi_{\mathbf{f}}).$$

The reversal of the two components introduces the conjugate that is needed in the complex case to compensate for the fact that ϕ fails to be an isomorphism only because

$$\phi_{a\mathbf{f}} = \bar{a}\phi_{\mathbf{f}}.$$

Exercises

1. Prove Theorem 8.34.

2. Let A be a real matrix for which every characteristic value is real. Deduce that A is orthogonally diagonable if and only if A is normal.

3. Prove that an $n \times n$ matrix A is normal if and only if there exists a set of n mutually orthogonal characteristic vectors.

4. To illustrate Exercises 2 and 3, refer to the matrix A given in Exercise 1(i), § 7.5. Show that the characteristic values of A are real, that A is diagonable, but that A is not orthogonally diagonable.

5. Prove that $\mathbf{T}^*$ is linear.

6. Prove Theorem 8.37.

7. Prove the following assertions about a normal transformation $\mathbf{T}$ and its adjoint.

    (i) $\|\xi\mathbf{T}\| = \|\xi\mathbf{T}^*\|$ for every $\xi \in \mathcal{V}$.

    (ii) λ is a characteristic value of $\mathbf{T}$ if and only if $\bar{\lambda}$ is a characteristic value of $\mathbf{T}^*$.

    (iii) ξ is a characteristic vector of $\mathbf{T}$ if and only if ξ is a characteristic vector of $\mathbf{T}^*$.

    (iv) If ξ_1 and ξ_2 are characteristic vectors of $\mathbf{T}$ associated with distinct characteristic values, then ξ_1 and ξ_2 are orthogonal.

8. Let $\mathcal{V}$ be a finite-dimensional complex inner product space, $\mathcal{V}'$ its dual space, and ϕ the one-to-one mapping of $\mathcal{V}'$ onto $\mathcal{V}$ defined in the text. Let p^* be the mapping of $\mathcal{V}' \times \mathcal{V}$ into $\mathcal{C}$ defined by

$$p^*(\mathbf{f}, \mathbf{g}) = p(\phi_{\mathbf{g}}, \phi_{\mathbf{f}}).$$

Prove that p^* is an inner product on $\mathcal{V}'$.

9. Carry out the details of the following derivation of the *polar decomposition* of a nonsingular matrix A as the product of a positive definite Hermitian matrix H and an isometric matrix Q.

(i) AA^* is Hermitian.

(ii) For some isometry P, $PAA^*P^* = D$ is diagonal with a positive real number in each diagonal position.

(iii) There exists a diagonal matrix E for which $E^2 = D$ and $e_{ii} > 0$ for every i.

(iv) Let $H = P^*EP$; then H is Hermitian and positive definite.

(v) Let $Q = H(A^*)^{-1}$; then Q is an isometry.

(vi) $A = HQ$.

CHAPTER 9

Combinatorial Equivalence

§9.1. *Preliminary Remarks*

Up to this point most of the material we have considered is central to a general study of matrices. This is not to claim that we have investigated every central idea, nor that every previous result is basic for any given application of matrix theory. Certainly only the surface has been scratched on some important topics, and a considerable body of material remains to be investigated. But almost any introductory course in linear algebra will be concerned with the material of Chapters 2 to 8, perhaps with a different ordering of these topics and with variations of the degree of generality with which each is considered.

The question of what topics should be studied next would receive different answers according to the interests of the individual. For prospective mathematicians there are many important applications to geometry, analysis, probability theory, and algebra. The generalization to infinite-dimensional vector spaces is of special interest and importance. The physicist may be more interested in applications to Newtonian mechanics, quantum mechanics, and relativity, the chemist to crystal structure or spectroscopy. The engineer will find applications to elasticity, electrical networks, wave propagation, and aircraft flutter. The economist might prefer to learn how to apply matrices to linear programming and game theory in order to solve problems in transportation, logistics, communications, and assignments. The biologist would wish to relate matrix theory to genetics, the psychologist to theory of learning or to dominance relations, and the sociologist to group relations and social customs.

Such applications of matrix theory are of genuine interest, not only for their effectiveness in solving significant problems of social and scientific import, but also because applications stimulate the development of new knowledge about matrices. Thus there is a strong temptation to discuss a number of these applications in the remainder of this book. Several considerations militate against this. First, the fields of application are sufficiently technical that a brief account of the background material would be necessarily fragmentary and perhaps superficial. Second, the range of applications is so broad that the selection of only a few topics would be either biased or capricious.

Therefore you are strongly encouraged to consult other sources for information on applications of matrix theory. In particular, Chapters 6 and 7 of Reference 29 contain an introductory exposition of several of these topics, and References 6 and 26 contain extensive references to applications, listed according to subject matter.

In the present chapter we shall develop some of the mathematics that is used to formulate and to solve a linear program. In the final chapter we shall draw upon the content of normal undergraduate work in function theory, extending to matrices the concepts of sequences, series, and functions.

§9.2. *Linear Inequalities*

As a generalization of the systems of linear equations studied in Chapter 5, we now consider a system of linear inequalities of the form

$$
\begin{aligned}
a_{11}x_1 + a_{12}x_2 + \cdots + a_{1n}x_n &\geq b_1 \\
a_{21}x_1 + a_{22}x_2 + \cdots + a_{2n}x_n &\geq b_2 \\
&\vdots \\
a_{m1}x_1 + a_{m2}x_2 + \cdots + a_{mn}x_n &\geq b_m,
\end{aligned}
$$

(9.1)

where each a_{ij} and each b_k is real and where $X = (x_1, \ldots, x_n)$ is a vector in Euclidean n-space $\mathcal{E}_n$. Each expression

$$a_{i1}x_1 + a_{i2}x_2 + \cdots + a_{in}x_n$$

defines a linear functional on $\mathcal{E}_n$, and we previously observed that the set of all $X \in \mathcal{E}_n$, for which

$$a_{i1}x_1 + a_{i2}x_2 + \cdots + a_{in}x_n = b_i$$

is a hyperplane in $\mathcal{E}_n$, a translation of an $(n-1)$-dimensional subspace. The set of all X for which

$$a_{i1}x_1 + a_{i2}x_2 + \cdots + a_{in}x_n \geq b_i$$

is called a *closed half-space* because it is the set of all points in $\mathcal{E}_n$ that lie
either on a hyperplane or on one side of that hyperplane. Hence the solution
of *(9.1)* consists of all points of $\mathcal{E}_n$ which are in the intersection of the m half-
spaces determined by the given inequalities. Clearly the solution can be the
void set, a single point, or an infinite set. It seems geometrically obvious,
and is not difficult to prove, that the solution set must be *convex*, meaning
that whenever two points lie in the set, the line segment joining them also
lies in the set.

As a two-dimensional example consider the system

$$4x + 3y \leq 12$$
$$x - 2y \leq 0$$
$$2x - y \geq -4.$$

The solution set consists of all points in the triangular region sketched. In
the example the third inequality relation is opposite in sense to the first two,

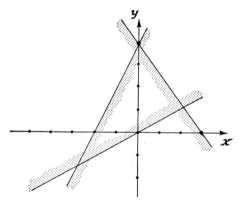

Figure 9.1

but this can be remedied by multiplying the first two inequalities by -1 to
obtain a system in the form *(9.1)*. Indeed any system of linear inequalities
can be converted to the form *(9.1)*.

Now let $(u_1, u_2, \ldots, u_n)$ be any solution of *(9.1)*; define the m-component
vector $(v_1, v_2, \ldots, v_m)$ by

$$v_i = (a_{i1}u_1 + \cdots + a_{in}u_n) - b_i, \qquad \text{for } i = 1, \ldots, m,$$

and observe that

$$v_i \geq 0 \qquad \text{for each } i = 1, 2, \ldots, m.$$

Hence each solution of the system *(9.1)* of m linear *inequalities* in n variables
determines a solution of the system of m linear *equations* in $m + n$ variables,
given by

$$-v_1 \qquad\qquad + a_{11}x_1 + \cdots + a_{1n}x_n = b_1$$

$$(9.2)$$

$$-v_m + a_{m1}x_1 + \cdots + a_{mn}x_n = b_m,$$

and furthermore the values of v_i for that solution are *nonnegative*. Conversely, any solution of (9.2) for which the v_i are nonnegative determines a solution of (9.1). This observation allows us to treat the problem of solving a system of linear inequalities by the techniques used for solving systems of linear equations, with the added restriction that certain of the variables must be nonnegative.

As in § 5.5, (9.2) can be expressed in matrix notation,

$$(-I|A) \begin{pmatrix} V \\ X \end{pmatrix} = B.$$

Here I is $m \times m$, A is $m \times n$, V is $m \times 1$, X is $n \times 1$, and B is $m \times 1$. The condition that no component of V be negative can be expressed

$$V \geq Z.$$

An inequality relation for vectors has not been defined previously; in general, for two real n-component vectors we write

$$X \geq Y$$

if and only if *each* component of X is as large as the corresponding component of Y:

$$x_i \geq y_i \qquad \text{for } i = 1, 2, \ldots, n.$$

This relation is reflexive and transitive, but unlike the ordering relation for real numbers, it does not follow that for any two n-component vectors either $X \geq Y$ or $Y \geq X$, since some but not all components of X might exceed the corresponding component of Y. Such a relation is called a *partial* ordering. Our discussion can be summarized as follows.

Theorem 9.1. A system $AX \geq B$ of real linear inequalities has a solution X_0 if and only if there exists a vector $V_0 \geq Z$ such that

$$(-I|A) \begin{pmatrix} V_0 \\ X_0 \end{pmatrix} = B.$$

There is another interpretation of (9.1) which is sometimes helpful. The left-hand side of each inequality is simply the inner product of X and a row vector of A, relative to a normal orthogonal basis for $\mathcal{E}_n$. A solution X_0 is simply a vector whose inner product with each of n given row vectors A_i exceeds a given value b_i.

Exercises

1. Sketch the graphs of each of the following systems of linear inequalities, indicating the solution set.

(i)
$$x_1 - 2x_2 \geq 4$$
$$x_1 + x_2 \leq 7$$
$$x_2 \geq 0$$

(ii)
$$x_1 - 2x_2 \geq 4$$
$$x_1 + x_2 \geq 7$$
$$x_1 \geq 0$$
$$x_2 \geq 0$$

(iii)
$$x_1 - 2x_2 \leq 4$$
$$x_1 + x_2 \leq 7$$
$$2x_1 - x_2 \leq -8$$
$$x_1 \geq 0$$
$$x_2 \geq 0$$

2. Determine the maximum and minimum of the function $3x_1 + 2x_2$ on each of the solution sets of Exercise 1.

3. In $\mathcal{E}_n$ the line segment joining two points ξ and η is defined to be the set of all vectors ζ of the form
$$\zeta = k\xi + (1 - k)\eta, \qquad 0 \leq k \leq 1.$$
A subset C of $\mathcal{E}_n$ is said to be *convex* if and only if each point of the line segment joining any two points of C also belongs to C.

(i) Prove that any half-space, defined in $\mathcal{E}_n$ by a linear inequality, is convex.

(ii) Prove that the intersection of two convex sets is convex.

(iii) Deduce that the solution set of a system of linear inequalities is convex.

4. Given a closed convex subset C of $\mathcal{E}_n$, and a linear form f defined for each $\xi = (x_1, \ldots, x_n)$ by
$$f(\xi) = c_1x_1 + c_2x_2 + \cdots + c_nx_n.$$

(i) Show that f is a monotone function along any line segment in $\mathcal{E}_n$.

(ii) Show that if f assumes a maximal or minimal value on C, then that extremal value must occur on the boundary of C.

(iii) Deduce that if C is defined by a system of linear inequalities, then any extremal value of f must occur at a "corner" point, the intersection of two or more half-spaces that bound C.

§9.3. *Linear Programming*

In this section we shall see how systems of linear inequalities arise in a natural way in problems of economic interest. As usual, however, the mathematical formulation of such problems and the methods of solution also apply to problems which are far removed from economic motivation. We begin with a simple example.

A metal processor wishes to produce an alloy of tin and lead, containing at least 60 percent lead and at least 35 percent tin. He can purchase four different alloys having the percentage compositions and hundredweight prices shown in the table below.

ALLOYS

	A_1	A_2	A_3	A_4	*Desired*
Lead	40	60	80	70	≥ 60
Tin	60	40	20	30	≥ 35
Costs	240	180	160	210	Minimal

How should the processor blend the alloys in order to minimize his costs? Suppose that $x_1, \ldots, x_4$ represent the proportions of the corresponding alloys in any hundredweight mixture. The explicit conditions of the problem may be expressed as a system of linear inequalities of the form (9.1):

$$\text{Lead:} \quad 40x_1 + 60x_2 + 80x_3 + 70x_4 \geq 60$$

$$\text{Tin:} \quad 60x_1 + 40x_2 + 20x_3 + 30x_4 \geq 35$$

$$\text{Cost:} \quad 240x_1 + 180x_2 + 160x_3 + 210x_4 = C.$$

But there are also some intrinsic conditions, namely that each x_i be *nonnegative* and

$$x_1 + x_2 + x_3 + x_4 = 1.$$

The problem is to determine the x_i such that all conditions are satisfied and the value of C is minimized.

The definition of a primal linear programming problem is a direct generalization of this example. Given a system of m linear inequalities in n variables

$$a_{11}x_1 + a_{12}x_2 + \cdots + a_{1n}x_n \geq b_1$$
$$a_{21}x_1 + a_{22}x_2 + \cdots + a_{2n}x_n \geq b_2$$
$$\vdots$$
$$a_{m1}x_1 + a_{m2}x_2 + \cdots + a_{mn}x_n \geq b_m,$$

the condition that each variable be nonnegative,

$$x_1 \geq 0$$
$$x_2 \geq 0$$
$$\vdots$$
$$x_n \geq 0,$$

and a linear form

$$v = c_1x_1 + c_2x_2 + \cdots + c_nx_n;$$

determine, from among all n-tuples $(x_1, \ldots, x_n)$ that satisfy all of the specified restrictions, one which makes the value of v as small as possible.

Stated in matrix form, a primal linear programming problem becomes this: given a real $m \times n$ matrix A, a real $m \times 1$ vector B, and a real $n \times 1$ vector C; determine a real $n \times 1$ vector X for which

$$AX \geq B$$
$$X \geq Z,$$

and such that the linear form

$$C \cdot X$$

is minimized.

It is also of interest to state the problem in vector space terminology. Of course A determines a linear transformation and X a vector. In order to convert to right-hand notation, as in § 5.1, it is necessary to take transposes: $X'A' \geq B'$. The transformation $\mathbf{T}$ corresponding to A' maps $\mathcal{E}_n$ into $\mathcal{E}_m$; X' corresponds to a vector in $\mathcal{E}_n$ and B' to a vector in $\mathcal{E}_m$. The vector C' determines a linear form on $\mathcal{E}_n$; hence we let C' correspond to a vector in the dual space $\mathcal{E}_n'$. Thus the primal linear programming problem may be stated as follows: given a linear transformation $\mathbf{T}$ from $\mathcal{E}_n$ to $\mathcal{E}_m$, a vector $\beta \in \mathcal{E}_m$, and a linear functional $\mathbf{c} \in \mathcal{E}_n'$, determine a vector $\xi \in \mathcal{E}_n$ such that

$$\xi\mathbf{T} \geq \beta$$
$$\xi \geq \theta,$$

and such that the value of the linear functional

$$\xi\mathbf{c}$$

is minimized.

The introduction of the dual space suggests a symmetry in the linear programming problem which is of great importance. We recall that the transpose $\mathbf{T}'$ of $\mathbf{T}$ is a mapping from $\mathcal{E}'_m$ to $\mathcal{E}'_n$ defined by the equation

$$\alpha(f\mathbf{T}') = (\alpha\mathbf{T})\mathbf{f} \text{ for all } \alpha \in \mathcal{E}_n \text{ and all } \mathbf{f} \in \mathcal{E}'_m.$$

Hence the situation is as indicated in Figure 9.2.

$$\mathcal{E}_n \xrightarrow{\mathbf{T}} \mathcal{E}_m$$
$$\beta$$

$$\mathcal{E}'_n \xleftarrow{\mathbf{T}'} \mathcal{E}'_m$$
$$\mathbf{c}$$

Figure 9.2

The symmetry makes clear that a linear programming problem defined by $\mathbf{T}$, β, and $\mathbf{c}$ determines a similar problem defined by $\mathbf{T}'$, $\mathbf{c}$, and β. The symmetry becomes even more apparent if we alter notation so that the elements of the dual space are written as vectors with Greek letters; for example, write γ for $\mathbf{c}$. Since any vector is also a linear functional on its dual space we shall write a Greek letter in bold face if we wish to emphasize its role as a linear functional.

Now choose any $\xi \in \mathcal{E}_n$ and any $\eta \in \mathcal{E}'_m$ such that $\xi \geq \theta$ and $\eta \geq \theta$. If $\xi\mathbf{T} \geq \beta$, then

$$\beta\boldsymbol{\eta} \leq (\xi\mathbf{T})\boldsymbol{\eta} = \xi(\eta\mathbf{T}').$$

If we further require that $\eta\mathbf{T}' \leq \gamma$, then we have

$$\xi(\eta\mathbf{T}') \leq \xi\boldsymbol{\gamma}.$$

Since the values of $\beta\boldsymbol{\eta}$ and $\xi\boldsymbol{\gamma}$ are obtained as the scalar product of two m-tuples and two n-tuples respectively, we therefore conclude that

$$\beta \cdot \eta \leq \gamma \cdot \xi.$$

Hence any $\eta \geq \theta$ which satisfies $\eta\mathbf{T}' \leq \gamma$ determines with β a lower bound of the function which the primal problem seeks to minimize. If we maximize $\beta \cdot \eta$ for all such η we still have a lower bound,

$$\max(\beta \cdot \eta) \leq \gamma \cdot \xi,$$

valid for all ξ which satisfy $\xi \geq \theta$ and $\xi\mathbf{T} \geq \beta$. Hence we conclude that

$$\max(\beta \cdot \eta) \leq \min(\gamma \cdot \xi)$$

as ξ is varied over all such vectors.

We recall from § 8.5 that in the real case $\mathbf{T}' = \mathbf{T}^*$ and therefore $\mathbf{T}'$ can be regarded as a mapping from $\mathcal{E}_m$ to $\mathcal{E}_n$ without referring to the dual space; with β and η regarded as vectors in the same space the calculation of $\beta \cdot \eta$ is fully justified. Now it is easy to state what is called the *dual* linear programming problem; for comparison we repeat the statement of the primal problem.

Given fixed vectors $\beta \in \mathcal{E}_m$ and $\gamma \in \mathcal{E}_n$ and given a fixed linear transformation $\mathbf{T}$ from $\mathcal{E}_n$ to $\mathcal{E}_m$:

Primal problem. Determine $\xi \in \mathcal{E}_n$ such that $\xi\mathbf{T} \geq \beta$, $\xi \geq \theta$, and $\gamma \cdot \xi$ is *minimal.*

Dual problem. Determine $\eta \in \mathcal{E}_m$ such that $\eta\mathbf{T}' \leq \gamma$, $\eta \geq \theta$ and $\beta \cdot \eta$ is *maximal.*

Stated in matrix notation, the primal and dual problems of linear programming assume this form: Given a real $m \times n$ matrix A, and column vectors B and C of dimension m and n, respectively;

Primal problem. Determine a *nonnegative* column vector X of dimension n such that

$$AX \geq B,$$

$$CX \text{ is minimal.}$$

Dual problem. Determine a *nonnegative* column vector Y of dimension m such that

$$A'Y \leq C,$$

$$BY \text{ is maximal.}$$

The information of both problems can be displayed in a tabular form introduced by A. W. Tucker.

Primal

Dual	$0 \leq$	x_1	x_2	$\cdots$	x_n	$\geq$	
	y_1	a_{11}	a_{12}	$\cdots$	a_{1n}	b_1	
	y_2	a_{21}	a_{22}	$\cdots$	a_{2n}	b_2	
	$\vdots$						
	y_m	a_{m1}	a_{m2}	$\cdots$	a_{mn}	b_m	
	$\leq$						max
		c_1	c_2	$\cdots$	c_m	min	

For the primal problem the inequalities are read by taking the inner product of the top row with each interior row of the table; the linear form to be minimized is the inner product of the top and bottom rows. For the dual problem columns are used instead of rows.

In order to state the major theorems of linear programming, some additional terminology is convenient. A vector $\xi \in \mathcal{E}_n$ is called *feasible* for the primal problem if and only if $\xi\mathbf{T} \geq \beta$ and $\xi \geq \theta$. A vector $\eta \in \mathcal{E}_m$ is called *feasible* for the dual problem if and only if $\eta \mathbf{T}' \leq \gamma$ and $\gamma \geq \theta$. An *optimal* vector for the primal problem is a primal-feasible vector ξ_0 for which $\gamma \cdot \xi_0$ is minimal. An *optimal* vector for the dual problem is a dual-feasible vector η_0 for which $\beta \cdot \eta_0$ is maximal.

The fundamental inequality which we derived previously can be stated thus: if ξ is primal-feasible and if η is dual-feasible, then

$$\max(\beta \cdot \eta) \leq \min(\gamma \cdot \xi).$$

It follows immediately that if ξ_0 and η_0 are feasible vectors for which

$$\beta \cdot \eta_0 = \gamma \cdot \xi_0,$$

then both ξ_0 and η_0 are optimal. Furthermore, it can be proved that a feasible ξ_0 is optimal only if that equality holds for some feasible η_0. This result is known as the *duality theorem* of linear programming. Of course the existence of optimal, or even feasible, vectors is not guaranteed. The fundamental *existence theorem* of linear programming asserts that a necessary and sufficient condition for *either* the primal or dual problem to have a solution (that is, an optimal vector) is that *both* problems have a feasible vector.

Even when the existence of a solution is guaranteed, an effective method of finding an optimal vector is needed to make linear programming a practical tool for decision making. In the next section we briefly discuss the *simplex method* and examine some of the matrix theory that underlies the method. For a full account of the theory and techniques of linear programming you are urged to consult Reference 22 and the excellent bibliography contained therein.

Exercises

1. Given a general primal linear programming problem as first stated in the text, write a corresponding statement of the dual problem. Do not use matrix or vector notation to abbreviate this statement.

2. A metal craftsman has on hand a supply of 30 ounces of gold and 60 ounces of silver from which to make gold rings, silver and gold pins, and silver earrings. Each ring uses $\frac{1}{2}$ ounce of gold, each pin uses $\frac{1}{4}$ ounce of gold and $\frac{1}{2}$ ounce of silver, and each pair of earrings uses one ounce of silver. He can make a profit of $5 for each ring, $4 for each pin, and $3 for each pair of earrings, and he seeks to maximize his profit.

   (i) Write this information in the form of a (dual) linear programming problem.

   (ii) Write the inequalities of the corresponding primal problem.

   (iii) Sketch a graph of the inequalities of the primal problem, determine an optimal solution, and use it to evaluate the minimum of the objective function of the primal problem.

(iv) Use the duality theorem to find (by inspection) a solution of the craftsman's problem.

3. Refer to the text example of the metal alloys, ignoring for the moment the condition that $x_1 + x_2 + x_3 + x_4 = 1$.

(i) State and sketch the graphs of four linear inequalities in y_1 and y_2 which, together with the linear form $60y_1 + 35y_2$, describe the dual of the modified primal problem.

(ii) Find an optimal solution of (i) and observe that 168 is the maximum value of the given linear form. At the same point, the maximum value of $65y_1 + 35y_2$ is 175.

(iii) Find a feasible solution of the original alloy problem, for which the cost function is 175, and explain why this solution is optimal.

§9.4. *Combinatorial Equivalence*

A very effective algorithm for solving any linear programming problem has been developed by G. B. Dantzig; it is called the simplex method. We shall describe the method generally but not go into details, which are fully covered in Reference 22. The first step is to convert the system of linear inequalities into the standard form

$$(I|A_1) \begin{pmatrix} V_1 \\ X_1 \end{pmatrix} = B_1$$

in which all components of V_1, X_1 and B_1 are nonnegative. The simplex algorithm then proceeds in two stages. In the first stage pivot methods are used to exchange the v_i for some of the x_j, leading either to the determination of a feasible vector or to a proof that no feasible vector exists. If a feasible vector exists, the second stage operates with pivots on a modified version of the system of equations, finally producing either an optimal vector or a proof that no optimal vector exists.

Our objective here is to study the pivot operation on matrices and to develop an associated concept of *combinatorial equivalence*, first introduced by A. W. Tucker. (See Reference 38.) In contrast to other equivalence relations we have studied, each $m \times n$ matrix is combinatorially equivalent to only a *finite* number of matrices. Starting with a linear program defined by a given matrix, the simplex method examines the finite set of matrices which are combinatorially equivalent to it, providing after each pivot a means of deciding whether a solution has been achieved, and if not, indicating which matrix should be examined next.

From § 5.5 we recall that if A is a given matrix for which $a_{ij} \neq 0$, then a pivot operation on a_{ij} results in a matrix which we shall denote by A_{ij}^*, where

$$
A_{ij}^* = a_{ij}^{-1}
\begin{pmatrix}
d_{11} & d_{12} & -a_{1j} & \cdots & d_{1n} \\
 & & & & \\
a_{i1} & a_{i2} & 1 & \cdots & a_{in} \\
 & & & & \\
d_{m1} & d_{m2} & -a_{mj} & \cdots & d_{mn}
\end{pmatrix},
$$

and where for $r \neq i$ and $s \neq j$,

$$
d_{rs} = a_{rs}a_{ij} - a_{rj}a_{is}.
$$

From our earlier analysis of systems of linear equations we know that a pivot operation always replaces a given system by a system having the same solution. Since the rows of A correspond to the equations of the system, a permutation of rows corresponds merely to a change in the order in which the equations are written. Each column specifies the coefficients of some x_j; hence a column permutation on A simply permutes the variables $x_1, \ldots, x_n$. Hence any finite sequence of pivots, row permutations, and column permutations leads to a system of linear equations which has the same solution as the original system. This fact is the motivation of the definition of combinatorial equivalence.

Definition 9.1. Let A and B be two $m \times n$ matrices. B is said to be *combinatorially equivalent* to A if and only if B can be obtained from A by a finite sequence of row permutations, column permutations, and pivot operations on nonzero elements.

As in § 6.2, P_{ij} will denote the elementary matrix obtained by permuting rows i and j of I. Premultiplication of A by P_{ij} interchanges rows i and j, and postmultiplication by P_{ij} interchanges columns i and j.

Theorem 9.2. Combinatorial equivalence is an equivalence relation on the set of all $m \times n$ matrices.

PROOF : Clearly the relation is reflexive and transitive. By Exercise 2 (i), if $a_{ij} \neq 0$ then $(A_{ij}^*)_{ij}^* = A$. Also $P_{ij}P_{ij}A = A = AP_{ij}P_{ij}$. Since each of the basic operations of combinatorial equivalence is self-inverse, the relation is symmetric.

In the next theorem we establish a matrix characterization of combinatorial equivalence which is more convenient to apply than the formal definition and which leads directly to other characterizations.

Theorem 9.3. B is combinatorially equivalent to A if and only if there exists an $(m + n) \times (m + n)$ permutation matrix P and an $m \times m$ nonsingular matrix Q, such that

$$Q(I|A)P = (I|B).$$

P R O O F : By a permutation matrix P we mean a product of elementary permutation matrices P_{ij}. Suppose that B can be derived from A by a finite sequence of row permutations, column permutations, and pivots. For an elementary permutation matrix P_{ij}, where $i, j \leq m$, we have

$$(I|P_{ij}A) = P_{ij}(I|A)P_{ij};$$

hence any row permutation of A can be effected by multiplying $(I|A)$ on the left by a nonsingular matrix and on the right by a permutation matrix. Similarly, for $i, j \leq n$

$$(I|AP_{ij}) = (I|A)P_{m+i,m+j},$$

so a column permutation on A can be performed by multiplying $(I|A)$ on the left by the nonsingular matrix I and on the right by a permutation matrix. We now show that the same is true for a pivot on any nonzero element. Beginning with the matrix $(I|A)$, let i and j be fixed such that $a_{ij} \neq 0$. Perform the following operations in succession: for each $k \neq i$ multiply row k by a_{ij}; for each $k \neq i$ add $-a_{kj}$ times row i to row k; permute column i and column $m + j$; multiply each row by a_{ij}^{-1}. It can be verified that the result is $(I|A_{ij}^*)$. Since all of the row operations are elementary and since the only column operation is a permutation $P_{i,m+j}$, we have

$$Q_0(I|A)P_{i,m+j} = (I|A_{ij}^*).$$

Hence if a finite succession of row permutations, column permutations, and pivots transforms A into B, then

$$Q(I|A)P = (I|B)$$

for some nonsingular matrix Q and some permutation matrix P.

Conversely, suppose that the last equation holds. Write P in any way as a product of elementary permutation matrices,

$$P = T_1 T_2 \cdots T_k.$$

We proceed by induction on k. If $k = 0$, we have

$$Q(I|A) = (Q|QA) = (I|B).$$

Hence $Q = I$ and $A = B$, so B is combinatorially equivalent to A. Assume that if

$$\hat{Q}(I|A)\hat{P} = (I|C)$$

whenever $\hat{P}$ is a product of fewer than k elementary permutation matrices, then C is combinatorially equivalent to A. Then we have

$$(I|B) = Q(I|A)P = Q(I|A)\hat{P}T_k,$$

where $\hat{P} = T_1 T_2 \cdots T_{k-1}$. Hence

$$(I|B)T_k = Q(I|A)\hat{P}.$$

Now T_k transposes two of the $m + n$ columns of the matrix on which it operates, and we need to distinguish three separate cases, according to whether T_k transposes

(1) two of the first m columns, or
(2) two of the last n columns, or
(3) one of the first m columns and one of the last n columns.

(1) If T_k transposes two of the first m columns of $(I|B)$, then T_k is of the form P_{ij}, where $i, j \leq m$. We have

$$P_{ij}(I|B)P_{ij} = (I|P_{ij}B) = P_{ij}Q(I|A)\hat{P} = \hat{Q}(I|A)\hat{P},$$

so by the induction hypothesis $P_{ij}B$ is combinatorially equivalent to A; since B is combinatorially equivalent to $P_{ij}B$, B is combinatorially equivalent to A.

(2) If T_k transposes two of the last n columns of $(I|B)$, then T_k is of the form $P_{m+i,m+j}$, where $i, j \leq n$. We then have

$$(I|B)P_{m+i,m+j} = (I|BP_{ij}) = Q(I|A)\hat{P}.$$

As in (1) BP_{ij} is combinatorially equivalent to A and to B.

(3) If T_k transposes one of the first m columns and one of the last n columns, then T_k is of the form $P_{i,m+j}$, where $i \leq m$ and $j \leq n$. We have

$$(I|B)P_{i,m+j} = Q(I|A)\hat{P}.$$

From the first part of the proof we know that if $b_{ij} \neq 0$ then row operations together with $P_{i,m+j}$ perform a pivot on b_{ij}. Hence

$$(I|B_{ij}^*) = Q_1(I|B)P_{i,m+j} = Q_1Q(I|A)\hat{P}.$$

As before, B_{ij}^* is combinatorially equivalent to A and to B.

In fact, however, it can happen that $b_{ij} = 0$, in which case the pivot described above cannot be performed. To complete the proof we use an argument suggested by P. J. L. Grant which makes a more careful analysis of the permutation P. P is a permutation on $M \cup N$, where $M = \{1, \ldots, m\}$ and $N = \{m + 1, \ldots, m + n\}$, which maps as many elements of M into N as it maps elements of N into M. Let $\{i_1, \ldots, i_t\} \subset M$ and $\{m + j_1, \ldots, m + j_t\} \subset N$ be the two sets of elements which are interchanged between M and N by P. Then P can be represented as

$$P = P_1 P_2 P_3,$$

where P_i is a product of transpositions of type (i), $i = 1, 2, 3$, and where

$$P_3 = P_{i_1, m+j_1} P_{i_2, m+j_2} \cdots P_{i_t, m+j_t}.$$

The subscripts of this representation of P_3 are all distinct, so these transpositions commute. For simplicity we denote the last of these by $P_{i, m+j}$. The equation

$$(I|B) = Q(I|A)P = Q(IP_1|AP_2)P_3 = (QP_1|QAP_2)P_3$$

shows that t columns of Q are simply a rearrangement of the $j_1, \ldots, j_t$ columns of B; the other columns of Q are certain columns of I. This implies that if $b_{i_s, j} = 0$ for $s = 1, 2, \ldots, t$, then the corresponding column of Q is a linear combination of the columns of Q which are columns of I, contradicting the nonsingularity of Q. Hence for some i_s, $b_{i_s, j} \neq 0$. Now we commute $P_{i_s, m+j_s}$ to the next to the last position in P_3 and write $i_s = h$ and $j_s = k$ to obtain

$$P = \overline{P} P_{h, m+k} P_{i, m+j},$$

where $\overline{P}$ is the product of P_1, P_2, and $t - 2$ transpositions of P_3. We have

$$(I|P_{hi}B) = P_{hi}(I|B)P_{hi} = P_{hi}Q(I|A)\overline{P}P_{h, m+k}P_{i, m+j}P_{hi}.$$

Now $C = P_{hi}B$ is combinatorially equivalent to B and $c_{ij} = b_{hj} \neq 0$. Hence if we multiply on the left by a suitable Q_1 and on the right by $P_{i, m+j}$, we pivot on c_{ij} to obtain

$$(I|C_{ij}^*) = Q_1 P_{hi}Q(I|A)\overline{P}P_{h, m+k}P_{i, m+j}P_{hi}P_{i, m+j}$$
$$= \overline{Q}(I|A)\overline{P}P_{m+j, m+k}P_{h, m+k},$$

where C_{ij}^* is combinatorially equivalent to C, hence to B. Now $P_{m+j, m+k}$ is a type (2) transposition which commutes with each type (3) transposition appearing in $\overline{P}$, since neither subscript occurs on a type (3) permutation of $\overline{P}$. In effect, these operations have replaced

$$(I|B) = Q(I|A)P$$

by
$$(I|\hat{B}) = \hat{Q}(I|A)\hat{P},$$

where $\hat{B}$ is combinatorially equivalent to B. P and $\hat{P}$ can be represented by the same number of transpositions, but $\hat{P}$ can be represented by one *fewer* transpositions of type (3) than can P. Repeating this argument, and using the earlier results concerning transpositions of type (1) and (2), we obtain

$$(I|D) = R(I|A)P_{p,m+q},$$

where D is combinatorially equivalent to B. Then $d_{iq} = r_{ip}$ for all i, so $d_{pq} = r_{pp}$. Except in column p, R coincides with I, so $r_{pp} \neq 0$. Hence we pivot on d_{pq} to finish the proof.

It is helpful to compare Theorem 9.3 with Theorem 6.12.

Theorem 9.4. B is combinatorially equivalent to A if and only if some permutation of the columns of $(I|A)$ produces the matrix $(G|H)$, where G is $m \times m$ and nonsingular and $GB = H$.

P R O O F : Suppose $Q(I|A)P = (I|B)$, and let $(I|A)P = (G|H)$. Then $(QG|QH) = (I|B)$, so $I = QG$ and $B = QH = G^{-1}H$. Conversely, if G, H exist as stated, then $(I|A)P = (G|H) = (G|GB)$ for some permutation matrix P. Then $G^{-1}(I|A)P = (I|B)$.

There are $(m + n)!$ possible permutations of the columns of $(I|A)$, not all of which necessarily produce a nonsingular G in the first m columns. But for each P, $(I|A)P$ is row equivalent to a uniquely determined matrix in reduced echelon form. Thus Q is uniquely determined by A and P such that $Q(I|A)P$ is in reduced echelon form. This may or may not have the form $(I|B)$ for some B.

Theorem 9.5. There are at most $(m + n)!$ matrices which are combinatorially equivalent to A; this maximal number is achieved if and only if every set of m columns of $(I|A)$ is linearly independent.

P R O O F : Our previous remarks show that each of the $(m + n)!$ permutations of the columns of $(I|A)$ determines at most one matrix which is combinatorially equivalent to A. If every set of m columns of $(I|A)$ is linearly independent, then each permutation determines a nonsingular matrix G as in Theorem 9.4. Then A is combinatorially equivalent to $G^{-1}H$. If there exists a set of m linearly dependent columns of $(I|A)$, let P be the permutation which places these columns in the first m columns of $(I|A)P$. Since linear dependence of columns is preserved by row operations, the reduced echelon form of $(I|A)P$ has linearly dependent columns in the first m positions and hence is not of the form $(I|B)$.

Theorem 9.6. B is combinatorially equivalent to A if and only if the systems of linear equations

$$Y + AX = Z$$
$$V + BU = Z$$

are equivalent, where the set of variables $\{v_1, \ldots, v_m, u_1, \ldots, u_n\}$ is some permutation of the variables $\{y_1, \ldots, y_m, x_1, \ldots, x_n\}$.

P R O O F : If B is combinatorially equivalent to A, then $(I|A)P$ is row equivalent to $(I|B)$. Hence the systems

$$(I|A)P \binom{Y}{X} = Z$$

and

$$(I|B) \binom{V}{U} = Z$$

are equivalent. Conversely, if these systems are equivalent for some permutation P of the variables,

$$P \binom{Y}{X} = \binom{V}{U},$$

their matrices are row equivalent, so $Q(I|A)P = (I|B)$.

Theorem 9.7. If A is nonsingular, A and A^{-1} are combinatorially equivalent.

P R O O F : $Y + AX = Z$ and $X + A^{-1}Y = Z$ are equivalent systems.

This implies, of course, that A^{-1} can be computed by a sequence of pivot operations. Since the number of such operations need not exceed the dimension n of A, and since each pivot can be performed by $n^2 - n$ multiplications and n divisions, A^{-1} can be computed by n^3 or fewer multiplications and divisions.

Theorem 9.8. B is combinatorially equivalent to A if and only if $-B'$ is combinatorially equivalent to $-A'$.

P R O O F : As an exercise you may verify that

$$-(A_{ij}^*)' = (-A')_{ji}^*.$$

Thus any pivot operation on A produces a matrix whose negative transpose is combinatorially equivalent to $-A'$. The remainder of the proof follows easily from this fact.

Finally we remark that the statement of Theorem 9.8 would not be valid if either the negative signs or the transpose signs were omitted. This essential combination of negative and transpose expresses the form of duality which we observed for linear programs.

Exercises

1. Assume that combinatorial equivalence had been defined by means of the equation $Q(I|A)P = (I|B)$ as described in Theorem 9.3. Prove that the resulting relation is an equivalence relation.

2. Given a matrix A for which a_{ij}, a_{ik}, and a_{kj} are nonzero, prove the following statements.

  (i) $(A_{ij}^*)_{ij}^* = A$.
  (ii) $(A_{ij}^*)_{kj}^* = P_{ik}A_{kj}^*$, if $k \neq i$.
  (iii) $(A_{ij}^*)_{ik}^* = A_{ik}^* P_{jk}$, if $k \neq j$.
  (iv) $((A_{ij}^*)_{kj}^*)_{ij}^* = P_{ik}A$, if $k \neq i$.
  (v) $((A_{ij}^*)_{ik}^*)_{ij}^* = AP_{kj}$, if $k \neq j$.

3. (i) Write out all matrices which are combinatorially equivalent to

$$A = \begin{pmatrix} 2 & 5 \\ 0 & 3 \end{pmatrix}.$$

By Theorem 9.5 there are at most 24 (actually 20) such matrices, which can be computed by four pivot operations together with row and column permutations.

  (ii) Verify that A^{-1} is in the list.

4. Calculate the inverse of each matrix of Exercise 1, § 6.3, by means of pivot operations.

5. Verify in detail the statements in the proof of Theorem 9.8.

6. Describe explicitly the uniquely determined matrix R such that if $a_{ij} \neq 0$ then $(I|A_{ij}^*) = R(I|A)P_{i,m+j}$.

CHAPTER 10

Functions of Matrices

§10.1. *Sequences and Series of Matrices*

It is assumed that you are already familiar with the basic facts about infinite sequences and series of complex numbers, or at least about real power series. In particular we shall refer to the following:

The definitions of convergence of infinite sequences and series of numbers.

The circle of convergence of a complex power series (interval of convergence in the real case).

Taylor series expansions for such functions as

$$e^x = \sum_{n=0}^{\infty} \frac{x^n}{n!}, \text{ valid for all complex } x,$$

$$\sin x = \sum_{n=0}^{\infty} (-1)^n \frac{x^{2n+1}}{(2n+1)!}, \text{ valid for all complex } x,$$

$$\cos x = \sum_{n=0}^{\infty} (-1)^n \frac{x^{2n}}{(2n)!}, \text{ valid for all complex } x,$$

$$\log(1+x) = \sum_{n=1}^{\infty} (-1)^{n+1} \frac{x^n}{n}, \text{ valid for all complex } x \text{ such that } |x| < 1,$$

$$\frac{1}{1-x} = \sum_{n=0}^{\infty} x^n, \text{ valid for all complex } x \text{ such that } |x| < 1.$$

Definition 10.1. A *sequence* $\{A^{(k)}\} = A^{(1)}, A^{(2)}, \ldots, A^{(n)}, \ldots$ of $m \times n$ matrices is a function whose domain is the natural numbers and whose range is a set of $m \times n$ matrices. Let $A^{(k)} = (a_{ij}^{(k)})$. The sequence $\{A^{(k)}\}$ is said to *converge* to the matrix $A = (a_{ij})$ if and only if for every $i = 1, 2, \ldots, m$ and every $j = 1, 2, \ldots, n$, the number sequence $\{a_{ij}^{(k)}\}$ converges to a_{ij}.

Example

Let
$$A^{(k)} = \begin{pmatrix} 1 + \dfrac{1}{k} & \dfrac{-1}{k^2} \\[2mm] \dfrac{k-2}{k^2+2} & 1 - \dfrac{1}{k^3} \end{pmatrix}.$$

Then $\{A^{(k)}\}$ converges to I, since $\{a_{ij}^{(k)}\}$ converges to δ_{ij} for $i, j = 1, 2$.

Theorem 10.1. If $\{A^{(k)}\}$ converges to A, if P is a fixed $h \times m$ matrix, and if Q is a fixed $n \times t$ matrix, then $\{PA^{(k)}Q\}$ converges to PAQ.

P R O O F : Let $B^{(k)} = PA^{(k)}Q$. For fixed i, j,

$$b_{ij}^{(k)} = \sum_{r=1}^{m} \sum_{s=1}^{n} p_{ir} a_{rs}^{(k)} q_{sj}.$$

By hypothesis, $\{a_{rs}^{(k)}\}$ converges to a_{rs}, for every $r = 1, 2, \ldots, m$ and every $s = 1, 2, \ldots, n$. Hence $\{p_{ir} a_{rs}^{(k)} q_{sj}\}$ converges to $p_{ir} a_{rs} q_{sj}$, and

$$\sum_{r=1}^{m} \sum_{s=1}^{n} \{p_{ir} a_{rs}^{(k)} q_{sj}\} \text{ converges to } \sum_{r=1}^{m} \sum_{s=1}^{n} p_{ir} a_{rs} q_{sj},$$

since a linear combination of convergent number sequences converges to the same linear combination of their limits. Hence $\{PA^{(k)}Q\}$ converges to PAQ.

The significance of this theorem is that convergence is preserved under the various equivalence relations that we have considered for matrices, and particularly by similarity. Thus it is possible to define convergence of a sequence of linear transformations by means of convergence of the matrices that represent those linear transformations in any coordinate system.

Definition 10.2. An *infinite series*

$$\sum_{k=0}^{\infty} A^{(k)} = A^{(0)} + A^{(1)} + \cdots + A^{(p)} + \cdots$$

of $m \times n$ matrices is said to *converge* to the matrix A if and only if for every $i = 1, 2, \ldots, m$ and every $j = 1, 2, \ldots, n$, the series $\sum_{k=0}^{\infty} a_{ij}^{(k)}$ converges to a_{ij}.

Thus convergence of a series of matrices is defined by the convergence of the mn number series of the elements in the same position. We shall consider only *power series* of matrices, that is, series for which

$$A^{(k)} = a_k X^k,$$

where a_k is a scalar and X is a square matrix. (Previously we used X only to denote row vectors.)

Definition 10.3. Given a scalar power series, $\sum_{k=0}^{\infty} a_k x^k$, let f be the function defined by

$$f(x) = \sum_{k=0}^{\infty} a_k x^k$$

for all x for which the series converges. The *matrix-valued function f of the square matrix X* is defined by

$$f(X) = \sum_{k=0}^{\infty} a_k X^k, \qquad X^0 = I$$

for all matrices X for which the series converges.

We recognize, of course, that the Hamilton-Cayley theorem makes it possible to avoid calculating powers of X higher than $n - 1$, since X^n is a linear combination of lower powers of X. If all such higher powers are thus converted, the infinite series

$$f(X) = \sum_{k=0}^{\infty} a_k X^k$$

is changed into the form

$$f(X) = \sum_{k=0}^{n-1} s_k X^k,$$

where each s_k is an infinite series of scalars. The convergence of $f(X)$ is then a question of the convergence of each of the s_k. (In this connection see Exercise 4.)

It is clear that Definition 10.3 is an extension of the correspondence between scalar polynomials and matrix polynomials with scalar coefficients. When we speak of the matrix functions e^X, $(I - X)^{-1}$, $\cos X$, we mean

$$e^X = \sum_{k=0}^{\infty} \frac{X^k}{k!},$$

$$(I - X)^{-1} = \sum_{k=0}^{\infty} X^k,$$

$$\cos X = \sum_{k=0}^{\infty} (-1)^k \frac{X^{2k}}{(2k)!}.$$

Two questions arise immediately:

For what matrices X does a power series converge?

If a series converges for some X, to what matrix does it converge?

Our method of answering these questions will be to reduce X to Jordan form J with diagonal blocks of a simple form, to answer the questions for J, and then to extract corresponding answers for X. The following three theorems, which may be proved as exercises, pertain to this method. In these theorems f refers to a function defined by a power series, $\sum_{k=0}^{\infty} a_k X^k$.

Theorem 10.2. If $f(X)$ converges and if $Y = PXP^{-1}$, then $f(Y)$ converges to $Pf(X)P^{-1}$.

P R O O F : Exercise. Apply Theorem 10.1 and the definition of convergence of a series of matrices.

Theorem 10.3. If X is a diagonal block matrix,

$$X = \begin{pmatrix} X_1 & Z \\ Z & X_2 \end{pmatrix}, \; X_1 \text{ and } X_2 \text{ square matrices,}$$

then

(a) $f(X)$ converges if and only if $f(X_1)$ and $f(X_2)$ converge, and
(b) if $f(X)$ converges, then

$$f(X) = \begin{pmatrix} f(X_1) & Z \\ Z & f(X_2) \end{pmatrix}.$$

P R O O F : Exercise. Observe that this theorem can be generalized by induction to the case in which there are any finite number of diagonal blocks.

Theorem 10.4. If X is nilpotent, $f(X)$ converges.

P R O O F : Exercise.

Theorems 10.2 and 10.3 reduce the questions of convergence of a matrix series to questions about the convergence of the series for a matrix in the form

$$J_1 = \begin{pmatrix} \lambda_1 & 1 & & & \\ & \lambda_1 & \cdot & & \\ & & \cdot & \cdot & \\ & & & \cdot & 1 \\ & & & & \lambda_1 \end{pmatrix},$$

since any X is similar to a diagonal block matrix where each block is of this form. Thus our attention is focused on the convergence of the series

$$\sum_{k=0}^{\infty} a_k(\lambda I + N)^k,$$

where λ is a characteristic value of X and N is nilpotent.

Theorem 10.5. If $\sum_{k=0}^{\infty} a_k x^k$ converges for all x such that $|x| < r$, and if $|\lambda| < r$ for every characteristic value λ of X, then $\sum_{k=0}^{\infty} a_k X^k$ converges.

P R O O F : Consider the diagonal block J_1 of the Jordan matrix similar to X such that λ appears in every diagonal position and 1 in every superdiagonal position. Let

$$S_m(J_1) = \sum_{k=0}^{m} a_k(\lambda I + N)^k.$$

Since N is nilpotent of some index p, there are no more than p terms in the expansion of $(\lambda I + N)^k$ even for large k. Let $m > p$. Then

$$
\begin{aligned}
S_m(J_1) = \quad & a_0 I \\
+ \quad & a_1 \lambda I + && a_1 N \\
+ \quad & a_2 \lambda^2 I + && 2a_2 \lambda N + a_2 N^2 \\
& \cdot && \cdot \\
& \cdot && \cdot \\
& \cdot && \cdot \\
+ \quad & a_{m-1}\lambda^{m-1}I + C_1^{m-1}a_{m-1}\lambda^{m-2}N + \cdots + C_{p-1}^{m-1}a_{m-1}\lambda^{m-p}N^{p-1} \\
+ \quad & a_m\lambda^m I + && C_1^m a_m \lambda^{m-1}N + \cdots + C_{p-1}^m a_m \lambda^{m-p+1}N^{p-1},
\end{aligned}
$$

where $C_s^m = \dfrac{m!}{s!(m-s)!}$ is the binomial coefficient.

Summing on like powers of N, we have

$$
S_m(J_1) = \sum_{r=0}^{p-1} \left(\sum_{k=r}^{m} a_k C_r^k \lambda^{k-r} \right) N^r.
$$

But

$$
a_k C_r^k \lambda^{k-r} = \frac{a_k}{r!} \frac{k!}{(k-r)!} \lambda^{k-r} = \frac{a_k}{r!} \frac{d^r}{dx^r}(x^k) \bigg]_{x=\lambda},
$$

so

$$
\sum_{k=r}^{m} a_k C_r^k \lambda^{k-r} = \frac{1}{r!} \sum_{k=r}^{m} a_k \frac{d^r}{dx^r}(x^k) \bigg]_{x=\lambda} = \frac{1}{r!} S_m^{(r)}(\lambda),
$$

where $S_m^{(r)}(\lambda)$ is the rth derivative of $S_m(x)$, evaluated at $x = \lambda$. Therefore, $S_m(J_1)$ has the upper triangular form,

$$
S_m(J_1) = \begin{pmatrix}
S_m(\lambda) & S_m^{(1)}(\lambda) & \tfrac{1}{2}S_m^{(2)}(\lambda) \cdots & \dfrac{1}{(p-1)!} S_m^{(p-1)}(\lambda) \\[2ex]
 & S_m(\lambda) & S_m^{(1)}(\lambda) \cdots & \dfrac{1}{(p-2)!} S_m^{(p-2)}(\lambda) \\[2ex]
 & & S_m(\lambda) \cdots & \dfrac{1}{(p-3)!} S_m^{(p-3)}(\lambda) \\[2ex]
 & & & \cdot \\
 & & & \cdot \\
 & & & \cdot \\
 & & & S_m(\lambda)
\end{pmatrix}
$$

By hypothesis, $\sum_{k=0}^{\infty} a_k \lambda^k$ converges, since $|\lambda| < r$. Thus the sequence $\{\sum_{k=0}^{m} a_k \lambda^k\} = \{S_m(\lambda)\}$ converges. But from the theory of infinite series it is known that the series obtained by differentiating $\sum_{k=0}^{\infty} a_k x^k$ term by term will converge for $|x| < r$. Hence the sequence $\{S_m(J_1)\}$ converges, which means that the series $\sum_{k=0}^{\infty} a_k J_1^k$ converges, so the proof is complete.

This theorem shows that such functions as e^X, $\sin X$, and $\cos X$ exist for all X, since the corresponding scalar series converge for all x. However, we cannot assume that the matrix function possesses all the properties of the corresponding scalar function; for example,

$$e^X e^Y \neq e^{X+Y},$$

although equality does hold if X and Y commute.

Another important consequence of Theorem 10.5 is the special role played by the characteristic value of largest absolute value. If f is defined by an infinite series whose radius of convergence is r, and if λ_0 is the characteristic value of largest magnitude of a matrix X, then $f(X)$ converges if $|\lambda_0| < r$ and diverges if $|\lambda_0| > r$. If $|\lambda_0| = r$, $f(X)$ may or may not converge. A simple relation between the characteristic values of X and those of $f(X)$ is given in the next theorem.

Theorem 10.6. If $f(X)$ converges and if λ is a characteristic value of X, then $f(\lambda)$ is a characteristic value of $f(X)$.

PROOF : If $J = PXP^{-1}$ is the Jordan form of X, then X and J have the same characteristic values, and $f(J) = Pf(X)P^{-1}$. But the proof of Theorem 10.5 shows that $f(J)$ is an upper triangular matrix with $f(\lambda_1), f(\lambda_2), \ldots, f(\lambda_n)$ as the diagonal elements. Hence these are the characteristic values of $f(J)$ and of the similar matrix $f(X)$.

Theorem 10.7. For every matrix X, $\det e^X = e^{\operatorname{tr} X}$ and therefore e^X is nonsingular. Furthermore, $(e^X)^{-1} = e^{-X}$.

PROOF : Exercise.

Exercises

1. Prove each of the following theorems:
    (i) Theorem 10.2,
    (ii) Theorem 10.3,
    (iii) Theorem 10.4,
    (iv) Theorem 10.7.

2. Evaluate e^A, given

(i) $A = \begin{pmatrix} -1 & 0 \\ 0 & 1 \end{pmatrix}$,

(ii) $A = \begin{pmatrix} -1 & 3 \\ 1 & 1 \end{pmatrix}$,

(iii) $A = \begin{pmatrix} 2 & 0 & 0 \\ 0 & -1 & 3 \\ 0 & 1 & 1 \end{pmatrix}$,

(iv) $A = \begin{pmatrix} 0 & 1 & 1 \\ 0 & 0 & 1 \\ 0 & 0 & 0 \end{pmatrix}.$

3. Prove that a series $\sum_{k=0}^{\infty} A^{(k)}$ of matrices converges if and only if the sequence $\{S^{(n)}\}$ of matrices converges, where $S^{(n)} = A^{(0)} + A^{(1)} + \cdots + A^{(n)}$.

4. Let $f(x) = \sum_{k=0}^{\infty} a_k x^k$, let A be a matrix with distinct characteristic values $\lambda_1, \lambda_2, \ldots, \lambda_n$ for which $f(A)$ converges. It can be proved that

$$f(A) = D^{-1}[D_0 I + D_1 A + \cdots + D_{n-1} A^{n-1}],$$

where D is the Vandermonde determinant

$$D = \begin{vmatrix} 1 & 1 & \ldots 1 \\ \lambda_1 & \lambda_2 & \ldots \lambda_n \\ \lambda_1^2 & \lambda_2^2 & \ldots \lambda_n^2 \\ \cdot & \cdot & \cdot \\ \cdot & \cdot & \cdot \\ \cdot & \cdot & \cdot \\ \lambda_1^{n-1} & \lambda_2^{n-1} & \ldots \lambda_n^{n-1} \end{vmatrix},$$

and D_k is the determinant that coincides with D except that the $(k+1)$ row vector is $(f(\lambda_1), f(\lambda_2), \ldots, f(\lambda_n))$. (This formula is reminiscent of Cramer's rule.)

(i) Apply the method described above to calculate $f(A)$, where

$$A = \begin{pmatrix} 3 & 2 & 2 \\ 1 & 4 & 1 \\ -2 & -4 & -1 \end{pmatrix}.$$

(ii) Check your result in (i) by using it to compute A^2.

(iii) For A as given in (i) find necessary and sufficient conditions on f that $f(A)$ be a scalar matrix.

(iv) Calculate e^A.

§10.2. *Matrices of Functions*

We now consider an $m \times n$ matrix whose entries are not scalars, but scalar-valued functions. To be specific, let

$$X(t) = (x_{ij}(t)), \quad i = 1, 2, \ldots, m; j = 1, 2, \ldots, n,$$

where $x_{ij}(t)$ is a real-valued function defined for all t in an interval $a \leq t \leq b$. Now X is a function whose domain includes $a \leq t \leq b$, and whose value at t is an $m \times n$ matrix of real numbers. In this section we shall indicate how a calculus of matrices of functions can be defined.

The idea is extremely simple, since continuity, derivative, and integral are defined component by component.

Definition 10.4. Let X be an $m \times n$ matrix of real-valued functions x_{ij} which are defined for all t in some set of real numbers.

(a) X is *continuous* at t_0 if and only if x_{ij} is continuous at t_0 for $i = 1, 2, \ldots, m; j = 1, 2, \ldots, n$.

(b) The *derivative* $\mathfrak{D}X$ of X is defined by

$$\mathfrak{D}X(t_0) = \left(\frac{d}{dt} x_{ij}(t_0)\right),$$

if and only if $\dfrac{d}{dt} x_{ij}(t_0)$ exists for $i = 1, 2, \ldots, m; j = 1, 2, \ldots, n$.

(c) The *definite integral* $\int_a^b X$ is defined by

$$\int_a^b X = \left(\int_a^b x_{ij}(t)dt\right),$$

if and only if $\int_a^b x_{ij}(t)dt$ exists for $i = 1, 2, \ldots, m; j = 1, 2, \ldots, n$.

We shall develop only enough calculus of matrices to enable us to apply our results to the solution of a differential equation.

Theorem 10.8. If X is $n \times n$, if Y is $n \times p$, and if $\mathfrak{D}X$ and $\mathfrak{D}Y$ exist, then

(a) $\mathfrak{D}(XY) = (\mathfrak{D}X)Y + X(\mathfrak{D}Y)$,

(b) $\mathfrak{D}(X^p) = \sum_{i=1}^p X^{p-i}(\mathfrak{D}X)X^{i-1}$, p a positive integer,

(c) $\mathfrak{D}(X^{-1}) = -X^{-1}(\mathfrak{D}X)X^{-1}$, if X is nonsingular.

P R O O F : Exercise.

Observe that these rules are generalizations of the corresponding results for scalar functions, which reduce to the usual differentiation formulas if all of the matrices involved commute with each other. In general, however, even X and $\mathfrak{D}X$ do not commute, so we must be careful to preserve the order of the matrices in these formulas.

Theorem 10.9. If A is an $n \times n$ matrix of scalars, then

$$\mathfrak{D}(e^{At}) = Ae^{At} = e^{At}A.$$

P R O O F : By definition, we have

$$e^{At} = \sum_{k=0}^\infty \frac{(At)^k}{k!} = I + \frac{At}{1} + \frac{A^2 t^2}{2!} + \cdots.$$

Thus

$$\mathfrak{D}(e^{At}) = \sum_{k=0}^\infty \frac{kA^k t^{k-1}}{k!} = \sum_{k=1}^\infty \frac{A(At)^{k-1}}{(k-1)!} = \sum_{j=0}^\infty \frac{A(At)^j}{j!}$$

$$= Ae^{At} = e^{At}A.$$

This result is reminiscent of the corresponding property of the exponential function

$$\frac{d}{dt} e^{at} = ae^{at},$$

which plays such an important role in the solution of certain differential equations. In the next theorem we consider the analogous problem for matrices.

Theorem 10.10. Consider the matrix differential equation

$$\mathfrak{D}X(t) = X(t)A,$$

where $X(t)$ is an $m \times n$ matrix of differentiable functions and A is an $n \times n$ matrix of scalars. Then

(a) for any fixed value t_0 of t, the matrix

$$X(t) = X(t_0)e^{(t-t_0)A}$$

   is a solution of the differential equation,

(b) any solution is of the form specified in (a) for some value of t_0,

(c) the rank of a given solution $X(t)$ is the same for all values of t.

P R O O F : Conclusion (a) follows directly from Theorem 10.9. To prove (b) let $X(t)$ be any solution, and let

$$Y(t) = X(t)e^{-At}.$$

Then

$$\mathfrak{D}Y(t) = [\mathfrak{D}X(t)]e^{-At} + X(t)\mathfrak{D}e^{-At}$$

$$= [\mathfrak{D}X(t)]e^{-At} - X(t)Ae^{-At}$$

$$= [\mathfrak{D}X(t) - X(t)A]e^{-At}$$

$$= Z,$$

since $\mathfrak{D}X(t) = X(t)A$ by hypothesis. Then Y is a constant $m \times n$ matrix C. For any value t_0 of t,

$$Y(t_0) = C = X(t_0)e^{-At_0},$$

so

$$X(t) = Ce^{At} = X(t_0)(e^{-At_0})e^{At}$$

$$= X(t_0)e^{(t-t_0)A},$$

where the last equality is valid since At_0 and At commute. Furthermore, by Theorem 10.7, $e^{(t-t_0)A}$ is nonsingular, so the rank of $X(t)$ is the same as the rank of $X(t_0)$, which proves (c).

In the next section we shall apply Theorem 10.10 in the special case in which X is a row vector.

Exercises

1. Prove that $\mathfrak{D}X$ as given in Definition 10.4 satisfies

$$\mathfrak{D}X(t_0) = \lim_{h \to 0} \frac{1}{h}\,[X(t_0 + h) - X(t_0)]$$

if limit is understood to operate on each component.

2. Prove Theorem 10.8.

3. Does an analogue of the fundamental theorem of calculus hold for matrix calculus? Explain.

4. Does an analogue of the mean value theorem of the derivative hold for matrix calculus? Explain.

5. Derive an expression for the derivative of $\det X(t)$.

6. Derive an expression for the derivative of $\operatorname{tr} X(t)$, and prove that

$$\frac{d}{dt}\,[\operatorname{tr} X(t)] = \operatorname{tr}[\mathfrak{D}X(t)].$$

§10.3. *An Application to Differential Equations*

We now consider the problem of determining all solutions of a linear, homogeneous, nth order differential equation with constant coefficients,

$$(10.1) \qquad \frac{d^n}{dt^n}\,x + a_1 \frac{d^{n-1}}{dt^{n-1}}\,x + \cdots + a_{n-1}\frac{d}{dt}\,x + a_n x = 0.$$

Most of the essential facts concerning the solutions of this equation can be verified easily by direct calculations. Our first observations are that any scalar multiple of a solution is also a solution, and that the sum of any two solutions is a solution. Therefore, the set of all solutions of (10.1) forms a vector space, called the *solution space*. Furthermore, the dimension of the solution space is n, a fact which follows from a theorem concerning the uniqueness of solutions of (10.1). Therefore, the problem of finding all solutions of (10.1) reduces to the problem of finding a basis for the solution space, a set of n linearly independent solutions.

If we let $x = e^{rt}$, then x is a solution if and only if r satisfies the polynomial equation

$$(10.2) \qquad r^n + a_1 r^{n-1} + \cdots + a_{n-1}r + a_n = 0.$$

At this point we separate the discussion into two cases. First, if the roots $r_1, r_2, \ldots, r_n$ of (10.2) are distinct, then the solution set $\{e^{r_1 t}, e^{r_2 t}, \ldots, e^{r_n t}\}$ is linearly independent, so any solution has the form

$$x = \sum_{i=1}^{n} c_i e^{r_i t},$$

where the c_i are suitable scalars. As the alternative to the case in which (10.2) has n distinct roots, suppose that the distinct roots are $r_1, r_2, \ldots, r_k$, and that r_i is a root of multiplicity m_i, for $i = 1, 2, \ldots, k$. Then for each i each of the functions

$$\{e^{r_it}, te^{r_it}, \ldots, t^{m_i-1}e^{r_it}\}$$

is a solution, and this set of solutions is linearly independent. The collection of all solutions obtained in this way by letting i vary from 1 to k forms a basis for the solution space. Thus we have full information concerning the solutions of (10.1).

Although verification of the preceding statements is not difficult, this approach is not completely satisfying because the success of the method seems to depend upon a mystic process of guessing that functions such as $t^2e^{r_it}$ are solutions. In this section we shall restate and resolve the problem in matrix notation, observing that the solutions arise in a natural way from the Jordan form of a matrix determined by (10.1).

First we make a change of variables in order to replace the single equation (10.1) of order n by a set of n equations of order 1. Let $y_1 = x$, $y_2 = \dfrac{d}{dt} y_1, \ldots, y_n = \dfrac{d}{dt} y_{n-1}$. Then we obtain the n equations

$$(10.3) \quad \left\{ \begin{array}{l} \dfrac{d}{dt} y_1 = y_2 \\[2mm] \dfrac{d}{dt} y_2 = y_3 \\[2mm] \quad \vdots \\[2mm] \dfrac{d}{dt} y_{n-1} = y_n \\[2mm] \dfrac{d}{dt} y_n = -a_ny_1 - a_{n-1}y_2 - \cdots - a_1y_n. \end{array} \right.$$

Let

$$Y = (y_1, y_2, \ldots, y_n),$$

and let

$$A = \begin{pmatrix} 0 & 0 & 0 \ldots 0 & -a_n \\ 1 & 0 & 0 \ldots 0 & -a_{n-1} \\ 0 & 1 & 0 \ldots 0 & -a_{n-2} \\ \vdots & \vdots & \vdots & \vdots \\ 0 & 0 & 0 \ldots 1 & -a_1 \end{pmatrix}.$$

Then (10.3) or, equivalently, (10.1) is written simply $\mathfrak{D}Y = YA$, and by Theorem 10.10 any solution is of the form

$$Y(t) = Y(t_0)e^{(t-t_0)A}.$$

Now for some nonsingular matrix P, $J = P^{-1}AP$, where J is a Jordan matrix. Let $W = YP$; then

$$W(t) = Y(t)P = [Y(t_0)P]P^{-1}e^{(t-t_0)A}P$$
$$= W(t_0)e^{(t-t_0)J}$$
$$= W(t_0)e^{(t-t_0)[\text{diag}(\lambda_1, \ldots, \lambda_n)+N]}.$$

The characteristic values λ_i of A are the solutions of (10.2) because the characteristic equation of A is

$$\lambda^n + a_1\lambda^{n-1} + \cdots + a_{n-1}\lambda + a_n = 0.$$

(See Exercise 7, § 7.3, and apply the result to A'.) We now consider the form of $W(t)$ for two special cases.

Case I. $\lambda_1, \lambda_2, \ldots, \lambda_n$ all distinct. Then $N = Z$, and we have

$$W(t) = W(t_0)e^{(t-t_0)\text{diag}(\lambda_1, \ldots, \lambda_n)}$$
$$= W(t_0)\text{diag}(e^{\lambda_1(t-t_0)}, \ldots, e^{\lambda_n(t-t_0)})$$
$$= (w_1(t_0)e^{\lambda_1(t-t_0)}, \ldots, w_n(t_0)e^{\lambda_n(t-t_0)}),$$

where the kth component of the vector $W(t_0)$ is denoted $w_k(t_0)$. Thus any solution vector is a linear combination of the vectors determined by the distinct characteristic values,

$$(0, \ldots, 0, e^{\lambda_k(t-t_0)}, 0, \ldots, 0).$$

Case II. $\lambda_1 = \lambda_2 = \cdots = \lambda_n$. Then N has zeros and ones on the super-diagonal, and

$$W(t) = W(t_0)e^{(t-t_0)[\lambda I+N]}$$
$$= W(t_0)[e^{\lambda(t-t_0)I}][e^{(t-t_0)N}]$$
$$= W(t_0)e^{\lambda(t-t_0)}\left[I + (t-t_0)N + \cdots + \frac{(t-t_0)^{n-1}}{(n-1)!}N^{n-1}\right].$$

Thus an arbitrary solution vector has for its kth component an expression of the form

$$p_k(t)e^{\lambda(t-t_0)},$$

where $p_k(t)$ is a polynomial in t of degree less than k. Those polynomials are generated by the various powers of the nonvanishing nilpotent part of the Jordan form of the matrix A. Thus a basis for the solution space can be chosen to be the vectors

$$\{e^{\lambda t}, te^{\lambda t}, \ldots, t^{n-1}e^{\lambda t}\}.$$

The general case in which there are r distinct characteristic values λ_i, each of multiplicity m_i, is a combination of the two cases described, any solution vector being a linear combination of the vectors

$$p_j(t)e^{\lambda_j t},$$

where $p_j(t)$ is a polynomial of degree less than m_j, $j = 1, 2, \ldots, r$. Hence a basis for the solution space is

$$\{e^{\lambda_1 t}, te^{\lambda_1 t}, \ldots, t^{m_1-1}e^{\lambda_1 t}, e^{\lambda_2 t}, te^{\lambda_2 t}, \ldots, t^{m_2-1}e^{\lambda_2 t}, \ldots, e^{\lambda_r t}, te^{\lambda_r t}, \ldots, t^{m_r-1}e^{\lambda_r t}\}.$$

Exercises

1. Work through the method of the text to solve the differential equation

$$\frac{d^3}{dt^3}x - \frac{d^2}{dt^2}x - \frac{d}{dt}x + x = 0,$$

showing that any solution vector can be written in the form

$$(ae^t, (at + b)e^t, ce^{-t}).$$

Observe the manner in which the second component arises from the nilpotent part of the Jordan form of the matrix determined by the equation.

APPENDIX A

Algebraic Concepts

The objective of this appendix is to formulate fundamental algebraic concepts in terms of the notion of sets, thus supplementing the discussion of abstract systems in Chapter 1. The treatment is brief and somewhat formal, but exercises are provided to augment the reader's understanding of this material.

§A.1. *Cartesian Product of Sets*

In § 1.3 we defined the cartesian product $S \times S$ of a set S with itself. It is quite clear that this definition can be generalized in two ways: first by considering the cartesian product $S \times T$ of *any* two sets, and then by extending the number of sets involved from two to n.

Definition A.1. Let $S_1, S_2, \ldots, S_n$ be any sets. The *cartesian product* $S_1 \times S_2 \times \cdots \times S_n$ is the set of all ordered n-tuples,

$$S_1 \times S_2 \times \cdots \times S_n = \{(s_1, s_2, \ldots, s_n) \mid s_i \in S_i \text{ for } i = 1, \ldots, n\}.$$

Two n-tuples are *equal*

$$(s_1, s_2, \ldots, s_n) = (t_1, t_2, \ldots, t_n)$$

if and only if $s_i = t_i$ for every $i = 1, 2, \ldots, n$.

Thus for each i, the ith component of any element of $S_1 \times S_2 \times \cdots \times S_n$ is an element of S_i, and $S_1 \times S_2 \times \cdots \times S_n$ consists of all n-tuples which can be formed in this manner.

Exercises

1. If S_i is a set of m_i elements, for $i = 1, 2, \ldots, n$, how many elements are in the set $S_1 \times S_2 \times \cdots \times S_n$?

2. Let I denote the set of all integers, and let R denote the set of all real numbers. Describe by means of a graph each of the following sets:

   (i) $I \times R$,

   (ii) $R \times I$.

3. Let S and T be arbitrary sets.

   (i) Prove that $S \times T$ and $T \times S$ have an element in common if and only if S and T have an element in common.

   (ii) If S and T have m elements in common, how many elements do $S \times T$ and $T \times S$ have in common?

   (iii) If $T \subseteq S$, show that $T \times T = (T \times S) \cap (S \times T)$.

4. For each $i = 1, 2, \ldots, n$ let $S_i = \{E_i; o_i\}$ be an abstract system having one binary operation o_i, which is closed on E_i. An operation $*$ is defined on $E_1 \times E_2 \times \cdots \times E_n$ by the rule

$$(a_1, a_2, \ldots, a_n) * (b_1, b_2, \ldots, b_n) = (c_1, c_2, \ldots, c_n),$$

where $c_i = a_i \, o_i \, b_i$ for each i. Prove the following.

   (i) $*$ is closed on $E_1 \times E_2 \times \cdots \times E_n$.

   (ii) $*$ is associative if and only if each o_i is associative.

   (iii) If each E_i has an identity element e_i relative to o_i, then $E_1 \times E_2 \times \cdots \times E_n$ has an identity element relative to $*$.

§A.2. *Binary Relations*

Definition A.2. A *binary relation* **R** from a set A into a set B is a subset of $A \times B$. If $(a, b) \in \mathbf{R}$, we say that a *is related to* b, and write

$$a \, \mathbf{R} \, b.$$

The *domain* of **R** is the set of all elements of A which are related by **R** to at least one element of B;

$$\text{dom } \mathbf{R} = \{a \in A \mid a \, \mathbf{R} \, y \text{ for some } y \in B\}.$$

The *range* of **R** is the set of all elements of B to which at least one element of A is related by **R**;

$$\text{range } \mathbf{R} = \{b \in B \mid x \, \mathbf{R} \, b \text{ for some } x \in A\}.$$

A binary relation from A into A is called a *relation in* A.

It is sometimes convenient to think of a relation in geometric terms as an *association*, or many-valued correspondence, from A into B. Each element in dom $\mathbf{R}$ is associated by $\mathbf{R}$ with one or more elements in range $\mathbf{R}$. For example, let $A = \{a_1, a_2, a_3\}$, $B = \{b_1, b_2, b_3, b_4\}$; let $\mathbf{R}$ be the subset of $A \times B$, which consists of the pairs (a_1, b_1), (a_1, b_2), (a_2, b_1), (a_2, b_4), and (a_3, b_4). Then dom $\mathbf{R} = A$ and range $\mathbf{R} = \{b_1, b_2, b_4\} \subset B$. $\mathbf{R}$ can be represented geometrically by the following diagram.

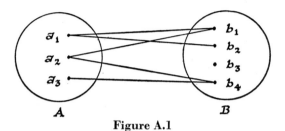

A $\qquad\qquad\qquad\qquad\qquad\qquad$ B

Figure A.1

Exercises

1. How many different binary relations can be defined from a set of m elements to a set of n elements?

2. Describe the number pairs that comprise each of the following relations.

(i) The order relation $<$ for real numbers.

(ii) The relation "a divides b evenly" for positive integers.

3. A binary relation $\mathbf{R}$ on a set A is called a *partial ordering* of A whenever $\mathbf{R}$ is

reflexive:	$a \mathbf{R} a$ for every $a \in A$,
anti-symmetric:	if $a \mathbf{R} b$ and $b \mathbf{R} a$, then $a = b$,
transitive:	if $a \mathbf{R} b$ and $b \mathbf{R} c$, then $a \mathbf{R} c$.

(i) Show that the subset relation is a partial ordering of the collection K of all subsets of a set S.

(ii) Show that "a divides b" defines a partial ordering of the positive integers.

(iii) Show that "$f(x) \leq g(x)$ for all $x \in [0, 1]$" defines a partial ordering of the set of all real valued functions whose domain of definition includes the interval $[0, 1]$.

§A.3. *Functions*

Definition A.3. A *function* $\mathbf{F}$ from a set A to a set B is a binary relation from A into B that satisfies the additional properties

(a) dom $\mathbf{F} \neq \Phi$,

(b) if $a\,\mathbf{F}\,b_1$ and $a\,\mathbf{F}\,b_2$, then $b_1 = b_2$.

The *domain* and *range* of $\mathbf{F}$ are its domain and range as defined for relations.

The essential condition that distinguishes a function from an arbitrary relation is the requirement that each $a \in$ dom $\mathbf{F}$ be associated with one and only one $b \in$ range $\mathbf{F}$. Because b is uniquely determined by a and $\mathbf{F}$, the relation notation $a\,\mathbf{F}\,b$ can be replaced for functions by the notation described in § 1.4,

$$b = a\mathbf{F}.$$

Thus

$$\text{dom } \mathbf{F} = \{a \in A \mid y = a\mathbf{F} \text{ for some } y \in B\},$$

$$\text{range } \mathbf{F} = \{b \in B \mid b = x\mathbf{F} \text{ for some } x \in A\}.$$

If range $\mathbf{F} = B$, we say that $\mathbf{F}$ is a function from A *onto* B.

Described geometrically, each $a \in$ dom $\mathbf{F}$ is associated with one and only one image $a\mathbf{F} \in$ range $\mathbf{F}$. To distinguish the unique association of a function from the multiple association of an arbitrary relation, we say that a function is a *mapping*. Each *image* $a\mathbf{F}$ of the mapping $\mathbf{F}$ is uniquely determined by its antecedent a. However, it is possible that different antecedents, $a \neq x$, determine the same image, $a\mathbf{F} = x\mathbf{F}$. In general, mappings are *many-to-one*, which means that many distinct points of the domain are mapped into the same image point of the range.

Definition A.4. A mapping $\mathbf{F}$ from A to B is said to be one-to-one (or *reversible*) if and only if for all a, $x \in$ dom $\mathbf{F}$ whenever $a\mathbf{F} = x\mathbf{F}$, then $a = x$. The *inverse* $\mathbf{F}^*$ of a one-to-one mapping is the mapping from B to A defined by

$$\text{dom } \mathbf{F}^* = \text{range } \mathbf{F},$$

$$\text{range } \mathbf{F}^* = \text{dom } \mathbf{F},$$

$$y\mathbf{F}^* = x,$$

where x is the uniquely determined element of dom $\mathbf{F}$ such that $x\mathbf{F} = y$. $\mathbf{F}^*$ is frequently denoted by $\mathbf{F}^{-1}$.

Exercises

1. By recalling the definition of a function in terms of sets, state what it means for two functions to be equal.

2. How many different functions can be defined from a set A having m elements to a set B having n elements? (Recall that the domain of such a function can be any nonvoid subset of A.)

3. Consider the function F of two real variables defined by

$$F(x, y) = x\sqrt{1 - y}\,\sin(x + y).$$

Show how this function is described by Definition A.3. Specify the domain and range of F.

4. Let R be the set of all real numbers. Give a specific example of a function F from R to R for each of the following conditions.

   (i) dom $F \subset R$, range $F \subset R$.
   (ii) dom $F = R$, range $F \subset R$, F one-to-one.
   (iii) dom $F \subset R$, range $F = R$, F not one-to-one.
   (iv) dom $F = R$, range $F = R$, F not one-to-one.
   (v) dom $F = R$, range $F = R$, F one-to-one.

5. Let $\mathbf{F}$ be a one-to-one mapping with domain A and range B. Describe each of the mappings $\mathbf{FF}^*$ and $\mathbf{F}^*\mathbf{F}$.

6. Prove that the inverse of a one-to-one mapping $\mathbf{F}$ is uniquely determined.

§A.4. *Binary Operations*

Definition A.5. A *binary operation* on a set A is a function from $A \times A$ into A. An operation on A is said to be *closed* if and only if the domain of the operation is the full set $A \times A$. More generally, an *n-ary operation* on A is a function whose domain is the set $A \times A \times \cdots \times A$ (n times) of ordered n-tuples of elements of A and whose range is a subset of A.

It is customary to use special symbols, rather than function notation, for binary operations. Thus $a_1 * a_2$ denotes the image in A of the ordered pair $(a_1, a_2) \in A \times A$ under the mapping that defines the operation $*$.

Exercises

1. Explain how a closed binary operation on a set S can be considered as a subset of $S \times S \times S$, having special properties. List all properties needed to make your description precise.

2. How many closed binary operations can be defined on a set having n elements?

3. Let R be the set of real numbers, described geometrically by a coordinate axis. State what is meant by a graph of each of the following, listing any special restrictions you need to make your description accurate.

(i) A binary relation on R.
(ii) A function from R to R.
(iii) A closed binary operation on R.

§A.5. *Summary of Abstract Systems*

In § 1.5 an abstract system

$$\mathbb{S} = \{E; R; O\}$$

was described as a set E of elements, a set R of binary relations in E, and a set O of closed operations on E, together with a set of postulates which endow the elements, relations, and operations with their distinctive properties. Each binary relation is a subset of $E \times E$; each n-ary operation is a function from $E \times E \times \cdots \times E$ (n times) into E. Since a function is a type of relation, each n-ary operation can be described as a subset of $E \times E \times \cdots \times E$ ($n + 1$ times). In this way the components of an abstract system are represented as subsets of sets formed from the set of elements of the system.

§A.6. *Boolean Algebras*

As an illustration of an abstract system, we return to the specific example of the collection K of all subsets of a given set S, considered in § 1.2. This system can be denoted

$$\mathbb{S} = \{K; =, \subseteq; \cup, \cap, '\}.$$

The two binary relations, two binary operations, and one unary operation were described in our introductory discussion of sets in terms of the undefined concepts of "set" and "membership"; in effect, therefore, our only postulate for the system $\mathbb{S}$ was that we understood these two notions. Therefore our approach was intuitive and concrete rather than formal and abstract.

We now undertake to develop an abstract system which will serve as a model for the algebra of sets. We consider a system $\mathfrak{B}$ composed of any set E of elements, two binary operations on E, and one unary operation on E:

$$\mathfrak{B} = \{E; \vee, \wedge, *\}.$$

To make sure that the abstract system $\mathfrak{B}$ contains the concrete system $\mathbb{S}$ as a specific example, we shall assume as postulates for $\mathfrak{B}$ statements which are valid in $\mathbb{S}$ when we interpret the three operations of $\mathfrak{B}$ to mean union, intersection, and complementation of sets. In selecting such postulates, various choices are possible; what we seek is a simple set of statements about the operations that will produce an accurate model of the algebra of sets. The following axioms were first given by E. V. Huntingdon in 1904.

B1. The operations $\vee$ and $\wedge$ are commutative: for all $x, y \in E$,

$$x \vee y = y \vee x,$$
$$x \wedge y = y \wedge x.$$

B2. Each of the operations $\vee$ and $\wedge$ is distributive over the other: for all $w, x, y \in E$

$$w \vee (x \wedge y) = (w \vee x) \wedge (w \vee y),$$
$$w \wedge (x \vee y) = (w \wedge x) \vee (w \wedge y).$$

B3. There exist in E distinct elements z and u which are identity elements for $\vee$ and $\wedge$ respectively; for all $x \in E$,

$$x \vee z = x,$$
$$x \wedge u = x.$$

B4. For all $x \in E$ the operation $*$ satisfies

$$x \vee x^* = u,$$
$$x \wedge x^* = z.$$

Definition A.6. Any system $\mathcal{B} = \{E; \vee, \wedge, *\}$ satisfying axioms B1–B4 is called a *Boolean algebra*.

In terms of our intuitive concept of membership and our understanding of the meaning of the words used to define set union, intersection, and complementation, we observe that the system S of all subsets of a given nonvoid set S is indeed a Boolean algebra whose identity elements are Φ and S. It is remarkable, however, that the postulates for $\mathcal{B}$ do not mention any relations on E, whereas our description of S made frequent use of the subset relation. In effect, equality in $\mathcal{B}$ is defined implicitly by the four postulates. Furthermore, a relation $<$ can be defined on E in terms of the operation $\vee$: for all $x, y \in E$

$$x < y \text{ if and only if } x \vee y = y.$$

Observe that this definition is consistent with the result of Exercise 3(i), § 1.2.

Having recognized that the algebraic system S of all subsets of a given set S is a Boolean algebra, we may ask whether the converse is true. Given any Boolean algebra $\mathcal{B}$, does a set S exist such that $\mathcal{B}$ represents the system S of all subsets of S? An affirmative answer to this question was given by M. H. Stone in 1936, showing that the abstract system which we call Boolean algebra is in all respects an accurate model of the concrete example of the algebra of subsets.

Exercises

Following is a list of theorems, statements which are valid for all elements w, x, y of any Boolean algebra. Theorems in the second column are dual to those in the first, obtained by interchanging $\lor$ and $\land$, u and z, and reversing the relation $<$. Duality occurs because of the symmetric nature of the postulates for a Boolean algebra. Prove as many of these statements as you can, using only the postulates or preceding statements in this sequence.

1. $x \lor x = x$.   1'. $x \land x = x$.

2. $x \lor u = u$.   2'. $x \land z = z$.

3. $x \lor (x \land y) = x$.   3'. $x \land (x \lor y) = x$.

4. $w \lor (x \lor y) = (w \lor x) \lor y$.   4'. $w \land (x \land y) = (w \land x) \land y$.

5. x^* is unique.

6. $(x^*)^* = x$.

7. $u^* = z$.   7'. $z^* = u$.

8. $(x \lor y)^* = x^* \land y^*$.   8'. $(x \land y)^* = x^* \lor y^*$.

9. $x < y$ if and only if $x \land y = x$.

10. If $w < x$ and $x < y$, then $w < y$.

11. If $x < w$ and $y < w$, then $x \lor y < w$.

12. If $w < x$ then $w < x \lor y$ for any y.

13. $x < y$ if and only if $y^* < x^*$.

§A.7. *Groups*

Another important example of a general algebraic system is a *group*, which was mentioned briefly in the discussion of fields in § 1.6.

Definition A.7. A group is any system $\mathcal{G} = \{G; *\}$ having one closed binary operation and satisfying the following postulates.

        G1. $*$ is associative.

        G2. An identity element i exists in G.

        G3. Each $g \in G$ has an inverse $g' \in G$.

A group is said to be *commutative* if and only if

        G4. $*$ is commutative.

Examples of Groups

(a) The integers (or the rational, real, or complex numbers) with addition as operation.

(b) The positive rational (or real) numbers with multiplication as operation.

(c) The nonzero rational (or real or complex) numbers with multiplication as operation.

(d) The mappings of Exercise 4, § 1.5.

Exercises

1. The n complex nth roots of unity are the numbers

$$e_k = \cos\frac{2k\pi}{n} + i\sin\frac{2k\pi}{n}, \; k = 0, 1, \ldots, (n-1),$$

where $i^2 = -1$.

(i) Prove that for $n = 3$ the three cube roots of unity, together with multiplication of complex numbers, form a group.

(ii) Prove the corresponding result for any n.

2. For any group $\mathcal{G}$ prove that

(i) there is only one identity element,

(ii) each element has only one inverse,

(iii) $(x')' = x$,

(iv) $(x * y)' = y' * x'$, where $*$ denotes the group operation.

3. Let $\mathcal{G} = \{G; *\}$ be any group, and let g be a fixed element of G.

(i) Show that the mapping

$$\mathbf{R}_g : x \longrightarrow x * g$$

is a one-to-one mapping of G onto G.

(ii) Show that the successive mapping $\mathbf{R}_g\mathbf{R}_h$ is the same mapping as $\mathbf{R}_{g*h}$.

4. Let $\{S; *\}$ be a system for which

$*$ is associative,

there exists $e \in S$ such that $x * e = x$ for all $x \in S$,

for each $x \in S$ there exists $\bar{x} \in S$ such that $x * \bar{x} = e$.

Prove that $\{S; *\}$ is a group. (e is called a *right* identity and $\bar{x}$ is called a *right* inverse.)

5. Let $\{S; *\}$ be a nonvoid system in which $*$ is associative and $yx^2 = y$ for every $x, y \in S$. Prove that $\{S; *\}$ is a commutative group.

6. Consider the real coordinate plane, and let $\mathbf{R}_A$ denote the rotation of the points of the plane through the angle A around the origin, counterclock-

wise if $A > 0$ and clockwise if $A < 0$. The "product" $\mathbf{R}_A * \mathbf{R}_B$ is defined to be the transformation which results when $\mathbf{R}_A$ is followed by $\mathbf{R}_B$.

(i) Find a simple expression for $\mathbf{R}_A * \mathbf{R}_B$.

(ii) Prove that the system $\mathcal{R} = \{R; *\}$ is a commutative group, where R is the set of all rotations of the plane around the origin.

7. In three-dimensional space let $\mathbf{X}_A$, $\mathbf{Y}_A$, and $\mathbf{Z}_A$ denote rotations of the points of space about the x, y, and z axes, respectively, through the angle A, where the positive direction of rotation is chosen to be counterclockwise as viewed toward the origin from the positive side of the axis of rotation. As in Exercise 6, the product of two rotations is defined to be the transformation which results when the first rotation is followed by the second. Show that this product is not commutative.

8. Consider the system $\{E; \odot\}$, where E is the set of three symbols $\{-, \S, /\}$, and where $\odot$ is defined in the table below by the rule that $x \odot y$ is the symbol in the row which is labeled x at the left and in the column which is labeled y at the top.

$\odot$	$-$	$\S$	$/$
$-$	$-$	$\S$	$/$
$\S$	$\S$	$/$	$-$
$/$	$/$	$-$	$\S$

Show that this system is a commutative group.

9. Discuss whatever similarities and distinctions you can detect between the systems of Exercise 8 and the group of Exercise 1 (i).

§A.8. *Homomorphisms and Isomorphisms*

We begin by defining homomorphism in the simple case of two systems, $\mathcal{S} = \{E; *\}$ and $\mathcal{S}' = \{E'; \star\}$, each having one operation.

Definition A.8. A mapping $\mathbf{H}$ of E into E' is called a *homomorphism* of $\mathcal{S}$ into $\mathcal{S}'$ if and only if for all $a, b \in E$

$$(a * b)\mathbf{H} = a\mathbf{H} \star b\mathbf{H}.$$

The domain of $\mathbf{H}$ is E; whenever the range of $\mathbf{H}$ is the full set E', $\mathbf{H}$ is called a homomorphism of $\mathcal{S}$ *onto* $\mathcal{S}'$. A homomorphism $\mathbf{H}$ of $\mathcal{S}$ onto $\mathcal{S}'$ is called an *isomorphism* if and only if $\mathbf{H}$ is a one-to-one mapping of E onto E'.

Thus a homomorphism is a many-to-one mapping of the elements of one system into those of another, having the special property that the operation

is preserved by the mapping. By this we mean that the image in E' of the
$*$-product of any two elements of E equals the $\star$-product in E' of the images
in E' of those two elements of E. Similarly, an isomorphism of S onto S' is a
one-to-one mapping of E onto E' that preserves the operation.

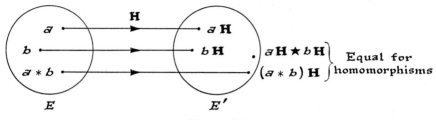

Figure A.2

Now consider the more general case of homomorphism of two systems S
and S', each of which has m relations and n operations. As before, a homomorphism is a mapping of E into E' that preserves the corresponding relations and operations. However, it is not immediately clear what is meant by
"corresponding." Suppose we make a one-to-one pairing of the relations of S
with the relations of S', and a one-to-one pairing of the operations of S with
the operations of S'; say, $r_i \longleftrightarrow r'_i, i = 1, \ldots, m$, and $o_j \longleftrightarrow o'_j, j = 1, \ldots, n$.

Definition A.9. A *homomorphism* of S into S' is a mapping $\mathbf{H}$ of E into
E' such that
(a) if $a\ r_i\ b$ in E, then $a\mathbf{H}\ r'_i\ b\mathbf{H}$ in E', $i = 1, \ldots, m$,
(b) $(a\ o_j\ b)\mathbf{H} = a\mathbf{H}\ o'_j\ b\mathbf{H}$ for all $a, b \in E$, $j = 1, \ldots, n$.
If $E' = $ range $\mathbf{H}$, then $\mathbf{H}$ is called a homomorphism of S *onto* S'. A
homomorphism $\mathbf{H}$ of S onto S' is called an *isomorphism* if and only if $\mathbf{H}$
is a one-to-one mapping of E onto E'.

Although the notation of (b), above, implicitly assumes that all operations
are binary, it is not difficult to formulate a corresponding statement for a
homomorphism of systems which have n-ary operations.

Exercises

1. Determine whether each of the following mappings is a homomorphism,
an isomorphism, or neither.

(i) The mapping $m \longrightarrow 2m$ of the additive group of integers into
the additive group of even integers.

(ii) The mapping $a \longrightarrow 1/a$ of the multiplicative group of nonzero
real numbers into the additive group of real numbers.

(iii) The mapping $a \longrightarrow 1/a^2$ of the multiplicative group of nonzero real numbers into the multiplicative group of positive real numbers.

2. Referring to Exercise 9, § 1.5 show by the mapping

$$(a, b) \longrightarrow a + ib$$

that $\{C; +, \bullet\}$ is isomorphic to the field of complex numbers.

3. Show that the additive group of real numbers is mapped homomorphically onto the multiplicative group of all complex numbers which lie on the unit circle by the mapping

$$x \longrightarrow \cos x + i \sin x.$$

4. Let $\mathcal{G} = \{G; *\}$ be any group, and let $\mathcal{J}$ be the additive group of the integers. For any fixed $g \in G$ show that the mapping

$$n \longrightarrow g * g * g * \cdots * g \ (n \ \text{times})$$

is a homomorphism of $\mathcal{J}$ into $\mathcal{G}$. Is this mapping a homomorphism of $\mathcal{J}$ onto $\mathcal{G}$?

5. Let $\mathbf{H}$ be a homomorphism of $\mathcal{S} = \{E; *\}$ onto $\mathcal{S}' = \{E'; \star\}$.

(i) Prove that if $\mathcal{S}$ has an identity element i, then $\mathcal{S}'$ must have an identity element i', and that $i' = i\mathbf{H}$.

(ii) Prove that if $a \in E$ has an inverse b, then $a\mathbf{H}$ has an inverse which must be $b\mathbf{H}$.

6. Is the additive group of all real numbers isomorphic to the multiplicative group of all positive real numbers? Explain.

7. Refer to Exercise 3, § A.7, where the mappings $\mathbf{R}_g$ are defined for any group $\mathcal{G} = \{G; *\}$. The product $\mathbf{R}_{g_1} \odot \mathbf{R}_{g_2}$ of two such mappings is defined as the mapping which results when $\mathbf{R}_{g_1}$ is followed by $\mathbf{R}_{g_2}$. Let $R_G = \{\mathbf{R}_g | g \in G\}$.

(i) Show that $\{R_G; \odot\}$ is a group.

(ii) Show that the mapping $g \longrightarrow \mathbf{R}_g$ is an isomorphism of $\{G; *\}$ onto $\{R_G; \odot\}$, thus proving *Cayley's Theorem:* Every group is isomorphic to a transformation group.

§A.9. *Equivalence Relations and Partitions*

Definition A.10. An *equivalence relation* on a set A is a binary relation $\mathbf{R}$ in A which is reflexive, symmetric, and transitive.

(a) *Reflexive:* $a \mathbf{R} a$ for every $a \in A$.

(b) *Symmetric:* If $a \mathbf{R} b$, then $b \mathbf{R} a$.

(c) *Transitive:* If $a \mathbf{R} b$ and $b \mathbf{R} c$, then $a \mathbf{R} c$.

It follows from (a) that dom $\mathbf{R} = A = $ range $\mathbf{R}$.

We now consider the effect imposed by an equivalence relation **R** on a non-void set A. For each $a \in A$ let $[a]_\mathbf{R}$ denote the set of all elements which are related to a by **R**:

$$[a]_\mathbf{R} = \{x \in A \mid x \mathbf{R} a\}.$$

The set $[a]_\mathbf{R}$ is called the *equivalence class determined by* a. Since **R** is reflexive, $a \mathbf{R} a$, so $a \in [a]_\mathbf{R}$. This implies that the set union of all the equivalence classes equals A. If $b \in [a]_\mathbf{R}$, then $b \mathbf{R} a$, and $a \mathbf{R} b$ since **R** is symmetric. Hence if $b \in [a]_\mathbf{R}$, then $a \in [b]_\mathbf{R}$. Suppose also that $y \in [b]_\mathbf{R}$. Then $y \mathbf{R} b$ and $b \mathbf{R} a$, so transitivity implies $y \mathbf{R} a$; hence $y \in [a]_\mathbf{R}$, and $[b]_\mathbf{R} \subseteq [a]_\mathbf{R}$. By reversing the roles of a and b we obtain $[a]_\mathbf{R} \subseteq [b]_\mathbf{R}$, so $[b]_\mathbf{R} = [a]_\mathbf{R}$ whenever $b \in [a]_\mathbf{R}$. This implies that two equivalence classes are either equal or have no elements in common.

Therefore, an equivalence relation **R** on a set A decomposes A into disjoint subsets, called equivalence classes. Such a decomposition of a set is called a *partition*.

> **Definition A.11.** A *partition* of a set A is a collection $\mathcal{P}$ of subsets of A, called classes of the partition, such that
> (a) if $x \in A$, then $x \in C$ for some $C \in \mathcal{P}$, and
> (b) if $C, D \in \mathcal{P}$, then either $C = D$ or $C \cap D = \Phi$.

Now suppose we reverse the situation and start with any partition $\mathcal{P}$ of A. A relation **R** can be defined on A by writing $a \mathbf{R} b$ if and only if a and b are in the same class of $\mathcal{P}$. It can be proved as an exercise that **R** is an equivalence relation on A for which the equivalence classes are the classes of $\mathcal{P}$. Therefore, each equivalence relation on A determines a partition of A, and, conversely, each partition determines an equivalence relation.

Exercises

1. Given a symmetric and transitive relation **R** in a set A. Is **R** reflexive? Distinguish between the cases dom **R** $= A$ and dom **R** $\subset A$.

2. Consider the points of a plane P as described in a rectangular coordinate system by pairs of real numbers, and let m be a fixed real number. Define on P the relation **M** as follows:

$$(x_1, y_1)\mathbf{M}(x_2, y_2) \qquad \text{if and only if } y_1 - y_2 = m(x_1 - x_2).$$

  (i) Prove that **M** is an equivalence relation.
  (ii) Describe geometrically the equivalence classes of **M**.

3. Given a partition $\mathcal{P}$ of a set A. Show, as indicated in the text, that a corresponding equivalence relation **R** can be defined on A such that the equivalence classes of **R** are the classes of the partition $\mathcal{P}$.

4. Let $E(n)$ denote the number of different partitions which can be defined on a set of n identical objects.

  (i) Evaluate $E(n)$ for $n = 1, 2, 3, 4$.

  (ii) Relate $E(n)$ to the number of different ways the integer n may be written as the sum of positive integers in nonincreasing order, for example,

$$5 = 3 + 2 = 3 + 1 + 1 = 4 + 1 \text{ and so on.}$$

§A.10. *Cosets*

We conclude this discussion of general algebraic concepts with one further notion of widespread applicability in the study of algebraic systems. In doing so we shall discover an intimate connection between mappings, equivalence relations, homomorphisms, and isomorphisms.

Let **R** be a relation from A into B, and suppose $A = \text{dom } \mathbf{R}$. We first show how **R** can be used to define a relation $\bar{\mathbf{R}}$ in A. Each $a \in A$ is related to one or more $b \in B$. Another element $x \in A$ might also be related to one or more of those same elements of B. With this fact in mind we make the following definition.

Definition A.12. The **R**-*coset* of $a \in A$ is the set

$$(a)_{\mathbf{R}} = \{x \in A \mid x \mathbf{R} b \text{ and } a \mathbf{R} b \text{ for some } b \in B\}.$$

We immediately deduce from the definition that

$$a \in (a)_{\mathbf{R}}$$

and

$$x \in (a)_{\mathbf{R}} \qquad \text{if and only if } a \in (x)_{\mathbf{R}}.$$

A relation $\bar{\mathbf{R}}$, which we call the *relation induced in A by the* **R**-*cosets*, is defined by writing

$$x \, \bar{\mathbf{R}} \, a \qquad \text{if and only if } x \in (a)_{\mathbf{R}}.$$

It follows that dom $\bar{\mathbf{R}} = A = \text{range } \bar{\mathbf{R}}$, and that $\bar{\mathbf{R}}$ is both reflexive and symmetric. In the example illustrated in Figure A.1, we observe that $(a_1)_{\mathbf{R}} = \{a_1, a_2\}$, $(a_2)_{\mathbf{R}} = \{a_1, a_2, a_3\}$, and $(a_3)_{\mathbf{R}} = \{a_2, a_3\}$. This shows that $\bar{\mathbf{R}}$ is not always transitive.

However, suppose that the original relation **R** is actually a mapping **F**, so that each $a \in A$ has a unique image $a\mathbf{F} \in B$. Then the **F**-coset of a is

$$(a)_{\mathbf{F}} = \{x \in A \mid x\mathbf{F} = a\mathbf{F}\}.$$

Therefore, the relation $\bar{\mathbf{F}}$ induced in A by the **F**-cosets is characterized by the statement

$$x \, \overline{\textbf{F}} \, a \qquad \text{if and only if } x\textbf{F} = a\textbf{F}.$$

We now prove that this reflexive and symmetric relation is also transitive. Let $y \, \overline{\textbf{F}} \, x$ and $x \, \overline{\textbf{F}} \, a$; then $y\textbf{F} = x\textbf{F} = a\textbf{F}$, so $y \, \overline{\textbf{F}} \, a$. Hence $\overline{\textbf{F}}$ is an equivalence relation. Furthermore, the $\overline{\textbf{F}}$-equivalence class which contains a is simply the $\textbf{F}$-coset of a, for

$$[a]_{\overline{\textbf{F}}} = \{x \in A \mid x \, \overline{\textbf{F}} \, a\} = \{x \in A \mid x\textbf{F} = a\textbf{F}\} = (a)_{\textbf{F}}.$$

These results are summarized and an additional fact asserted in the following theorem.

Theorem A.1. Let $\textbf{R}$ be a relation from A into B for which $A = \text{dom } \textbf{R}$, and let $\overline{\textbf{R}}$ be the relation induced on A by the $\textbf{R}$-cosets of A. Then $\overline{\textbf{R}}$ is reflexive and symmetric. If $\textbf{R}$ is a mapping $\textbf{F}$, then $\overline{\textbf{F}}$ is an equivalence relation whose equivalence classes are the $\textbf{F}$-cosets. Let $\overline{A}$ be the collection of these equivalence classes; there exist a mapping $\textbf{K}$ from A onto $\overline{A}$ and a one-to-one mapping $\textbf{J}$ of $\overline{A}$ onto range $\textbf{F} \subseteq B$ such that

$$\textbf{F} = \textbf{KJ}.$$

P R O O F : To verify the last sentence of the theorem we define the mapping $\textbf{K}$ from A onto $\overline{A}$ as follows:

$$\textbf{K}: \qquad a \longrightarrow [a]_{\overline{\textbf{F}}}.$$

$\textbf{K}$ maps each $a \in \text{dom } \textbf{F}$ into the equivalence class ($\textbf{F}$-coset) of all elements x for which $x\textbf{F} = a\textbf{F}$. The mapping $\textbf{J}$ of $\overline{A}$ onto range $\textbf{F}$ is defined by

$$\textbf{J}: \qquad [a]_{\overline{\textbf{F}}} \longrightarrow a\textbf{F}.$$

It is necessary now to consider an important technical point: the description just given as a definition of the mapping $\textbf{J}$ is open to criticism, since the $\textbf{J}$-image of the equivalence class $[a]_{\overline{\textbf{F}}}$ was specified as $a\textbf{F}$, the $\textbf{F}$-image of one of the members of $[a]_{\overline{\textbf{F}}}$. At first glance it appears that this definition might be ambiguous, because different members of $[a]_{\overline{\textbf{F}}}$ might have different $\textbf{F}$-images in B. But $x \in [a]_{\overline{\textbf{F}}}$ if and only if $x\textbf{F} = a\textbf{F}$, which shows that all members of $[a]_{\overline{\textbf{F}}}$ do have the same $\textbf{F}$-image. Hence, $\textbf{J}$ is properly defined, after all.

To prove that $\textbf{J}$ is one-to-one, suppose $[a]_{\overline{\textbf{F}}}\textbf{J} = [b]_{\overline{\textbf{F}}}\textbf{J}$. Then $a\textbf{F} = b\textbf{F}$, so $b \in [a]_{\overline{\textbf{F}}}$. But two equivalence classes which are not disjoint must be equal, so $[a]_{\overline{\textbf{F}}} = [b]_{\overline{\textbf{F}}}$. Finally, $a\textbf{K} = [a]_{\overline{\textbf{F}}}$, and $a\textbf{KJ} = [a]_{\overline{\textbf{F}}}\textbf{J} = a\textbf{F}$, so $\textbf{KJ} = \textbf{F}$.

The following diagram might help to fix in mind the essential points of this theorem.

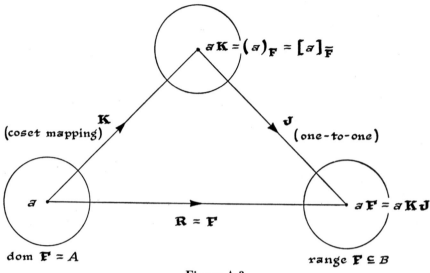

Figure A.3

This analysis of the role of cosets in the theory of mappings takes on special significance when it is applied to homomorphisms of abstract systems. Let **H** be a homomorphism of $S = \{E; *\}$ onto $S' = \{E'; \star\}$. From the theorem just proved, we know that the **H**-cosets are equivalence classes which form a partition of E. Let $\overline{E}$ be the collection of the **H**-cosets of E. The mapping **H** can be represented as the successive mappings **KJ**, where **K** maps each $x \in E$ into its **H**-coset, $[x]_H$, and where **J** is the one-to-one mapping of $\overline{E}$ onto E' which assigns to $[x]_H$ the image xH:

$$x \xrightarrow{\text{K}} [x]_H \xrightarrow{\text{J}} xH.$$

But much more can be said; because of the operation which is defined on E, it is possible to define an operation $\bullet$ on $\overline{E}$ by the rule

$$[x]_H \bullet [y]_H = [x * y]_H.$$

It is necessary again to prove that the definition is not ambiguous; that is, to prove that the "product" of two cosets is independent of the choice of representative elements. Suppose $a \in [x]_H$ and $b \in [y]_H$. Then $aH = xH$ and $bH = yH$. Since **H** is a homomorphism,

$$(a * b)H = aH \star bH = xH \star yH = (x * y)H.$$

Hence, $a * b \in [x * y]_H$, and finally $[a * b]_H = [x * y]_H$ because the **H**-cosets form a partition of E. Therefore, the operation $\bullet$ is properly defined on $\overline{E}$, and $\overline{S} = \{\overline{E}; \bullet\}$ is an abstract system.

Now consider the mapping **K** of E onto $\overline{E}$. We have

$$(x * y)\mathbf{K} = [x * y]_H = [x]_H \bullet [y]_H = x\mathbf{K} \bullet y\mathbf{K}.$$

Hence **K** is a homomorphism of S onto S̄. Likewise, the one-to-one mapping **J** of $\overline{E}$ onto E' preserves the corresponding operation:

$$([x]_{\mathrm{H}} \bullet [y]_{\mathrm{H}})\mathbf{J} = [x * y]_{\mathrm{H}}\mathbf{J} = (x * y)\mathbf{H} = x\mathbf{H} \star y\mathbf{H} = [x]_{\mathrm{H}}\mathbf{J} \star [y]_{\mathrm{H}}\mathbf{J}.$$

Therefore **J** is an isomorphism of the systems S̄ and S'.

> **Fundamental Isomorphism Theorem.** Let **H** be a homomorphism of the system S $= \{E; *\}$ onto the system S' $= \{E'; \star\}$. Then a product
> • can be defined on the set $\overline{E}$ of **H**-cosets such that
> (a) there exists a mapping **K** which is a homomorphism of the system S onto the system S̄ $= \{\overline{E}; \bullet\}$,
> (b) there exists a mapping **J** which is an isomorphism of the system S̄ onto the system S',
> (c) **H = KJ.**

Finally, we remark that no specific properties of any of the systems were assumed, and therefore the preceding theorem is extremely general. In various applications the system S̄ of cosets is called the *factor-system*, *quotient-system*, or *difference-system* of S.

Exercises

1. Describe the **R**-cosets of each of the following relations.
    (i) The order relation $<$ for real numbers.
    (ii) The relation "a divides b" for positive integers.
    (iii) The relation "L_1 is perpendicular to L_2" for lines of the plane.

2. Let S be the set of all humans living at a given instant, and let **F** be the age function, $s\mathbf{F}$ being the age in years of s on his most recent birthday. Describe the **F**-cosets.

3. Refer to the relation **R** of congruence modulo n, as defined for integers in Exercise 4, § 1.3.

    (i) Describe the **R**-cosets.
    (ii) Let I_n denote the collection of these cosets, which we denote by $(0)_n, (1)_n, \ldots, (n-1)_n$. We define on I_n two operations:

$$(a)_n \oplus (b)_n = (a+b)_n,$$
$$(a)_n \odot (b)_n = (ab)_n.$$

Verify that these operations are unambiguously defined.
    (iii) Show that the system $\mathfrak{I}_n = \{I_n; \oplus\}$ is a commutative group.
    (iv) Show that the system $\mathfrak{I}_n = \{I_n; \oplus, \odot\}$ is a field if and only if n is prime.

(v) Show that the mapping $\mathbf{H}$ of the integers onto $\mathcal{J}_n$ is a homomorphism, where $\mathbf{H}$ is defined by

$$x\mathbf{H} = [a]_n \qquad \text{if and only if } x \equiv a(\mathrm{mod}\ n),\ a = 0, \ldots, n - 1.$$

4. Let $\mathcal{S} = \{E; *\}$ be a group whose identity is denoted i, and let $\mathbf{H}$ be a homomorphism of $\mathcal{S}$ onto $\mathcal{S}' = \{E'; \star\}$. From Exercise 5, § A.8 we know that $i\mathbf{H}$ is the identity of $\mathcal{S}'$. The $\mathbf{H}$-coset $(i)_\mathbf{H}$ is called the *kernel* of $\mathbf{H}$. Prove that $\mathbf{H}$ is an isomorphism if and only if the kernel of $\mathbf{H}$ has i as its only element.

5. Let $\mathbf{H}$ be a homomorphism of a field $\mathcal{F}$ into a field $\mathcal{F}'$, and suppose that $a\mathbf{H} \neq 0'$ for some $a \in \mathcal{F}$. Prove that $\mathbf{H}$ is an isomorphism.

APPENDIX B

Matrix Notation

A student beginning his study of linear algebra might find it disconcerting to discover that no two books on the subject seem to use the same notation. Some use Greek letters for scalars and Latin letters for vectors; others reverse the choice. Some use bold face type for vectors; others use it for mappings. But more basic than these simple typographical differences, some authors write the symbol for a mapping to the left of the symbol for the element that is mapped, others write it to the right. This lack of agreement among mathematicians about where to write symbols for mappings is a potential source of confusion for the inexperienced reader, and the purpose of this brief appendix is to reduce the confusion by examining the two most common conventions and their consequences in matrix algebra.

We begin by recognizing that a matrix can represent various mathematical objects, each in accordance with some notational convention. Different conventions for representing a given mathematical object by a matrix usually lead to different forms of the same matrix theorem. But it is the mathematical object itself, rather than its matrix representation, that attracts our interest. For this reason, algebraic operations for matrices are defined in such a way that the algebra of matrices reflects the algebra of the objects thus represented.

§B.1. *Mappings*

The most useful mathematical concept frequently represented by a matrix is a linear mapping, or a vector space homomorphism. If α is a vector and **T** a mapping, the image of α under **T** is usually denoted either by $\mathbf{T}\alpha$ or by $\alpha\mathbf{T}$. The latter notation, in which **T** is written to the right of α is called *right-hand notation;* the former, with **T** to the left of α is called *left-hand* *notation.* The image of α under the composite mapping, **T** followed by **S**, is denoted by α**TS** in right-hand notation and by **ST**α in left-hand notation. Of course, both symbols have exactly the same meaning: the vector α is mapped by **T**, and then the resulting vector is mapped by **S**. Thus in right-hand notation α**TS** is read *from left to right;* in left-hand notation **ST**α is read *from right to left.* Both describe the same sequence of events.

§B.2. *Linear Transformations*

Suppose that **T** is a vector space homomorphism from $\mathcal{V}_m$ to $\mathcal{W}_n$. As described in § 4.1, in order to represent **T** by a matrix we choose a basis $\{\alpha_1, \alpha_2, \ldots, \alpha_m\}$ for $\mathcal{V}_m$ and a basis $\{\beta_1, \beta_2, \ldots, \beta_n\}$ for $\mathcal{W}_n$, and we express the image of each vector of the α-basis as a linear combination of the vectors of the β-basis:

$$\alpha_1\mathbf{T} = a_{11}\beta_1 + a_{12}\beta_2 + \cdots + a_{1n}\beta_n = \mathbf{T}\alpha_1$$

$$\alpha_i\mathbf{T} = a_{i1}\beta_1 + a_{i2}\beta_2 + \cdots + a_{in}\beta_n = \mathbf{T}\alpha_i$$

$$\alpha_m\mathbf{T} = a_{m1}\beta_1 + a_{m2}\beta_2 + \cdots + a_{mn}\beta_n = \mathbf{T}\alpha_m$$

In right-hand notation **T** is represented by the $m \times n$ matrix A of coefficients of the β_j in the array of these equations.

$$(B.1\text{-R}) \qquad \mathbf{T} \longrightarrow A = \begin{pmatrix} a_{11} & a_{12} & \cdots & a_{1n} \\ & & & \\ a_{i1} & a_{i2} & \cdots & a_{in} \\ & & & \\ a_{m1} & a_{m2} & \cdots & a_{mn} \end{pmatrix}$$

Each row of the representative matrix A specifies the coefficients of the image of the corresponding basis vector:

$$(B.2\text{-R}) \qquad \alpha_i\mathbf{T} = \sum_{j=1}^{n} a_{ij}\beta_j.$$

A vector $\xi = \sum_{i=1}^{n} x_i\alpha_i \in \mathcal{V}_m$ is represented by the *row* vector $X = (x_1, \ldots, x_n)$. Then $\xi\mathbf{T}$ is represented by the row vector XA. If a linear mapping **S** from $\mathcal{W}_n$ to $\mathcal{Y}_p$ is represented by a matrix C relative to the β-basis for $\mathcal{W}_n$ and a γ-basis for $\mathcal{Y}_p$, then **TS** is represented by the matrix product AC. Similarly, $\xi\mathbf{TS}$ is represented by XAC.

In left-hand notation **T** is represented by the $n \times m$ matrix B of coefficients of the β_j in the *transposed* array of the equations.

$$(B.1\text{-}L) \qquad \mathbf{T} \longrightarrow B = \begin{pmatrix} a_{11} \cdots a_{i1} \cdots a_{m1} \\ a_{12} \cdots a_{i2} \cdots a_{m2} \\ \cdot \qquad \cdot \qquad \cdot \\ \cdot \qquad \cdot \qquad \cdot \\ \cdot \qquad \cdot \qquad \cdot \\ a_{1n} \cdots a_{in} \cdots a_{mn} \end{pmatrix}$$

Thus $b_{ji} = a_{ij}$, and $B = A'$. Each *column* of the representative matrix B specifies the coefficients of the image of the corresponding basis vector:

$$(B.2\text{-}L) \qquad \mathbf{T}\alpha_i = \sum_{j=1}^{n} b_{ji}\beta_j.$$

The vector $\xi = \sum_{i=1}^{m} x_i\alpha_i$ is represented by the column vector U, where

$$U = \begin{pmatrix} x_1 \\ \cdot \\ \cdot \\ \cdot \\ x_m \end{pmatrix} = X'.$$

Then $\mathbf{T}\xi$ is represented by the matrix product BU. We note that

$$BU = A'X' = (XA)';$$

thus the column vector BU which represents $\mathbf{T}\xi$ in left-hand notation is the transpose of the row vector which represents $\xi\mathbf{T}$ in right-hand notation. The transformation $\mathbf{S}$ from $\mathcal{W}_n$ to $\mathcal{Y}_p$ will be represented by a $p \times n$ matrix $D = C'$. Thus $\mathbf{ST}$ is represented by $DB = C'A' = (AC)'$, and $\mathbf{ST}\xi$ is represented by $DBU = C'A'X' = (XAC)'$.

In short, the matrix representation for vectors and linear transformations using left-hand notation is the transpose of the matrix representation obtained using right-hand notation. Furthermore, in both systems of representation the algebra of matrices reflects that of linear transformations.

These observations provide a direct method by which a statement about matrices which expresses a fact about linear transformations in either system of notation can be translated into a matrix statement which expresses the same result in the other system. For example, consider matrix equivalence, which in right-hand notation is expressed in § 6.5 by

$$(B.3\text{-}R) \qquad A = PCQ^{-1}.$$

Then

$$A' = (Q')^{-1}C'P' = (Q')^{-1}C'P'.$$

But each linear transformation is represented by a certain matrix in one system of notation and by the transpose of that matrix in the other system. Hence A and A' represent $\mathbf{T}$, C and C' represent $\mathbf{T}$ relative to another pair of bases, P and P' represent the change of basis in $\mathcal{V}_m$, and Q and Q' represent the change of basis in $\mathcal{W}_n$. If we let $B = A'$, $D = C'$, $R = P'$, and

$S = Q'$, then we obtain a characterization of matrix equivalence, expressed in left-hand notation: matrices B and D are equivalent if and only if there exist nonsingular matrices R and S such that

(B.3-L) $$B = S^{-1}DR.$$

Similarity takes the form

(B.4-R) $\qquad A = PCP^{-1} \qquad$ in right-hand notation,

(B.4-L) $\qquad B = R^{-1}DR \qquad$ in left-hand notation.

§B.3. *Systems of Linear Equations*

Now consider a system of linear equations of the form (5.1):

$$a_{11}x_1 + a_{12}x_2 + \cdots + a_{1n}x_n = y_1$$
$$a_{21}x_1 + a_{22}x_2 + \cdots + a_{2n}x_n = y_2$$
$$\vdots \qquad \vdots \qquad\qquad \vdots \qquad \vdots$$
$$a_{m1}x_1 + a_{m2}x_2 + \cdots + a_{mn}x_n = y_m$$

In order to represent this system by the matrix A of coefficients arranged precisely in the array given by the equations themselves, we use left-hand notation:

(6.5-L) $$AX = Y,$$

where X and Y are *column* vectors representing $\xi \in \mathcal{W}_n$ and $\eta \in \mathcal{V}_m$, and where A represents a linear transformation $\mathbf{T}$ from $\mathcal{W}_n$ to $\mathcal{V}_m$:

$$\mathbf{T}\beta_i = \sum_{j=1}^{m} a_{ji}\alpha_j,$$

$$\mathbf{T}\xi = \eta.$$

(The definitions of $\mathbf{T}$, ξ, η, X, and Y are different from those in § B.2.) But the system can also be expressed by

(6.5-R) $$X'A' = Y',$$

where X' and Y' are row vectors. Now in right-hand notation A' represents $\mathbf{T}$, X' and Y' represent ξ and η, and $\xi\mathbf{T} = \eta$.

§B.4. *Conjugate Bilinear Functions*

Finally, consider the matrix representation of a conjugate bilinear function f, as discussed in § 8.1. In either left-hand or right-hand notation, f is represented relative to bases $\{\alpha_i\}$ for $\mathcal{V}_m$ and $\{\beta_j\}$ for $\mathcal{W}_n$ by the matrix A where

$a_{ij} = f(\alpha_i, \beta_j)$. In right-hand notation, vectors ξ and η are represented by row vectors X and Y, and

$(B.6\text{-R})$ $$f(\xi, \eta) = XA\overline{Y}'.$$

Conjunctivity of A and C is expressed by

$(B.7\text{-R})$ $$A = PC\overline{P}',$$

and congruence is expressed by

$(B.8\text{-R})$ $$A = PCP'.$$

In left-hand notation, ξ and η are represented by column vectors U and V, and

$(B.6\text{-L})$ $$f(\xi, \eta) = U'A\overline{V}.$$

Conjunctivity of A and C is expressed by

$(B.7\text{-L})$ $$A = P'C\overline{P},$$

and congruence is expressed by

$(B.8\text{-L})$ $$A = P'CP.$$

Sometimes a further modification is employed for left-hand notation by defining a conjugate bilinear function to be conjugate linear in the *first* component and linear in the *second*. With that convention we have

$$f(\xi, \eta) = \overline{U}'AV,$$

and conjunctivity becomes

$$A = \overline{P}'CP.$$

Congruence remains in the form

$$A = P'CP.$$

You are strongly encouraged to verify the statements of this Appendix by direct computation, observing carefully how and where the distinctions arise, yet discerning that corresponding matrix statements have precisely the same meaning when interpreted as statements about mappings.

References

The references given here are intended as a guide for undergraduates, with no pretense of completeness, in the hope that students will make a habit of consulting the literature frequently. These references are classified somewhat arbitrarily into two categories: introductory textbooks, which roughly parallel the content of this book, and supplementary books on algebra, matrix theory, and applications. References to important journal articles can be found in some of these volumes and in *Mathematical Reviews*.

Textbooks

1. Beaumont, R. A., *Linear Algebra*. New York: Harcourt, Brace, and World, Inc., 1965.
2. Birkhoff, G., and MacLane, S., *A Survey of Modern Algebra*, Revised edition. New York: Macmillan Company, 1953.
3. Curtis, C. W., *Linear Algebra*. Boston: Allyn and Bacon, Inc., 1963.
4. Halmos, P. R., *Finite Dimensional Vector Spaces*, Second edition. Princeton: D. Van Nostrand Company, Inc., 1958.
5. Hoffman, K., and Kunze, R., *Linear Algebra*. Englewood Cliffs: Prentice-Hall, Inc., 1961.
6. Hohn, F. E., *Elementary Matrix Algebra*. New York: Macmillan Company, 1958.
7. Murdoch, D. C., *Linear Algebra for the Undergraduate*. New York: John Wiley and Sons, Inc., 1957.
8. Nering, E. D., *Linear Algebra and Matrix Theory*. New York: John Wiley and Sons, Inc., 1963.
9. Paige, L. J., and Swift, J. D., *Elements of Linear Algebra*. Boston: Ginn and Company, 1961.
10. Perlis, S., *The Theory of Matrices*. Cambridge, Mass.: Addison-Wesley Press, Inc., 1952.
11. Schwartz, J. T., *Introduction to Matrices and Vectors*. New York: McGraw-Hill Book Company, 1961.
12. Stewart, F. M., *Introduction to Linear Algebra*. Princeton: D. Van Nostrand Company, Inc., 1963.
13. Stoll, R. R., *Linear Algebra and Matrix Theory*. New York: McGraw-Hill Book Company, Inc., 1952.
14. Thrall, R. M., and Tornheim, L., *Vector Spaces and Matrices*. New York: John Wiley and Sons, Inc., 1957.

Supplementary Books

15. Aitken, A. C., *Determinants and Matrices*. New York: Interscience Publishers, 1954.
16. Artin, E., *Galois Theory*, Second edition. University of Notre Dame, 1944.
17. Artin, E., *Geometric Algebra*. New York: Interscience Publishers, Inc., 1957.
18. Beckenbach, E. F. (editor), *Modern Mathematics for the Engineer*. New York: McGraw-Hill Book Company, Inc., 1956.
19. Beckenbach, E. F. (editor), *Modern Mathematics for the Engineer* (Second series). New York: McGraw-Hill Book Company, Inc., 1961.
20. Bodewig, E., *Matrix Calculus*. Amsterdam: North Holland Publishing Company, 1956.
21. Bourbaki, N., *Algèbre*, Chapter II, "Algèbre linéaire." Paris: Hermann et Cie., 1947.
22. Dantzig, G. B., *Linear Programming and Extensions*. Princeton: Princeton University Press, 1963.
23. Faddeev, D. K., and Faddeeva, V. N., *Computational Methods of Linear Algebra*. San Francisco: W. H. Freeman and Company, 1963.
24. Feller, W., *An Introduction to Probability and its Applications*. New York: John Wiley and Sons, Inc., 1957.
25. Halmos, P. R., *Introduction to Hilbert Space*. New York: Chelsea Publishing Company, 1951.
26. Higman, B., *Applied Group-Theoretic and Matrix Methods*. London: Oxford University Press, 1955.
27. Householder, A. S., *The Theory of Matrices in Numerical Analysis*. New York: Blaisdell Publishing Company, 1964.
28. Jacobsen, N., *Lectures in Abstract Algebra*. Volume II. New York: D. Van Nostrand Company, 1953.
29. Kemeny, J. G., Snell, J. L., and Thompson, G. L., *Finite Mathematics*. Englewood Cliffs: Prentice-Hall, Inc., 1957.
30. König, D., *Theorie der Endlichen und Unendlichen Graphen*. Leipzig: Academische verlagsgesellschaft, 1936.
31. Kuiper, N. H., *Linear Algebra and Geometry*. Amsterdam: North Holland Publishing Company, 1962.
32. MacDuffee, C. C., *Vectors and Matrices*. Buffalo, N. Y.: Mathematical Association of America, 1943.
33. MacDuffee, C. C., *The Theory of Matrices*. New York: Chelsea Publishing Company, 1946.
34. Malčev, A. I., *Foundations of Linear Algebra*. San Francisco: W. H. Freeman and Company, 1963.
35. Margenau, H., and Murphy, G. M., *The Mathematics of Physics and Chemistry*, Second edition. Princeton: D. Van Nostrand Company, Inc., 1956.
36. Mirsky, L., *An Introduction to Linear Algebra*. Oxford: The Clarendon Press, 1955.

37. Schreier, O., and Sperner, E., *Modern Algebra and Matrix Theory*. New York: Chelsea Publishing Company, 1952.

38. Tucker, A. W., *A Combinatorial Equivalence of Matrices* (Proceedings of Symposia in Applied Mathematics, volume 10). Providence, R. I.: American Mathematical Society, 1960.

39. Turnbull, H. W., and Aiken, A. C., *An Introduction to the Theory of Canonical Matrices*. Glasgow: Blackie and Son, Ltd., 1932.

40. Wedderburn, J. H. M., *Lectures on Matrices*. New York: American Mathematical Society, 1934.

Suggestions and Answers for Selected Exercises

CHAPTER 1

§ 1.1. 1. (i) Let $\mathcal{K}$ represent the club, and let x and y represent any two distinct members of $\mathcal{K}$. By (b) there is a committee C to which x and y belong. By (c) there is a member z of $\mathcal{K}$ who does not serve on C. Now finish the proof by using (b) again.

(ii) Let C be any committee and let x be any member of C. Use (c) and (d) to obtain a student y not on C, and a committee C_1 which has no members in common with C. By (b) x and y serve on a uniquely determined committee C_2, and by (c) some student z does not serve on C_2. Then y and z determine a committee C_3. Now consider the possibilities of C and C_3 having a member in common; to complete the proof you will have to construct a C_4 also.

§ 1.2. 1. (i) There are 16 distinct subsets.

(ii) 2^m.

4. (iii) No.

5. (iii) Yes.

(v) Yes.

7. $n(A \cup B \cup C) = n(A) + n(B) + n(C) - n(A \cap B) - n(A \cap C)$
$$- n(B \cap C) + n(A \cap B \cap C).$$

§ 1.3. 1. (ii) There are six pairs in the subset.

(iii) There are six pairs in the subset.

2. $S \times S$ has at least sixteen elements; hence at least 2^{16} subsets.

§ 1.4. 1. (i) dom $\mathbf{FG}$ = dom $\mathbf{F}$ = S; range $\mathbf{FG} \subseteq$ range $\mathbf{G} \subseteq U$.

§ 1.5. 1. (i) Show that if both e and i are identities relative to $*$, then $e = i$.

(ii) Let $\bar{x}$ and x' be inverses of x, and consider $\bar{x} * (x * x')$.

3.　(i) Yes.

　(ii) Yes.

　(iii) No.

§ 1.6.　1.　(i) Consider $a \odot (o \oplus i)$.

　(ii) Consider $(a_- \odot b) \oplus (a \odot b)$, and use (i).

　(iii) Consider $b' \odot [b_- \odot (b_-)']$, and use (ii).

3. Show that the operations are closed and that the field postulates are satisfied.

CHAPTER 2

§ 2.1.　2. Only (v) and (x) form groups.

§ 2.2.　2. The space of all real n-tuples is isomorphic to the space of all real polynomials of degree not exceeding $n - 1$.

　5. No. Why not?

　6. Yes; yes; no; yes; no.

§ 2.3.　1. Yes; no; yes; no; yes; yes; yes; no; yes; yes.

　2. (iii) Not a group.

　4. $S \cap 3 = [(-3, 1, 5)]$.

　6. Let $\xi \in (\Re + S) \cap 3$ and write $\xi = \rho + \sigma$, where $\rho \in \Re$, and $\sigma \in S$. Prove that $\xi \in (\Re \cap 3) + (S \cap 3)$, and finally use the result of Exercise 5.

§ 2.4.　2. The number of vectors in a maximal linearly independent subset for each part is

　　(i) three;

　　(ii) four;

　　(iii) two.

§ 2.5.　5. $\epsilon_1 = \alpha_1 - \alpha_2$, $\epsilon_2 = \alpha_2 - \alpha_3$, $\epsilon_3 = \alpha_3 - \alpha_4$, $\epsilon_4 = \alpha_4$.

§ 2.6.　2. (a) n.

　　(b) 0.

　　(c) 1.

　　(d) $n + 1$.

　　(e) Infinite.

　4. (i) Choose a basis $\{\alpha_1, \ldots, \alpha_k\}$ for S; extend to a basis $\{\alpha_1, \ldots, \alpha_n\}$ for $\mathcal{V}$, and let $3 = [\alpha_{k+1}, \ldots, \alpha_n]$.

　5. Use Theorem 2.14 and Exercise 5, § 2.3.

§ 2.7.　1. Map $a_0 x^n + a_1 x^{n-1} + \cdots + a_n$ onto the $(n + 1)$-tuple

$$(a_0, a_1, \ldots, a_n).$$

　7. (i) Yes; no.

　　(iii) Yes; yes; no.

CHAPTER 3

§ 3.1. 4. Write $\theta = \alpha + (-\alpha)$.

    8. Only (ii) and (iv) are linear.

   10. (ii) No.

      (iii) Show that $\mathbf{MD} - \mathbf{DM}$ maps any polynomial into itself.

      (iv) Consider $\mathbf{D(MD} - \mathbf{DM)M}$.

§ 3.2. 1. If $\xi \in \mathscr{R}_{\mathbf{TS}}$, then $\xi = \eta\mathbf{TS}$ for some $\eta \in \mathcal{V}$. Hence $\xi = \alpha\mathbf{S}$, where $\alpha = \eta\mathbf{T} \in \mathcal{W}$. Hence $\xi \in \mathscr{R}_{\mathbf{S}}$.

    3. (i) Show that $\mathscr{R}_{\mathbf{T+S}} \subseteq \mathscr{R}_{\mathbf{T}} + \mathscr{R}_{\mathbf{S}}$ and then use Theorem 2.13.

      (iii) Choose a basis $\{\alpha_1, \ldots, \alpha_k\}$ for $\mathfrak{N}_{\mathbf{T}}$; extend to a basis $\{\alpha_1, \ldots, \alpha_m\}$ for $\mathfrak{N}_{\mathbf{TS}}$, and show that $\{\alpha_{k+1}\mathbf{T}, \ldots, \alpha_m\mathbf{T}\}$ is a basis for the space $\mathfrak{N}_{\mathbf{TS}}\mathbf{T}$. Finally, observe that $\mathfrak{N}_{\mathbf{TS}}\mathbf{T} \subseteq \mathfrak{N}_{\mathbf{S}}$, and complete the proof.

    7. If $\rho(\mathbf{T}) = 1$, each $\xi \in \mathcal{V}$ is mapped into a scalar multiple of some fixed vector α: $\xi\mathbf{T} = k_\xi\alpha$, where k_ξ depends upon ξ. Choose $c = k_\alpha$.

§ 3.3. 3. $ad \neq bc$.

    5. (ii) All except $\mathbf{DJ}$.

      (iii) All except $\mathbf{D}$ and $\mathbf{DJ}$.

§ 3.4. 1. Let $\xi = c(\alpha f)^{-1}\alpha$, where α is any vector for which $\alpha f \neq 0$.

    3. $(x_1, x_2, x_3)\mathbf{f}_i = \frac{1}{2}(x_1 + x_2 + x_3 - 2x_i)$, $i = 1, 2, 3$.

§ 3.5. 3. To show that $\mathbf{S}'$ is nonsingular, suppose that $f\mathbf{S}' = \theta \in \mathcal{V}'$, for some $f \in \mathcal{W}'$; then $\alpha\mathbf{S}f = 0$ for all $\alpha \in \mathcal{V}$. Since $\mathbf{S}$ is nonsingular, $\beta f = 0$ for all $\beta \in \mathcal{V}$, so $f = \theta \in \mathcal{W}'$.

§ 3.6. 1. (i) Let $\xi = \sum_{i=1}^{m} a_i\alpha_i$ and $\eta = \sum_{j=1}^{m} b_j\alpha_j$; calculate $\xi\eta$.

    2. (i) Calculate $(a_1 1 + a_2 i + a_3 j + a_4 k)(b_1 1 + b_2 i + b_3 j + b_4 k)$.

      (ii) Try $(a_1 1 - a_2 i - a_3 j - a_4 k)$ as an inverse of $(a_1 1 + a_2 i + a_3 j + a_4 k)$.

§ 3.7. 1. (iii) $(a, b)\mathbf{T} = (-a - b, -a + b)$.

      (iv) $\beta_1\mathbf{T} = -2\beta_1 + 2\beta_2$

           $\beta_2\mathbf{T} = -1\beta_1 + 2\beta_2$.

    2. (ii) $\alpha_1\mathbf{S} = \alpha_1 + 2\alpha_2$

         $\alpha_2\mathbf{S} = -\alpha_1 + \alpha_2$.

      (iii) $\epsilon_1\mathbf{S}^{-1} = (\epsilon_1 - 2\epsilon_2)/3$

         $\epsilon_2\mathbf{S}^{-1} = (\epsilon_1 + \epsilon_2)/3$.

    3. (iii) $(a, b)\mathbf{TS} = (-2b, -3a - b)$

         $(a, b)\mathbf{ST} = (-3a, a + 2b)$.

    5. (ii) Show that a basis for $\mathscr{R}_{\mathbf{T}}$ together with a basis for $\mathfrak{N}_{\mathbf{T}}$ form the desired basis for $\mathcal{V}$.

CHAPTER 4

§ 4.1. 3.   (i) $A = \begin{pmatrix} 1 & 0 \\ 0 & 0 \end{pmatrix}$, $B = \begin{pmatrix} 0 & 0 \\ 0 & 1 \end{pmatrix}$, $C = \begin{pmatrix} 0 & 1 \\ 1 & 0 \end{pmatrix}$.

   4.   (i) E_{ij} has 1 in the (i, j) position and 0 elsewhere.

§ 4.2. 3.   (ii) The (i, j) elements of AD and DA are $a_{ij}d_{jj}$ and $d_{ii}a_{ij}$, respectively. These will be equal for all choices of the d's if and only if $a_{ij} = 0$ when $i \neq j$.

   4. The major problem is to show that the inverse of a nonsingular triangular matrix is triangular. Assume that $AT = I$, and show that if $a_{rs} \neq 0$ for $r > s$, then one of the diagonal elements of T must be zero. You may use Exercise 3, § 4.4, to conclude that T must then be singular.

   8–12. Use Exercise 7.

   13.   (ii) $A = \begin{pmatrix} 1 & -2 & 0 \\ 1 & 1 & 1 \\ 0 & 1 & -1 \end{pmatrix}$.

   (iii) $B = \tfrac{1}{4} \begin{pmatrix} 2 & 2 & 2 \\ -1 & 1 & 1 \\ -1 & 1 & -3 \end{pmatrix}$.

§ 4.3. 2.   (i) A reflection across the x axis.
   (iii) A reflection across the line $y = x$, followed by a projection onto the y axis.

   3.   (i) Let $A = \begin{pmatrix} a & b \\ c & d \end{pmatrix}$ be idempotent. Show that

$$(a - d)(a + d - 1) = 0,$$

and consider separately the two cases which arise from this equation.
   (ii) As in (i), show that if A is nilpotent, then $(a - d)(a + d) = 0$, and consider separately the two cases which arise from this equation.

§ 4.4. 3. Determine necessary and sufficient conditions that the row vectors form a linearly independent set.

   4. To prove the assertion concerning dimension, choose a basis for $\mathcal{V}_n$ having ξ as its first vector. Then consider the effect on ξ of the linear transformations $\mathbf{T}_{ij}$ as defined in the proof of Theorem 3.16.

   5. Use Exercise 3, § 3.2.

   8. A Markov matrix can be singular.

   9. Yes.

   11.   (iii) $I, X, Y, iZ, -I, -X, -Y, -iZ$.

   12.   (ii) Show that $L(v_1)L(v_2) = L(v')$, where

$$v' = \frac{(v_1 + v_2)c^2}{v_1 v_2 + c^2}.$$

§ 4.5. 3. (i) The space spanned by $\{\alpha_1, \ldots, \alpha_k\}$ is **T**-invariant, as defined in Exercise 7, § 3.3.

CHAPTER 5

§ 5.1. 1. Interpret the system *(5.3)* as defining a linear transformation **T** from $\mathcal{W}_n$ to $\mathcal{V}_m$. Then $\rho(A') = \rho(\mathbf{T})$.

  3. $x_1 = -1 - 3x_4 + x_5$
  $x_2 = -1 - 3x_4$
  $x_3 = 1 + x_4 - 2x_5$
  x_4 and x_5 arbitrary.

  4. $x_1 = -1$, $x_2 = -2$, $x_3 = 4$. Solution is unique.

  5. No solution exists.

§ 5.2. 3. (i) If $\det \begin{pmatrix} a & b \\ c & d \end{pmatrix} = 0$, then $\det \begin{pmatrix} a & e \\ c & f \end{pmatrix} = 0$ and

$$\det \begin{pmatrix} e & b \\ f & d \end{pmatrix} = 0.$$

§ 5.3. 2. If $i \neq k$, $\sum\limits_{j=1}^{n} a_{ij}|A_{kj}|$ is the expression for expanding a determinant for which row i and row k are identical.

  4. Consider the various ways in which a nonzero product of n terms can be formed, one from each row and each column.

  6. (ii) $\det V$ is a polynomial of degree $n - 1$ in each x_i, which has the value zero if $x_i = x_j$ for $i \neq j$. Hence $(x_j - x_i)$ is a factor for each $j > i$, and $\det V = k \prod\limits_{1 \leq i < j \leq n} (x_j - x_i)$, where k is a constant, perhaps depending upon n. Prove that $k = 1$.

§ 5.4. 1. $x_1 = 2$, $x_2 = -2$, $x_3 = -1$.

  4. Use Theorem 5.12.

  5. $x = 1, 2, 3$.

  6. Use Exercise 6, § 5.3.

§ 5.5. 2. Multiply row i of B by a_{ij} and expand by Theorem 5.5(b) to obtain 2^{n-1} determinants, all but one of which are zero.

  3. (i) $\det A = -29$
    (ii) $\det B = -11$
    (iii) $\det C = -\frac{2}{7}$.

  4. Expand $\det B$ as the sum of 2^{n-1} determinants, all but n of which are zero; then apply Theorem 5.9.

  5. (i) Use Exercise 4, pivoting on d.

CHAPTER 6

§ 6.1.   3. (iii) A canonical form for $m \times n$ matrices of rank k is

$$\begin{pmatrix} I_k & Z \\ Z & Z \end{pmatrix}.$$

§ 6.2.   3. Consider the number of linearly independent rows of each type of matrix.

6. $M_i(c^{-1}) A_{ij} M_i(c)$.

7. $\det A_{ij} = 1 = -\det P_{ij}$; $\det M_i(c) = c$.

§ 6.3.   1.   (i) $\frac{1}{8} \begin{pmatrix} -2 & 6 & 4 \\ 1 & -3 & 2 \\ 1 & 5 & 2 \end{pmatrix}$.

(ii) $\frac{1}{2} \begin{pmatrix} 1 & 1 & 1 & 0 \\ 0 & 1 & 0 & 1 \\ 1 & 1 & -1 & 0 \\ 0 & 1 & 0 & -1 \end{pmatrix}$.

2. Convert each to reduced echelon form and compare.

7.   (i) The reduced echelon matrix E which is row equivalent to A has rank m. Hence there are m columns which have zero in all positions except one; these nonzero elements all equal 1 and appear in m distinct rows.

§ 6.4.   1. See the answer for Exercise 1, § 6.3.

4. All three matrices are of rank 2.

5. First observe that PAP' is symmetric if A is symmetric. If $a_{ij} \neq 0$, then $A_{ij} A (A_{ij})'$ has the element $2a_{ij}$ in the (j, j) position. A permutation of rows 1 and j and a like permutation of columns places $2a_{ij}$ in the $(1, 1)$ position. Multiplication of row 1 and column 1 by $(2a_{ij})^{-1/2}$ produces 1 in the $(1, 1)$ position. Row operations and corresponding column operations then produce zeros in the remaining positions of the first column and the first row.

6.   (i) Yes.

(ii) Not necessarily.

(iii) Not necessarily, if both A and B are singular. Yes, if either A or B is nonsingular.

§ 6.5.   4. $D = 3(e - 1) \begin{pmatrix} ez_1 + ez_2 + ez_3 & 0 & 0 \\ 0 & ez_1 + z_2 + e^2 z_3 & 0 \\ 0 & 0 & ez_1 + e^2 z_2 + z_3 \end{pmatrix}$.

6. $\begin{pmatrix} -2 & 0 & -1 \\ 4 & -3 & -1 \end{pmatrix}$.

7. Use the results of Exercise 5, § 3.7.

CHAPTER 7

§ **7.1.** 1. (i) $\lambda_1 = -3,$ $\quad X_1 = (2a, -3a)$
$\lambda_2 = 2,$ $\quad X_2 = (a, a).$
(ii) $\lambda_1 = -1 = \lambda_2$; two linearly independent characteristic vectors can be chosen.
$\lambda_3 = 8,$ $\quad X_3 = (2a, a, 2a).$
(iii) $\lambda_1 = 1 = \lambda_2 = \lambda_3,$ $\quad X_1 = (a, 0, -2a, 0)$
$\lambda_4 = 3,$ $\quad X_4 = (a, 0, 0, 0).$

10. M and M' have the same characteristic values. If $XM' = \lambda X$, let $m = \max |x_i|$, and show that $|\lambda x_i| \le m$ for all i.

§ **7.2.** 1. (i) $\lambda_1 = -2, \lambda_2 = 1, \lambda_3 = 3$. A suitable diagonalizing matrix is

$$P = \begin{pmatrix} 0 & 1 & -1 \\ 3 & -5 & 2 \\ 5 & 1 & 4 \end{pmatrix}.$$

(ii) $\lambda_1 = 3 = \lambda_2, \lambda_3 = 12$. A suitable diagonalizing matrix is

$$P = \begin{pmatrix} 1 & -1 & 0 \\ 1 & 0 & 1 \\ 4 & 4 & -1 \end{pmatrix}.$$

(iii) $\lambda_1 = 1 = \lambda_2, \lambda_3 = 2$. Since the characteristic vectors associated with the repeated characteristic value span only the one-dimensional space $[(5, 2, -5)]$, no diagonalizing matrix exists.

2. (i) and (ii) are similar to diagonal matrices; (iii) is not.
3. Use Exercise 8, § 7.1.
4. Use Exercise 7, § 7.1.
5. (i) Consider $\det(A - \lambda I)$, substituting each suggested value.
(ii) Use column operations on $\det(A - \lambda I)$.
6. (ii) Using D as defined in (i), let $C = Q^{-1}BP^{-1}$ and apply the results of (i).
8. An example which proves the assertion is given by

$$A = \begin{pmatrix} 0 & 1 & 0 \\ 0 & 0 & 1 \\ 0 & 0 & 0 \end{pmatrix}, \quad B = \begin{pmatrix} 0 & 1 & 0 \\ 0 & 0 & 0 \\ 0 & 0 & 0 \end{pmatrix}.$$

§ **7.3.** 6. (i) Let $A = \begin{pmatrix} a & b \\ c & d \end{pmatrix}$ and consider separately the cases $a + d = 0$
and $a + d \ne 0$.
(ii) If A is real and 3×3, the characteristic polynomial of A is of third degree with real coefficients; hence it has at least one real zero. Thus A^2 has at least one nonnegative characteristic value. This implies that $A^2 \ne -I$.

§ 7.4. 1. (i) $\mathfrak{M} = [(1, 1)],$ $\mathfrak{N} = [(-1, 1)],$ $\mathcal{E}_2 = \mathfrak{M} \oplus \mathfrak{N}.$

(ii) $A = \begin{pmatrix} 0 & 1 \\ 1 & 0 \end{pmatrix}.$

(iii) $B = \begin{pmatrix} 1 & 0 \\ 0 & -1 \end{pmatrix}.$

(iv) $P = \begin{pmatrix} 1 & 1 \\ 1 & -1 \end{pmatrix}.$

5. (iv) $\mathbf{E}_i$ is represented by a matrix which consists of zeros except for a square block I of size equal to the dimension of $\mathfrak{R}_{\mathbf{E}_i}$, beginning in the $(k + 1, k + 1)$ position, where $k = \dim \mathfrak{R}_{\mathbf{E}_1} + \cdots + \dim \mathfrak{R}_{\mathbf{E}_{i-1}}$.

§ 7.5. 1. (i) The minimal polynomial has distinct zeros.
(ii) The characteristic vectors do not span $\mathcal{V}_3$.
(iii) The characteristic vectors do not span $\mathcal{V}_3$.
(iv) The characteristic polynomial has distinct zeros.

2. A is similar to a diagonal matrix, which can be shown to be B.

5. Compute $E_j A$, and deduce that $A - a_j I$ is singular. Any nonzero vector of the form YE_j is characteristic.

§ 7.6. 2. (i) $\rho(A) = 2; \mathfrak{N}_A = [(0, 0, 1)]; A$ is nilpotent of index 3.
(ii) $\{\xi_1, \xi_1\mathbf{T}, \xi_1\mathbf{T}^2\}$ is a basis.
(iii) Relative to the basis of (ii), $\mathbf{T}$ is represented by the matrix

$$\begin{pmatrix} 0 & 1 & 0 \\ 0 & 0 & 1 \\ 0 & 0 & 0 \end{pmatrix}.$$

Hence $k = 1$ and $p_1 = 2$.

3. (i) By direct calculation, $AN = NA$ if and only if $a_{i,j-1} = a_{i+1,j}$ for $i < n$ and $j > 1$, $a_{nj} = 0$ if $j < n$, and $a_{i1} = 0$ if $i > 1$.

(ii) The only characteristic value of A is a_1, and the characteristic vectors can be shown to be those of the form $(0, 0, \ldots, 0, x_n)$.

(iii) Under the hypotheses, direct computation shows that the characteristic vectors are those of the form $(0, \ldots, 0, x_{n-k+1}, \ldots, x_n)$.

4. The characteristic polynomial of a nilpotent matrix must be $(-1)^n\lambda^n$; hence the conditions are $c_{n1} = c_{n2} = \cdots = c_{nn} = 0$.

5. If $\xi \in \mathfrak{R}_{\mathbf{T}^{p-k}}$, then $\xi\mathbf{T}^k = \theta$. Hence $\mathfrak{R}_{\mathbf{T}^{p-k}} \subseteq \mathfrak{N}_{\mathbf{T}^k}$. As in Theorem 3.5,

$$[\theta] \subseteq \mathfrak{R}_{\mathbf{T}^{p-1}} \subseteq \cdots \subseteq \mathfrak{R}_{\mathbf{T}} \subseteq \mathcal{V}$$

$$[\theta] \subseteq \mathfrak{N}_{\mathbf{T}} \subseteq \cdots \subseteq \mathfrak{N}_{\mathbf{T}^{p-1}} \subseteq \mathcal{V}.$$

Prove by induction that if $\mathfrak{R}_{\mathbf{T}^{p-1}} = \mathfrak{N}_{\mathbf{T}}$, then $\mathfrak{R}_{\mathbf{T}^{p-k}} = \mathfrak{N}_{\mathbf{T}^k}$. Then use Theorem 3.4 to show that if $\mathfrak{R}_{\mathbf{T}^{p-1}} \neq \mathfrak{N}_{\mathbf{T}}$, then $\mathfrak{R}_{\mathbf{T}} \neq \mathfrak{N}_{\mathbf{T}^{p-1}}$.

§ 7.7. 2. Find the Jordan form of A by determining whether A is similar to a diagonal matrix.

3. If A is not similar to a diagonal matrix, the two characteristic

values of A must coincide, and the characteristic vectors must span a one-dimensional space. Necessary and sufficient conditions are $(a - d)^2 + 4bc = 0$ and $b^2 + c^2 > 0$.

4. (i) $\begin{pmatrix} 1 & 1 & 0 \\ 0 & 1 & 0 \\ 0 & 0 & 2 \end{pmatrix}$.

(ii) $\begin{pmatrix} -1 & 1 & 0 \\ 0 & -1 & 1 \\ 0 & 0 & -1 \end{pmatrix}$.

(iii) $\begin{pmatrix} 1 & 1 & 0 \\ 0 & 1 & 0 \\ 0 & 0 & -1 \end{pmatrix}$.

6. Let $AJ = I$; for fixed i, let k be the smallest integer such that $a_{ik} \neq 0$. Then $\delta_{ik} = a_{ik}\lambda_k \neq 0$, so $k = i$. A 3×3 example shows that A need not be in Jordan form.

7. (iv) Segre characteristic: $\{(4, 2)(4)(1, 1)\}$.
    (v) Characteristic polynomial: $(\lambda - 2)^6(\lambda)^4(\lambda - 1)^2$.
    (vi) Minimal polynomial: $(\lambda - 2)^4(\lambda)^4(\lambda - 1)$.
    (vii) Elementary divisors: $(\lambda - 2)^4$, $(\lambda - 2)^2$, λ^4, $(\lambda - 1)$.

§ 7.8. 1. $A^3 = \begin{pmatrix} 2 & -6 & 2 & -4 \\ 0 & 2 & 0 & 2 \\ 2 & -2 & -2 & 0 \\ 0 & 2 & 0 & -2 \end{pmatrix}$, $A^{-1} = \frac{1}{2}\begin{pmatrix} 1 & 1 & 1 & 0 \\ 0 & 1 & 0 & 1 \\ 1 & 1 & -1 & 0 \\ 0 & 1 & 0 & -1 \end{pmatrix}$.

2. Consider the Jordan form of A.

5. (i) Yes.
    (ii) No.

6. (i) Recall that a projection is idempotent, and hence its characteristic values are zero or one.

7. Use Exercise 6, § 7.6.

8. $H_nAH_n^{-1}$ can be obtained from A by rotating each entry $180°$ about the center of A.

9. A is similar to a matrix J in Jordan form; let J have t diagonal sub-blocks. Let $P = \mathrm{diag}(B_1, \ldots, B_t)$ where each B_i is of the form H_{n_i} of Exercise 8, and where n_i is the size of the ith sub-block of J. Then $PJP^{-1} = J'$.

10. First show that $A^2 = (\mathrm{tr}A)A$

CHAPTER 8

§ 8.1. 2. (i) $\begin{pmatrix} 1 & 0 \\ -1 & 2 \end{pmatrix}$ and $\begin{pmatrix} 4 & 4 \\ 2 & 4 \end{pmatrix}$.

(ii) Yes.

9. Begin by moving a nonzero element a_{ij} into the $(1, 2)$ position by means of congruence operations. Then multiply row 1 and column 1 by $-a_{ij}^{-1}$. This produces a canonical block in the upper left. Reduce to zero the remaining elements of the first two rows and columns.

10. The canonical form has two diagonal blocks of the form $\begin{pmatrix} 0 & -1 \\ 1 & 0 \end{pmatrix}$, and all other elements are zero.

11.   (i) One correct answer is $\frac{1}{2}\begin{pmatrix} 5 & 0 & 0 \\ 0 & -20 & 0 \\ 0 & 0 & 0 \end{pmatrix}$.

   (ii) $\begin{pmatrix} 1 & 0 & 0 \\ 0 & -1 & 0 \\ 0 & 0 & 0 \end{pmatrix}$.

   (iii) $\begin{pmatrix} 1 & 0 & 0 \\ 0 & 1 & 0 \\ 0 & 0 & 0 \end{pmatrix}$.

12. $\begin{pmatrix} 1 & 0 & 0 \\ 0 & 1 & 0 \\ 0 & 0 & -1 \end{pmatrix}$.

§ 8.2.   5. If $\xi = k\eta$, direct calculations show that the Schwarz inequality reduces to equality. Conversely, if $|p(\xi, \eta)|^2 = p(\xi, \xi)p(\eta, \eta)$, let $k = \dfrac{-p(\xi, \eta)}{p(\eta, \eta)}$ and show that $p(\xi + k\eta, \xi + k\eta) = 0$.

§ 8.3.   1.   (i) Expand $p(\xi + \eta, \xi + \eta)$.
   (ii) Expand $p(\xi - \eta, \xi - \eta)$.
   (iii) Expand $p(\xi + \eta, \xi - \eta)$.
   5. Observe that $\|\alpha + c\beta\|^2 = \|\alpha\|^2 + c^2\|\beta\|^2 + 2cp(\alpha, \beta)$.
   7. Choose a normal orthogonal basis for S; extend to a normal orthogonal basis for $\mathcal{V}$.
   9. (ii) $(S + 5)^\perp$ is orthogonal to S and hence is a subspace of $S^\perp$. Likewise, $(S + 5)^\perp$ is a subspace of $5^\perp$, and hence a subspace of $S^\perp \cap 5^\perp$. The reverse relation can be established without difficulty.
   11. Compute $\xi \mathbf{T}^2$ and compare with $\xi \mathbf{T}$.

§ 8.4.   1.   (i) $\begin{pmatrix} \cos \Psi & \sin \Psi \\ -\sin \Psi & \cos \Psi \end{pmatrix}$.

   3. (i) $B = \begin{pmatrix} 0 & 1 & 0 \\ 1 & 0 & 0 \\ 0 & 0 & -1 \end{pmatrix}$.

   4. (i) $a^2 + b^2 = 1$, $c^2 + d^2 = 1$, $ac + bd = 0 = ab + cd$.
   7. If an isometry $\mathbf{T}$ is represented by a Jordan matrix J relative to the basis $\{\alpha_i\}$, then $\alpha_i \mathbf{T} = \lambda_i \alpha_i + k\alpha_{i+1}$, where $k = 0$ or 1. Deduce that $k = 0$, and therefore J is diagonal.

9. Consider $[(I - K)(I + K)^{-1}][(I - K)(I + K)^{-1}]'$, and observe that $I + K$ and $I - K$ commute.

§ 8.5. 1. (i) Complete the square.
2. (i) $r = 3$, $s = 3$.
    (ii) $r = 3$, $s = -1$.
    (iii) $r = 3$, $s = 1$.
3. Let $z = XKX^*$. Show that $\bar{z} = z$ and that z must be real.
7. There are three types of rank three, and two of rank two.
8. (ii) If A is nonsingular, $\rho(B_0) = n$. $XB_0X' \geq 0$, for all X. The canonical matrix which is congruent to B_0 must be I. Why?
    (iii) Observe that $C = DB_0D'$, where $D = \text{diag}(x_1, \ldots, x_n)$. Hence B_0 and C represent the same quadratic function.
    (iv) $\det C = \Pi\lambda_i$, where the λ_i are real and positive. But the geometric mean of any n positive real numbers never exceeds their arithmetic mean.
    (v) Show that $c_{ii} = 1$ for all i.
9. Since c_j is the coefficient of λ^{n-j} in the expansion of $\det(A - \lambda I)$, consider any choice of $n - j$ diagonal positions. Let D_j denote the determinant of the $j \times j$ matrix obtained by deleting from A the rows and columns corresponding to the $n - j$ diagonal positions. Then c_j is the signed sum of all the D_j obtained from different choices of the diagonal positions. There are $\binom{n}{j}$ such choices and, by Hadamard's inequality, $|D_j| \leq j^{i/2}k^i$.

§ 8.6. 2. Adapt the arguments of Theorems 8.35 and 8.36.
3. Use Theorem 8.36.
6. Choose a normal orthogonal basis $\{\alpha_i\}$ and calculate the two equal expressions $p(\alpha_i, \alpha_j\mathbf{T}^*)$ and $p(\alpha_i\mathbf{T}, \alpha_j)$.
7. (ii) First show that if $\mathbf{T}$ is normal, so is $\mathbf{T} - \lambda\mathbf{I}$. Then compute $p(\xi(\mathbf{T} - \lambda\mathbf{I}), \xi(\mathbf{T} - \lambda\mathbf{I}))$. This also solves (iii).
    (iv) Show that $\lambda_1p(\xi_1, \xi_2) = \lambda_2p(\xi_1, \xi_2)$, using (ii) and (iii).

CHAPTER 9

§ 9.2. 2. (i) Min $= 12$, max $= 21$.
    (ii) Min $= 20$, no max.
3. (i) The inequality $\sum_{i=1}^n a_ix_i \geq b$ can be expressed in vector form by $\alpha \cdot \xi \geq b$. Let ξ and η be solutions, and let $\zeta = k\xi + (1 - k)\eta$, where $0 \leq k \leq 1$. Compute.
4. (i) For any line segment $L \subseteq C$, let $\xi, \eta \in L$, and let ζ lie between ξ and η on L; then $\zeta = k\xi + (1 - k)\eta$ for some k, $0 \leq k \leq 1$. Then $f(\zeta) = \gamma \cdot \zeta$ is a convex linear combination of the numbers $f(\xi)$ and $f(\eta)$.

§ 9.3. 2.   (i)

$0 \leq$		gold x_1	silver x_2	$\geq$
ring	y_1	$\frac{1}{2}$	0	5
pin	y_2	$\frac{1}{4}$	$\frac{1}{2}$	4
earring	y_3	0	1	3
$\leq$		30	60	max / min

(ii) $x_1 \geq 10$, $x_2 \geq 3$, $x_1 + 2x_2 \geq 16$.

(iii) Min $v = 480$.

(iv) 60 rings, no pins, 60 pairs of earrings.

3.   (ii) The linear form is maximal at $y_1 = 1.4$, $y_2 = 2.4$.

(iii) The cost is 175 if $x_1 = x_3 = 0$, $x_2 = .75$, $x_4 = .25$.

§ 9.4. 2. (iv) Show that $(P_{rs}B)^*_{st} = P_{rs}B^*_{rt}$, and use (ii) and (i), recognizing that $P_{rs} = P_{sr}$.

(v) Show that $(BP_{rs})^*_{tr} = B^*_{ts}P_{rs}$, and use (iii) and (i).

3.   (ii) $A^{-1} = \frac{1}{6}\begin{pmatrix} 3 & -5 \\ 0 & 2 \end{pmatrix}$.

6. R coincides with I except for the entries in column i, which are of the form $-a_{rj}a_{ij}^{-1}$ in row $r \neq i$, and a_{rj}^{-1} in row i.

CHAPTER 10

§ 10.1. 2.   (i) $e^A = \begin{pmatrix} e^{-1} & 0 \\ 0 & e \end{pmatrix}$.

(ii) Diagonalize A to obtain $PAP^{-1} = J = \begin{pmatrix} 2 & 0 \\ 0 & -2 \end{pmatrix}$,

$$e^A = Pe^J P^{-1} = \frac{1}{4}\begin{pmatrix} e^2 + 3e^{-2} & 3e^2 - 3e^{-2} \\ e^2 - e^{-2} & 3e^2 + e^{-2} \end{pmatrix}.$$

(iii) Use the result of (ii), together with Theorem 10.3.

(iv) $e^A = \frac{1}{2}\begin{pmatrix} 2 & 2 & 3 \\ 0 & 2 & 2 \\ 0 & 0 & 2 \end{pmatrix}$. Observe that A is nilpotent.

4.   (i) Characteristic values: $\lambda_1 = 1$, $\lambda_2 = 2$, $\lambda_3 = 3$.

$$f(A) = \begin{pmatrix} -a + 2b & -2a + 2b & -2a + 2b \\ -b + c & -b + 2c & -b + c \\ a \quad -c & 2a \quad -2c & 2a \quad -c \end{pmatrix},$$

where $a = f(1)$, $b = f(2)$, $c = f(3)$.

(iii) Necessary and sufficient conditions are $f(1) = f(2) = f(3)$.

(iv) $e^A = \begin{pmatrix} -e + 2e^2 + 0 & -2e + 2e^2 + 0 & -2e + 2e^2 + 0 \\ 0 - e^2 + e^3 & 0 - e^2 + 2e^3 & 0 - e^2 + e^3 \\ e + 0 - e^3 & 2e + 0 - 2e^3 & 2e + 0 - e^3 \end{pmatrix}$.

§ 10.2. 5. $\dfrac{d}{dt} \det X(t) = \det(\dot{X}_1, X_2, \ldots, X_n) + \det(X_1, \dot{X}_2, \ldots, X_n) +$
$\cdots + \det(X_1, X_2, \ldots, \dot{X}_n)$, where X_i denotes column i of $X(t)$.

§ 10.3. 1. $\dot{Y} = YA$, where $A = \begin{pmatrix} 0 & 0 & -1 \\ 1 & 0 & 1 \\ 0 & 1 & 1 \end{pmatrix}$.

The characteristic values of A are $1, 1, -1$, and A is similar to

$$J = \begin{pmatrix} 1 & 1 & 0 \\ 0 & 1 & 0 \\ 0 & 0 & -1 \end{pmatrix}; \quad e^{(t-t_0)J} = \begin{pmatrix} e^{t-t_0} & (t - t_0)e^{t-t_0} & 0 \\ 0 & e^{t-t_0} & 0 \\ 0 & 0 & e^{-t+t_0} \end{pmatrix}.$$

APPENDIX A

§ A.1. 1. $m_1 m_2 \ldots m_n$ elements.
3. (ii) m^2 elements.

§ A.2. 1. 2^{mn} relations.
2. (ii) $\{(a, b) \in I \times I \mid b = ka$ for some $k \in I\}$.

§ A.3. 1. $\mathbf{F} = \mathbf{G}$ means that $\operatorname{dom} \mathbf{F} = \operatorname{dom} \mathbf{G}$, and $x\mathbf{F} = x\mathbf{G}$ for all $x \in \operatorname{dom} \mathbf{F}$.
2. $(n + 1)^m - 1$ functions.
5. $\mathbf{FF}^* = \mathbf{I}_A; \mathbf{F}^*\mathbf{F} = \mathbf{I}_B$.

§ A.4. 2. $n^{(n^2)}$ binary operations.
3. (i) The graph of a relation $\mathbf{R}$ on the real numbers is the set of all points (a, b) in the real plane such that $a \mathbf{R} b$.

§ A.7. 2. (i) If both i and e are identity elements, then $i = i * e = e$.
4. First show that $\bar{x}$ is also a left inverse of x; then show that e is also a left identity.
5. Use Exericse 4.
7. Consider 90° rotations about two fixed perpendicular axes, performed in each of the two possible orders.
9. The systems are isomorphic.

§ A.8. 1. (i) An isomorphism.
(ii) Neither.
(iii) A homomorphism onto.
6. Yes. The mapping $x \longrightarrow 2^x$, for example, is an isomorphism.

§ A.9.   1. **R** is reflexive if dom **R** $= A$, but not otherwise.

   2. Each equivalence class is a line of slope m, and each such line is an equivalence class.

   4. $E(4) = 5$.

§ A.10.   1.   (i) (a) is the set of all real numbers.

   (ii) (a) is the set of all positive integers.

   (iii) (L) is the set of all lines parallel to L.

   3.   (i) $(a)_n = \{x \in I \mid x = kn + a \text{ for some } k \in I\}$.

   (iv) To show that each $(a)_n$, $a \neq 0$, has an inverse if n is prime, consider $(1)_n(k)_n$, $(2)_n(k)_n$, $\ldots$, $(n-1)_n(k)_n$ for any fixed $k = 1, \ldots, n-1$. These $n-1$ cosets can be proved to be distinct from one another and from $(0)_n$. Hence one of them must be $(1)_n$, which means that $(k)_n$ has a multiplicative inverse.

INDEX

294 Index